Vauxhall/Opel Diesel Engine
Service and Repair Manual

by Matthew Minter and Christopher Rogers

Models covered

(1222-224-2AB1)

1488cc, 1598cc, 1686cc and 1699cc diesel engines
Fitted to the Vauxhall Nova, Corsa, Astra, Belmont and Cavalier as well as the Opel Corsa, Astra, Kadett, Ascona and Vectra and the Bedford/Vauxhall Corsa, Combi and Astra vans

© Haynes Publishing 1998

ABCDE
FGHI

A book in the **Haynes Service and Repair Manual Series**

2

ISBN 1 85960 226 6

British Library Cataloguing in Publication Data
A catalogue record for this book is available from the British Library.

Printed by **J H Haynes & Co Ltd, Sparkford, Nr Yeovil, Somerset BA22 7JJ, England**

Haynes Publishing
Sparkford, Nr Yeovil, Somerset BA22 7JJ, England

Haynes North America, Inc
861 Lawrence Drive, Newbury Park, California 91320, USA

Editions Haynes S.A.
Tour Aurore - La Défense 2, 18 Place des Reflets, 92975 PARIS LA DEFENSE Cedex, France

Haynes Publishing Nordiska AB
Box 1504, 751 45 UPPSALA, Sweden

Contents

LIVING WITH YOUR VAUXHALL/OPEL DIESEL

Introduction

The Diesel engine

MAINTENANCE

Routine maintenance and servicing

Contents

16D & 16DA engines

The 16D/DA engine is derived from the 16S petrol engine, which it closely resembles in many respects. Like the 16S, it is fitted in the Astra, Belmont and Cavalier and their commercial equivalents (sold in the UK under the Bedford label).

Although on paper this engine may appear to lack power when compared with its petrol relatives, on the road it copes well with all conditions up to maximum legal speeds. The slight trade-off in performance is potentially more than repaid by gains in fuel economy and engine longevity, and ultimately by a higher resale value.

The DIY mechanic will find routine maintenance straightforward, with good access to the commonly required items. Maintenance of the engine itself is in fact minimal, and apart from more frequent oil changing there is considerably less to do than on the petrol equivalent. Investment in one or two special tools will be necessary for some major tasks.

17D engine

The 17D engine closely resembles the 16DA unit from which it is derived and which it replaces, but embodies a number of detail changes designed to improve flexibility, and to reduce noise levels and vibration.

The most significant revision is the increase in cylinder bore size, giving increased capacity and improved torque output with a consequent improvement in mid-range acceleration. Internally, the unit is little changed from its predecessor, although the pistons have been lightened to reduce engine noise and vibration and the cylinder head has received detail modifications. These include thickening and reinforcement by means of internal ribbing of the lower section, the effect being to reduce valve leakage at cranking speed and thus improve cold starting.

External changes include a revised inlet system, employing a new cast aluminium alloy manifold and resonator assembly linked by flexible trunking to a remote filter unit located to the rear of the right-hand headlight. The camshaft cover has also been modified with the oil filler now located at the right-hand end. Changes have also been made to the camshaft drivebelt covers, two versions being fitted since the introduction of this engine type.

The GM Diesel Team

Haynes manuals are produced by dedicated and enthusiastic people working in close co-operation. The team responsible for the creation of this book included:

Authors	**Matthew Minter** **Christopher Rogers**
Sub-editor	**Carole Turk**
Editor & Page Make-up	**Bob Jex**
Workshop manager	**Paul Buckland**
Photo Scans	**Paul Tanswell** **Steve Tanswell**
Cover illustration	**Roger Healing**
Wiring diagrams	**Matthew Marke**

We hope the book will help you to get the maximum enjoyment from your car. By carrying out routine maintenance as described you will ensure your car's reliability and preserve its resale value.

In addition to the mechanical revisions to the engine, there have been a number of changes to the engine ancillaries. A new Lucas/CAV injection pump has been introduced, featuring an automatic cold start system in place of the previous manual arrangement. The new pump also includes an electronic speed governor and a solenoid-operated fuel shut-off valve which allows the engine to be stopped by turning the key to the off position. Detail changes have also been made to the existing Bosch injection pump, which continues as an alternative standard fitment on these engines. An electrically-heated fuel filter is used, allowing the engine to operate at lower ambient temperatures without the risk of fuel waxing.

17DR engine

The 17DR engine is a further development of the 17D unit, and features revisions to the swirl chambers, resulting in an increased power output. An exhaust gas recirculation system is also employed to ensure that the engine will meet existing and proposed diesel exhaust emission regulations.

The engine is also fitted with a spring-loaded automatic camshaft drivebelt tensioner, which ensures correct belt tensioning on assembly and eliminates the need for regular belt retensioning.

17DTL engine

At the time of writing this engine is fitted to the Astra only. Incorporating a low pressure turbocharger, the engine produces appreciably greater power and torque than its predecessor, the 17DR unit. Otherwise, it closely resembles the 17DR unit, from which it is derived.

There are however, a number of design changes incurred by the fitting of the turbocharger. One such change being the modification of the big-end and main bearing shells, both to facilitate improved lubrication and to cope with the increased power output. Modifications to the engine lubrication system include the incorporation of an oil cooler and thermostat, the fitting of an oil cooler between the oil filter and pump and the incorporation of spray nozzles to aid piston cooling

15D & 15DT engines

Installed in the Nova and Corsa, this engine is of completely new design and appears in non turbocharged (15D) and turbocharged (15DT) versions.

Both versions are of four-cylinder overhead camshaft design. The cylinder head is of light alloy construction and the block is iron, the crankshaft running in five main bearings.

The camshaft is belt-driven from the crankshaft sprocket. The same belt drives the oil pump and the fuel injection pump. Belt tension is automatically adjusted by means of a spring and pulley adjuster.

A coolant pump is driven by a V-belt which runs from the crankshaft pulley, as is the power steering pump (where fitted) and alternator (which has the vacuum pump attached).

Lubrication is by means of the crankshaft driven pump, oil being drawn from the sump and pumped through a full flow filter before entering the main oil galleries in the block and crankshaft. The oil is cooled by passing through a cooler unit located between the oil filter and cylinder block.

Valve clearance adjustment is by means of exchanging shims. Maintenance tasks are mostly straightforward but operations which involve disturbing or checking the valve timing should not be undertaken unless the necessary equipment is available.

17DT engine

Installed in the Astra and Cavalier, this engine is turbocharged and similar in design to the 15DT unit. The most significant difference being the increase in cylinder bore size and piston stroke, resulting in increased capacity and improved torque output.

Working on your car can be dangerous. This page shows just some of the potential risks and hazards, with the aim of creating a safety-conscious attitude.

General hazards

Scalding

• Don't remove the radiator or expansion tank cap while the engine is hot.
• Engine oil, automatic transmission fluid or power steering fluid may also be dangerously hot if the engine has recently been running.

Burning

• Beware of burns from the exhaust system and from any part of the engine. Brake discs and drums can also be extremely hot immediately after use.

Crushing

• When working under or near a raised vehicle, always supplement the jack with axle stands, or use drive-on ramps. *Never venture under a car which is only supported by a jack.*
• Take care if loosening or tightening high-torque nuts when the vehicle is on stands. Initial loosening and final tightening should be done with the wheels on the ground.

Fire

• Fuel is highly flammable; fuel vapour is explosive.
• Don't let fuel spill onto a hot engine.
• Do not smoke or allow naked lights (including pilot lights) anywhere near a vehicle being worked on. Also beware of creating sparks (electrically or by use of tools).
• Fuel vapour is heavier than air, so don't work on the fuel system with the vehicle over an inspection pit.
• Another cause of fire is an electrical overload or short-circuit. Take care when repairing or modifying the vehicle wiring.
• Keep a fire extinguisher handy, of a type suitable for use on fuel and electrical fires.

Electric shock

• Ignition HT voltage can be dangerous, especially to people with heart problems or a pacemaker. Don't work on or near the ignition system with the engine running or the ignition switched on.

• Mains voltage is also dangerous. Make sure that any mains-operated equipment is correctly earthed. Mains power points should be protected by a residual current device (RCD) circuit breaker.

Fume or gas intoxication

• Exhaust fumes are poisonous; they often contain carbon monoxide, which is rapidly fatal if inhaled. Never run the engine in a confined space such as a garage with the doors shut.
• Fuel vapour is also poisonous, as are the vapours from some cleaning solvents and paint thinners.

Poisonous or irritant substances

• Avoid skin contact with battery acid and with any fuel, fluid or lubricant, especially antifreeze, brake hydraulic fluid and Diesel fuel. Don't syphon them by mouth. If such a substance is swallowed or gets into the eyes, seek medical advice.
• Prolonged contact with used engine oil can cause skin cancer. Wear gloves or use a barrier cream if necessary. Change out of oil-soaked clothes and do not keep oily rags in your pocket.
• Air conditioning refrigerant forms a poisonous gas if exposed to a naked flame (including a cigarette). It can also cause skin burns on contact.

Asbestos

• Asbestos dust can cause cancer if inhaled or swallowed. Asbestos may be found in gaskets and in brake and clutch linings. When dealing with such components it is safest to assume that they contain asbestos.

Special hazards

Hydrofluoric acid

• This extremely corrosive acid is formed when certain types of synthetic rubber, found in some O-rings, oil seals, fuel hoses etc, are exposed to temperatures above 400ºC. The rubber changes into a charred or sticky substance containing the acid. *Once formed, the acid remains dangerous for years. If it gets onto the skin, it may be necessary to amputate the limb concerned.*
• When dealing with a vehicle which has suffered a fire, or with components salvaged from such a vehicle, wear protective gloves and discard them after use.

The battery

• Batteries contain sulphuric acid, which attacks clothing, eyes and skin. Take care when topping-up or carrying the battery.
• The hydrogen gas given off by the battery is highly explosive. Never cause a spark or allow a naked light nearby. Be careful when connecting and disconnecting battery chargers or jump leads.

Air bags

• Air bags can cause injury if they go off accidentally. Take care when removing the steering wheel and/or facia. Special storage instructions may apply.

Diesel injection equipment

• Diesel injection pumps supply fuel at very high pressure. Take care when working on the fuel injectors and fuel pipes.

⚠️ *Warning: Never expose the hands, face or any other part of the body to injector spray; the fuel can penetrate the skin with potentially fatal results.*

Remember...

DO

• Do use eye protection when using power tools, and when working under the vehicle.

• Do wear gloves or use barrier cream to protect your hands when necessary.

• Do get someone to check periodically that all is well when working alone on the vehicle.

• Do keep loose clothing and long hair well out of the way of moving mechanical parts.

• Do remove rings, wristwatch etc, before working on the vehicle – especially the electrical system.

• Do ensure that any lifting or jacking equipment has a safe working load rating adequate for the job.

DON'T

• Don't attempt to lift a heavy component which may be beyond your capability – get assistance.

• Don't rush to finish a job, or take unverified short cuts.

• Don't use ill-fitting tools which may slip and cause injury.

• Don't leave tools or parts lying around where someone can trip over them. Mop up oil and fuel spills at once.

• Don't allow children or pets to play in or near a vehicle being worked on.

Component or system	Lubricant or fluid	Capacity
Engine - 15D, 15DT	Multigrade engine oil, viscosity range SAE 5W/50 to 20W/50, to specification API SF/CD, SG/CD or CD (Duckhams Diesel, QXR, QS, Hypergrade Plus, or Hypergrade)	3.75 litres with filter
Engine - 16D, 16DA	Multigrade engine oil, viscosity range SAE 10W/40 to 20W/50, to specification SG/CD or better (Duckhams Diesel, QXR, QS, Hypergrade Plus, or Hypergrade)	3.75 litres with filter (pre-1984) 5.0 litres with filter (1985-on)
Engine - 17D	Multigrade engine oil, viscosity range SAE 10W/40 to 20W/50, to specification SG/CD or better (Duckhams Diesel, QXR, QS, Hypergrade Plus, or Hypergrade)	4.75 litres with filter
Engine - 17DR, 17DTL	Multigrade engine oil, viscosity range SAE 5W/50 to specification API SG/CD, SH/CD or CD (Duckhams QS)	5.0 litres with filter
Engine - 17DT	Multigrade engine oil, viscosity range SAE 5W/50 to 20W/50, to specification API SF/CD, SG/CD or CD (Duckhams Diesel, QXR, QS, Hypergrade Plus, or Hypergrade)	5.0 litres with filter
Power steering system	Dexron II type ATF (Duckhams Uni-Matic)	To dipstick mark
Fuel system	Commercial diesel fuel for road vehicles (DERV)	Dependent on model
Cooling system	Ethylene glycol based antifreeze to GME specification 13368 (Duckhams Antifreeze and Summer Coolant)	6.0 litres - 15D 6.3 litres - 15TD 7.7 litres - 16D, 16DA 9.1 litres - 17D, 17DR 6.8 litres - 17DTL 6.8 litres - 17DT

Choosing your engine oil

Oils perform vital tasks in all engines. The higher the engine's performance, the greater the demand on lubricants to minimise wear as well as optimise power and economy. Duckhams tailors lubricants to the highest technical standards, meeting and exceeding the demands of all modern engines.

HOW ENGINE OIL WORKS

• *Beating friction*

Without oil, the surfaces inside your engine which rub together will heat, fuse and quickly cause engine seizure. Oil, and its special additives, forms a molecular barrier between moving parts, to stop wear and minimise heat build-up.

• *Cooling hot spots*

Oil cools parts that the engine's water-based coolant cannot reach, bathing the combustion chamber and pistons, where temperatures may exceed 1000°C. The oil assists in transferring the heat to the engine cooling system. Heat in the oil is also lost by air flow over the sump, and via any auxiliary oil cooler.

• *Cleaning the inner engine*

Oil washes away combustion by-products (mainly carbon) on pistons and cylinders, transporting them to the oil filter, and holding the smallest particles in suspension until they are flushed out by an oil change. Duckhams oils undergo extensive tests in the laboratory, and on the road.

Note: It is antisocial and illegal to dump oil down the drain. To find the location of your local oil recycling bank, call this number free.

Engine oil types

Mineral oils are the "traditional" oils, generally suited to older engines and cars not used in harsh conditions. *Duckhams Hypergrade Plus* and *Hypergrade* are well suited for use in most popular family cars.
Diesel oils such as *Duckhams Diesel* are specially formulated for Diesel engines, including turbocharged models and 4x4s.
Synthetic oils are the state-of-the-art in lubricants, offering ultimate protection, but at a fairly high price. One such is *Duckhams QS*, for use in ultra-high performance engines.
Semi-synthetic oils offer high performance engine protection, but at less cost than full synthetic oils. *Duckhams QXR* is an ideal choice for hot hatches and hard-driven cars.

For help with technical queries on lubricants, call Duckhams Oils on 0181 290 8207

Chapter 1
The Diesel engine

Contents

1 History

Rudolf Diesel invented the first commercially successful compression ignition engine at the end of the 19th century. Compared with the spark ignition engine, the diesel had the advantages of lower fuel consumption, the ability to use cheaper fuel and the potential for much higher power outputs. Over the following two or three decades, such engines were widely adopted for stationary and marine applications but the fuel injection systems used were not capable of high-speed operation. This speed limitation, and the considerable weight of the air compressor needed to operate the injection equipment, made the first diesel engines unsuitable for use in road-going vehicles.

In the 1920s the German engineer Robert Bosch developed the in-line injection pump, a device which is still in extensive use today. The use of hydraulic systems to pressurise and inject the fuel did away with the need for a separate air compressor and made possible much higher operating speeds. The so-called high-speed diesel engine became increasingly popular as a power source for goods and public transport vehicles, but for a number of reasons (including specific power output, flexibility and cheapness of manufacture) the spark ignition engine continued to dominate the passenger car and light commercial market.

In the 1950s and 60s, diesel engines became increasingly popular for use in taxis and vans, but it was not until the sharp rises in oil prices in the 1970s that serious attention was paid to the small passenger car market.

Subsequent years have seen the growing popularity of the small diesel engine in cars and light commercial vehicles, not only for reasons of fuel economy and longevity but also for environmental reasons. Every major European car manufacturer now offers at least one diesel-engined model. The diesel's penetration of the UK market has been relatively slow, due in part to the lack of the considerable fuel price differential in favour of diesel which exists in other parts of Europe, but it has now gained widespread acceptance and this trend looks set to continue.

2 Principles of operation

1 All the diesel engines covered in this book operate on the familiar four-stroke cycle of induction, compression, power and exhaust (see illustration). Two-stroke diesels do exist, and may in future become important, but they are not used in light vehicles at present. Most have four cylinders, some larger engines have six, and five and three cylinder engines also exist.

Induction and ignition

2 The main difference between diesel and petrol engines is in the means by which the fuel/air mixture is introduced into the cylinder and then ignited. In the petrol engine the fuel is mixed with the incoming air before it enters the cylinder, and the mixture is then ignited at the appropriate moment by a spark plug. At all conditions except full throttle, the throttle butterfly restricts the airflow and cylinder filling is incomplete.

3 In the diesel engine, air alone is drawn into the cylinder and then compressed. Because of the diesel's high compression ratio (typically 20:1) the air gets very hot when compressed - up to 750°C (1382°F). As the piston approaches the end of the compression stroke, fuel is injected into the combustion chamber under very high pressure in the form of a finely atomised spray. The temperature of the air is high enough to ignite the injected fuel as it mixes with the air. The mixture then burns and provides the energy which drives the piston downwards on the power stroke.

4 When starting the engine from cold, the temperature of the compressed air in the cylinders may not be high enough to ignite the fuel. The preheating system overcomes this problem. The engines in this book have automatically-controlled preheating systems, using electric heater plugs (glow plugs) which heat the air in the combustion chamber just before and during start-up.

5 On most diesel engines there is no throttle valve in the inlet tract. Exceptions to this are those few engines which use a pneumatic governor, which depends on a manifold depression being created. Even more rarely a throttle valve may be used to create manifold depression for the operation of a brake servo, though it is more usual for a separate vacuum pump to be fitted for this purpose.

Direct and indirect injection

6 In practice, it is difficult to achieve smooth combustion in a small-displacement engine by injecting the fuel directly into the combustion chamber. To get around this

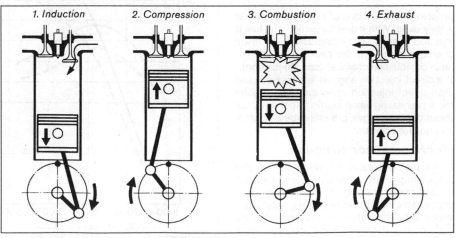

2.1 Four-stroke diesel cycle
© Robert Bosch Limited

1. Induction   2. Compression   3. Combustion   4. Exhaust

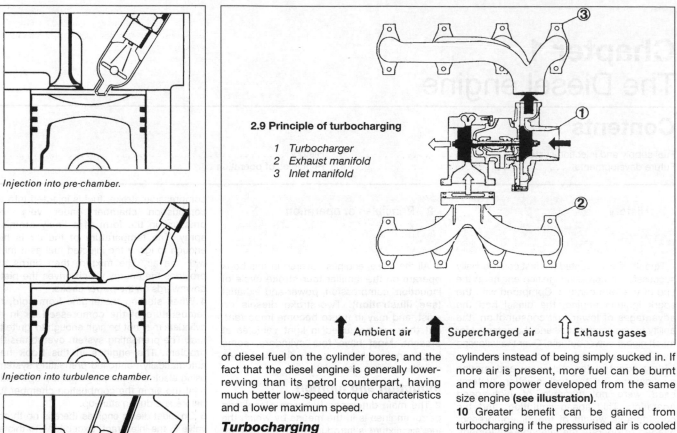

Injection into pre-chamber.

Injection into turbulence chamber.

Direct injection.

2.6 Direct and indirect injection
©Robert Bosch Limited

problem the technique of indirect injection is widely used. With indirect injection, the fuel is injected into a pre-combustion or swirl chamber in the cylinder head, alongside the main combustion chamber **(see illustration)**.

7 Indirect injection engines are less efficient than direct injection ones and also require more preheating when starting from cold, but these disadvantages are offset by smoother and quieter operation.

Mechanical construction

8 The pistons, crankshaft and bearings of a diesel engine are generally of more robust construction than in a petrol engine of comparable size, because of the greater loads imposed by the higher compression ratio and the nature of the combustion process. This is one reason for the diesel engine's longer life. Other reasons include the lubricating qualities

2.9 Principle of turbocharging

1 *Turbocharger*
2 *Exhaust manifold*
3 *Inlet manifold*

⬆ Ambient air   ⬆ Supercharged air   ⇧ Exhaust gases

of diesel fuel on the cylinder bores, and the fact that the diesel engine is generally lower-revving than its petrol counterpart, having much better low-speed torque characteristics and a lower maximum speed.

Turbocharging

9 Turbochargers have long been used on large diesel engines and are becoming common on small ones. The turbocharger uses the energy of the escaping exhaust gas to drive a turbine which pressurises the air in the inlet manifold. The air is forced into the cylinders instead of being simply sucked in. If more air is present, more fuel can be burnt and more power developed from the same size engine **(see illustration)**.

10 Greater benefit can be gained from turbocharging if the pressurised air is cooled before it enters the engine. This is done using an air-to-air heat exchanger called an intercooler or charge air cooler (CAC). The cooled air is denser and contains more oxygen in a given volume than warm air straight from the turbocharger **(see illustrations)**.

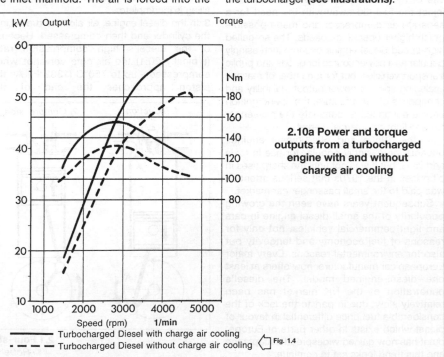

2.10a Power and torque outputs from a turbocharged engine with and without charge air cooling

Speed (rpm)   1/min

—— Turbocharged Diesel with charge air cooling
------ Turbocharged Diesel without charge air cooling   ◁ Fig. 1.4

2.10b Induction airflow in a turbocharged engine with charge air cooling

1	Air cleaner	4	Inlet manifold
2	Turbocharger	A	Inducted air
3	Intercooler		

B	Compressed air before cooling	
C	Compressed air after cooling	

Exhaust emissions

11 Because combustion in the correctly functioning diesel engine nearly always occurs in conditions of excess oxygen, there is little or no carbon monoxide (CO) in the exhaust gas. A further environmental benefit is that there is no added lead in diesel fuel.

12 At the time of writing there is no need for complicated emission control systems on the diesel engine, though simple catalytic converters are beginning to appear on production vehicles. Increasingly stringent emission regulations may result in the adoption of exhaust gas recirculation (EGR) systems and carbon particle traps **(see illustration)**.

Knock and smoke

13 The image of the diesel engine for many years was of a noisy, smoky machine, and to some extent this was justified. It is worth examining the causes of knock and smoke, both to see how they have been reduced in modern engines and to understand what causes them to get worse.

14 There is inevitably a small delay (typically 0.001 to 0.002 sec) between the start of fuel injection and the beginning of proper combustion. This delay, known as ignition lag, is greatest when the engine is cold and idling. The characteristic diesel knock is caused by the sudden increase in cylinder pressure which

occurs when the injected fuel has mixed with the hot air and starts burning. It is therefore an unavoidable part of the combustion process, though it has been greatly reduced by improvements in combustion chamber and

injection system design. A defective injector (which is not atomising the fuel as it should for optimum combustion) will also cause the engine to knock.

15 Smoke is caused by incorrect combustion, but unlike knock it is more or less preventable. During start-up and warm-up a certain amount of white or blue smoke may be seen, but under normal running conditions the exhaust should be clean. The thick black smoke which is all too familiar from old or badly-maintained vehicles is caused by a lack of air for combustion, either because the air inlet is restricted (clogged air cleaner) or because too much fuel is being injected (defective injectors or pump). Causes of smoke are examined in more detail in Chapter 7.

3 Fuel supply and injection systems

Fuel supply

1 The fuel supply system is concerned with delivering clean fuel, free of air, water or other contaminants, to the injection pump. It always includes a fuel tank, a water trap and a fuel filter (which may be combined in one unit), and the associated pipework. Some arrangement must also be made for returning fuel leaked from the injection pump and injectors to the tank **(see illustration)**.

2 A fuel lift pump is fitted between the tank and the filter on vehicles which use an in-line injection pump, or where the fuel tank outlet is significantly lower than the injection pump. When a distributor injection pump is fitted and the tank outlet is at about the same level as the injection pump (as is the case with many

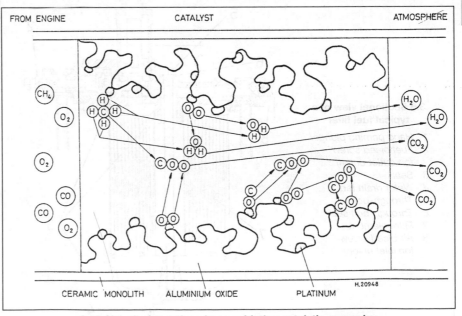

2.12 Chemical reactions in an oxidation catalytic converter

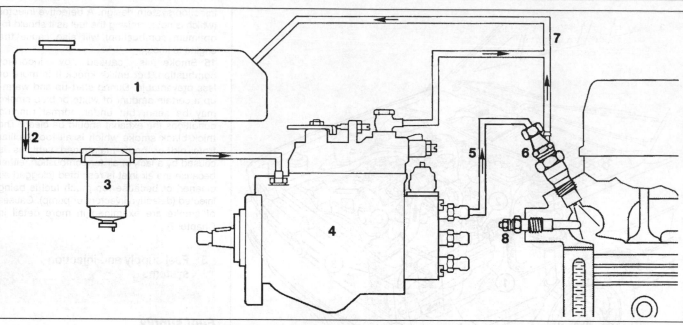

3.1 Fuel circulation - typical passenger car system
©Robert Bosch Limited

1 Fuel tank
2 Fuel feed line
3 Fuel filter / water trap
4 Injection pump with integral supply pump
5 Injector pipe
6 Injector
7 Fuel return (leak-off) line

passenger cars), a separate fuel lift pump is not fitted. In this case a hand priming pump is often provided for use when bleeding the fuel system.

3 Additional refinements may be encountered. These include a fuel heater, which may be integral with the filter or on the tank side of it, to prevent the formation of wax crystals in the fuel in cold weather. A "water in fuel" warning light on the instrument panel

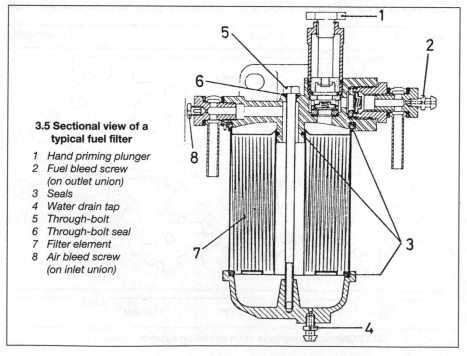

3.5 Sectional view of a typical fuel filter

1 Hand priming plunger
2 Fuel bleed screw (on outlet union)
3 Seals
4 Water drain tap
5 Through-bolt
6 Through-bolt seal
7 Filter element
8 Air bleed screw (on inlet union)

may be illuminated by a device in the water trap when the water reaches a certain level.

4 The water trap and fuel filter are vital for satisfactory operation of the fuel injection system. The water trap may have a glass bowl, in which case water build-up can be seen, or it may as already mentioned have some electrical device for alerting the driver to the presence of water. Whether or not these features are present, the trap must be drained at the specified intervals, or more frequently if experience shows this to be necessary. If water enters the injection pump it can cause rapid corrosion, especially if the vehicle is left standing for any length of time.

5 The fuel filter may be of the disposable cartridge type, or it may consist of a renewable element inside a metal bowl. Sometimes a coarser pre-filter is fitted upstream of the main filter. Whatever the type, it must be renewed at the specified intervals. Considering the damage which can be caused to the injection equipment by the entry of even small particles of dirt, it is not worth using cheap replacement filters, which may not be of the same quality as those of reputable manufacture **(see illustration)**.

Fuel injection pump

6 The pump is a mechanical device attached to the engine **(see illustrations)**. Its function is to supply fuel to the injectors at the correct pressure, at the correct moment in the combustion cycle and for the length of time necessary to ensure efficient combustion. The pump responds to depression of the accelerator pedal by increasing fuel delivery, within the limits allowed by the governor. It is also provided with some means of cutting off fuel delivery when it is wished to stop the engine.

7 Some kind of governor is associated with the injection pump, either integral with it or attached to it. All vehicle engine governors regulate fuel delivery to control idle speed and maximum speed; the variable-speed governor also regulates intermediate speeds. Operation of the

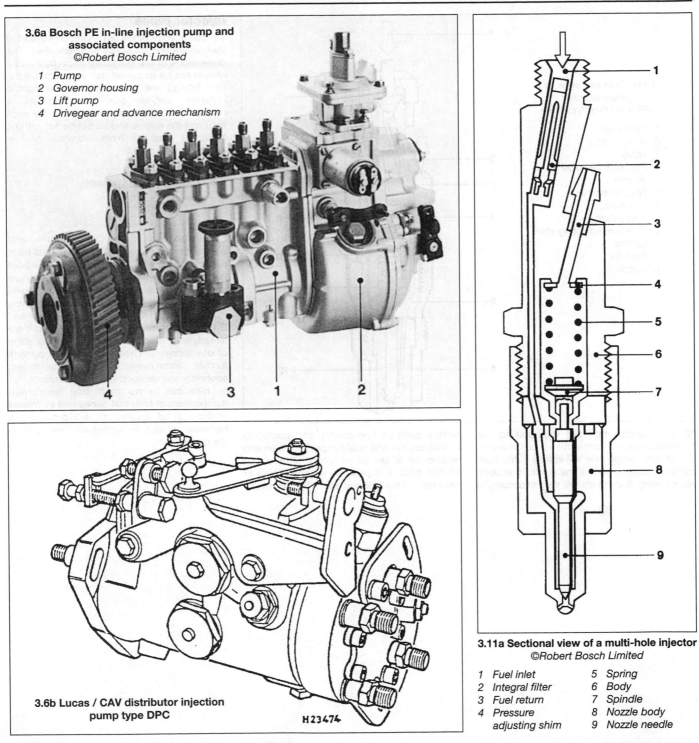

3.6a Bosch PE in-line injection pump and associated components
©Robert Bosch Limited

1 Pump
2 Governor housing
3 Lift pump
4 Drivegear and advance mechanism

3.6b Lucas / CAV distributor injection pump type DPC

H23474

3.11a Sectional view of a multi-hole injector
©Robert Bosch Limited

1 Fuel inlet   5 Spring
2 Integral filter   6 Body
3 Fuel return   7 Spindle
4 Pressure   8 Nozzle body
   adjusting shim   9 Nozzle needle

governor may be mechanical or hydraulic, or it may be controlled by manifold depression.

8 Other devices in or attached to the pump include cold start injection advance or fast idle units, turbo boost pressure sensors and anti-stall mechanisms.

9 Fuel injection pumps are normally very reliable. If they are not damaged by dirt, water or unskilled adjustment they may well outlast the engine to which they are fitted.

Fuel injectors

10 One fuel injector is fitted to each cylinder. The function of the injector is to spray an evenly atomised quantity of fuel into the combustion or pre-combustion chamber when the fuel pressure exceeds a certain value, and to stop the flow of fuel cleanly when the pressure drops. Atomisation is achieved by a spring-loaded needle which vibrates rapidly against its seat when fuel

under pressure passes it. The needle and seat assembly together are known as the injector nozzle.

11 Injectors in direct injection engines are usually of the multi-hole type **(see illustration)**, while those in indirect engines are of the pintle type **(see illustration)**. The "throttled pintle" injector gives a progressive build-up of injection, which is valuable in achieving smooth combustion.

1

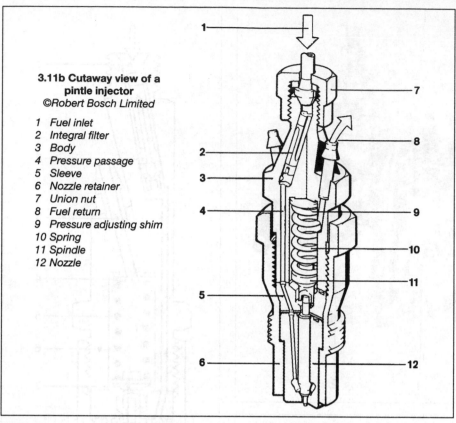

3.11b Cutaway view of a pintle injector
©Robert Bosch Limited

1 Fuel inlet
2 Integral filter
3 Body
4 Pressure passage
5 Sleeve
6 Nozzle retainer
7 Union nut
8 Fuel return
9 Pressure adjusting shim
10 Spring
11 Spindle
12 Nozzle

12 The injector tips are exposed to the temperatures and pressures of combustion, so not surprisingly they will in time suffer from carbon deposits and ultimately from erosion and burning. Service life will vary according to factors such as fuel quality and operating conditions, but one could expect to clean and recalibrate a set of injectors after about 50 000 miles, and perhaps to renew them or have them reconditioned after 100 000 miles.

Injector pipes

13 The injector pipes are an important part of the system and must not be overlooked. The dimensions of the pipes are important and it should not be assumed that just because the end fittings are the same, a pipe from a different engine can be used as a replacement. Securing clips must be kept tight and the engine should not be run without them, as damage from vibration or fuel cavitation may result.

4 Future developments

Development of the diesel engine, and particularly the fuel injection system, has been relatively slow compared with the advances which have been made in petrol engine fuel injection and management systems. However, new systems such as 'EPIC' (Electronically Programmed Injection Control) by Lucas and EDC (Electronic Diesel Control) by Bosch are already in production or in an advanced stage of development. These systems will provide further improvements in smoothness, economy and reduced exhaust emissions.

There can be no doubt that the current combination of high fuel prices and increased environmental awareness will provide the necessary stimuli for further improvements in the near future.

Chapter 2
Routine maintenance and servicing

Contents

2

Degrees of difficulty

Easy, suitable for novice with little experience	Fairly easy, suitable for beginner with some experience	Fairly difficult, suitable for competent DIY mechanic	Difficult, suitable for experienced DIY mechanic	Very difficult, suitable for expert DIY or professional

Oil filter types

15D and 15DT engines	Champion F126
16D and 16DA engines	Champion G105
17D and 17DR engines	Champion G105
17DTL engine	Champion F208
17DT engine	Champion F208

Battery capacity

15D and 15DT engines	60Ah
16D and 16DA engines	66Ah
17D and 17DR engines	60Ah
17DTL engine	60Ah
17DT engine	60Ah

Auxiliary drivebelts

15D, 15DT and 17DT engines

Tension (using gauge):

Alternator:	
New	440 to 540 N
Used	320 to 390 N
Power steering pump:	
New	450 N
Used	250 to 300 N

16D, 16DA, 17D, 17DR and 17DTL engines

Tension (using gauge):

Alternator:	
New	450 N
Used	250 to 400 N
Power steering pump:	
New	450 N
Used	250 to 300 N

Injection pump adjustment

Idle speed

15D and 15DT engines	830 to 930 rpm
16D and 16DA engines	825 to 875 rpm
17D engine	820 to 920 rpm
17DR and 17DTL engines:	
Below 20°C	1200 rpm
Above 20°C	850 rpm
17DT engine	780 to 880 rpm

Maximum speed

15D engine	5800 rpm
15DT engine	5600 rpm
16D and 16DA engines	5600 rpm
17D, 17DR and 17DTL engines	5500 to 5600 rpm
17DT engine	5100 to 5300 rpm

Fuel filter types

15D and 15DT engines	Champion L111
16D and 16DA engines	Champion L113
17D and 17DR engines:	
Cavalier from 1988, and Astra to 1991	Champion L113
Astra from 1991, and Astramax	Champion L111
17DTL engine	Champion L111
17DT engine	Champion L111

Air filter types

15D and 15DT engines	Champion U641
16D and 16DA engines	Champion U503
17D and 17DR engines:	
Astra 1988 to 1991, and Astramax	Champion U558
Astra from 1991	Champion U599
Cavalier from 1988	Champion U554
17DTL engine	Champion U548
17DT engine	Champion U548

Valve clearances (cold)

15D, 15DT and 17DT engines:

Inlet	0.15 mm
Exhaust	0.25 mm

16D, 16DA, 17D, 17DR and 17DTL engines:

Inlet	Automatically adjusted
Exhaust	Automatically adjusted

Camshaft drivebelt tension

15D and 15DT engines	Automatic tensioner

16D and 16DA engines (using tension gauge):

New belt, warm	9.0
New belt, cold	6.5
Run-in belt, warm	8.0
Run-in belt, cold	4.0

17D engine (using tension gauge):

New belt, warm	7.5
New belt, cold	9.5
Run-in belt, warm	5.0
Run-in belt, cold	9.0
17DR and 17DTL engines	Automatic tensioner
17DT engine	Automatic tensioner

Glow plugs

15D engine:

5 volt system	Champion CH-110, or equivalent
11 volt system	Champion CH-157, or equivalent
15DT engine	Champion CH-158, or equivalent
16D and 16DA engines	Champion CH-68, or equivalent
17D and 17DR engines	Champion CH-68, or equivalent
17DTL engine	Champion CH-158, or equivalent
17DT engine	Champion CH-158, or equivalent

Torque wrench settings

Glow plugs	Nm	lbf ft
15D and 15DT engines	20	15
16D and 16DA engines	40	30
17D and 17DR engines	20	15
17DT engine	20	15

2

The maintenance schedules which follow are basically those recommended by the manufacturer. Servicing intervals are determined by mileage or time elapsed - this is because fluids and systems deteriorate with age as well as with use. Follow the time intervals if the appropriate mileage is not covered within the specified period.

Vehicles operating under adverse conditions may need more frequent maintenance. Adverse conditions include climatic extremes, full-time towing or taxi work, driving on unmade roads, and a high proportion of short journeys. The use of inferior fuel can cause early degradation of the engine oil. Consult a Vauxhall/Opel dealer for advice on these points.

All models

Every 250 miles (400 km), weekly, or before a long journey

- ☐ Check engine oil level and top-up if necessary (Section 3)
- ☐ Check coolant level and top-up if necessary (Section 4)
- ☐ Check battery electrolyte level (if applicable) (Section 5)
- ☐ Check exhaust emission (Section 6)
- ☐ Check operation of glow plug warning light (Section 7)

Schedule A - 1982/83 model years

Every 3000 miles (5000 km) or 6 months, whichever comes first

- ☐ Renew engine oil and oil filter (Section 8)
- ☐ Drain fuel filter (Section 9)

Every 6000 miles (10 000 km) or 6 months

- ☐ Check idle speed and adjust if necessary (Section 12)
- ☐ Renew fuel filter element (Section 13)
- ☐ Renew air filter element (Section 14)
- ☐ Check auxiliary drivebelts for condition and tension (Section 15)
- ☐ Check coolant strength (Section 16)
- ☐ Check hoses for leaks and damage (Section 17)

Every 18000 miles (30 000 km) or 2 years

- ☐ Check condition and tension of camshaft drivebelt (Section 27)

Every 36 000 miles (60 000 km) or 4 years

- ☐ Renew camshaft drivebelt (Section 35)

Every 60 000 miles (100 000 km) or 5 years

- ☐ Renew glow plugs (Section 37)

Every 2 years, regardless of mileage

- ☐ Renew the engine coolant (Section 41)

Schedule B - 1984/85/86 model years

Every 3000 miles (5000 km) or 6 months, whichever comes first - 1984 only
- [ ] Renew engine oil and oil filter (Section 8)
- [ ] Drain fuel filter (Section 9)

Every 4500 miles (7500 km) or 6 months - 1985/86
- [ ] Renew engine oil and oil filter (Section 10)
- [ ] Drain fuel filter (Section 11)

Every 9000 miles (15 000 km) or 12 months
- [ ] Check idle speed and adjust if necessary (Section 18)
- [ ] Check auxiliary drivebelts for condition and tension (Section 21)
- [ ] Lubricate throttle linkage (Section 22)
- [ ] Check coolant strength (Section 23)
- [ ] Check hoses for leaks and damage (Section 17)

Every 18 000 miles (30 000 km) or 2 years
- [ ] Renew fuel filter element (Section 28)
- [ ] Renew air filter element (Section 29)
- [ ] Check condition and tension of camshaft drivebelt (Section 27)

Every 36 000 miles (60 000 km) or 4 years
- [ ] Renew camshaft drivebelt (Section 35)

Every 63 000 miles (105 000 km) or 7 years
- [ ] Renew glow plugs (Section 38)

Every 2 years, regardless of mileage
- [ ] Renew the engine coolant (Section 41)

Schedule C - 1987 model year on

Every 4500 miles (7500 km) or 6 months, whichever comes first
- [ ] Renew engine oil and filter (Section 10)
- [ ] Drain fuel filter (Section 11)

Every 9000 miles (15 000 km) or 12 months
- [ ] As for Schedule B

Every 18 000 miles (30 000 km) or 2 years
- [ ] As for Schedule B but without inspecting the camshaft drivebelt

Every 27 000 miles (45 000 km) or 3 years
- [ ] If operating in adverse driving conditions, check condition and tension of camshaft drivebelt (Section 32)

Every 36 000 miles (60 000 km) or 4 years
- [ ] When operating in normal driving conditions, check condition and tension of camshaft drivebelt (Section 33)

Every 54 000 miles (90 000 km) or 6 years
- [ ] If operating in adverse driving conditions, renew camshaft drivebelt (Section 36)

Every 63 000 miles (105 000 km) or 7 years
- [ ] Renew glow plugs (Section 38)
- [ ] When operating in normal driving conditions, renew camshaft drivebelt (Section 39)

Every 2 years, regardless of mileage
- [ ] Renew the engine coolant (Section 41)

2

Note: *The following Routine Maintenance Schedule is based on the vehicle being driven for 9000 miles per annum. Should the vehicle be driven for an appreciably lesser or greater mileage than this, then the Schedule must be modified to suit. Ask advice from your Vauxhall/Opel dealer.*

Every 250 miles (400 km), weekly, or before a long journey

- ☐ Check engine oil level and top-up if necessary (Section 3)
- ☐ Check coolant level and top-up if necessary (Section 4)
- ☐ Check battery electrolyte level (if applicable) (Section 5)
- ☐ Check exhaust emission (Section 6)
- ☐ Check operation of glow plug warning light (Section 7)

Every 4500 miles (7500 km) or 12 months, whichever comes first

- ☐ Renew engine oil and oil filter (Section 10)

Every 9000 miles (15 000 km) or 12 months

- ☐ Check the engine and gearbox for leaks (Section 24)
- ☐ Drain any accumulation of water from the fuel filter (Section 25)
- ☐ Renew the air filter element (Section 26)
- ☐ Check the engine idle speed (Section 18)
- ☐ Check the maximum speed (Section 19)
- ☐ Check the exhaust emissions (Section 20)
- ☐ Check the condition and tension (where applicable) of the auxiliary drivebelts (Section 21)

Every 18 000 miles (30 000 km) or 2 years

- ☐ Renew the fuel filter (Section 30)
- ☐ Check condition of camshaft drivebelt - 17DR and 17DTL engines (Section 27)
- ☐ Check valve clearances - 15D, 15DT and 17DT engines (Section 31)
- ☐ Renew engine coolant - every 2 years, regardless of mileage (Section 41)

Every 36 000 miles (60 000 km) or 4 years

- ☐ Check condition of camshaft drivebelt - 15D, 15DT and 17DT engines (Section 34)
- ☐ Renew camshaft drivebelt regardless of condition - 17D, 17DR and 17DTL engines (Section 35)

Every 63 000 miles (105 000 km) or 7 years

- ☐ Renew glow plugs (Section 38)
- ☐ Renew camshaft drivebelt regardless of condition - 15D and 15DT (up to 1991) engines (Section 39)

Every 72 000 miles (120 000 km) or 8 years

- ☐ Renew camshaft drivebelt regardless of condition - 15D, 15DT (from 1992-on) and 17DT engines (Section 40)

Note: *The manufacturers state that on 17DT engines from the 1995-on model year, the camshaft drivebelt renewal interval could be extended from 72 000 to 80 000 miles.*

Underbonnet view of 15D engine in Combi Van

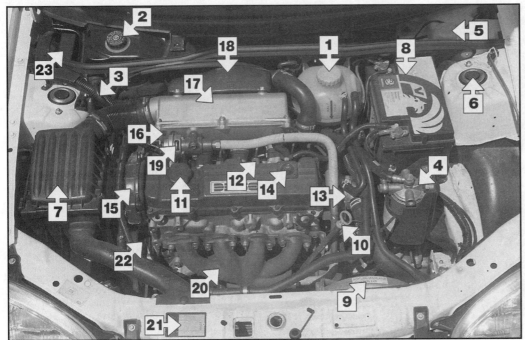

1 Cooling system filler/
   pressure cap
2 Brake fluid reservoir cap
3 Brake servo line
4 Fuel filter
5 Screen washer reservoir
6 Suspension turret
7 Air cleaner housing
8 Battery
9 Radiator fan
10 Engine oil dipstick
11 Engine oil filler cap
12 Fuel injector
13 Thermostat housing
14 Engine breather
15 Camshaft drivebelt cover
16 Inlet manifold
17 Plenum chamber
18 Air resonator box
19 EGR valve
20 Exhaust manifold
21 VIN plate
22 Coolant pump
23 Relay box

Underbonnet view of 15DT engine in Corsa

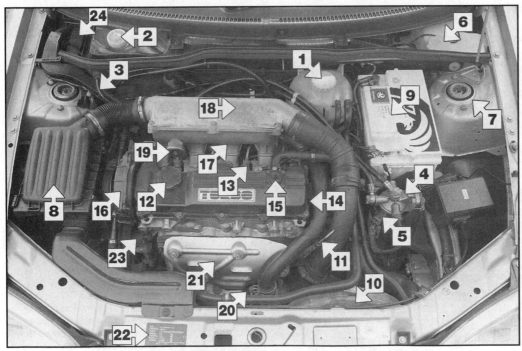

1 Cooling system filler/
   pressure cap
2 Brake fluid reservoir cap
3 Brake servo line
4 Fuel filter
5 Fuel heater
6 Screen washer reservoir
7 Suspension turret
8 Air cleaner housing
9 Battery
10 Radiator fan
11 Engine oil dipstick
12 Engine oil filler cap
13 Fuel injector
14 Thermostat housing
   (beneath hose)
15 Engine breather
16 Camshaft drivebelt cover
17 Inlet manifold
18 Plenum chamber
19 Charge air safety valve
20 Turbocharger
21 Exhaust manifold heat shield
22 VIN plate
23 Coolant pump
24 Relay box

Underbonnet view of 16D engine in Cavalier

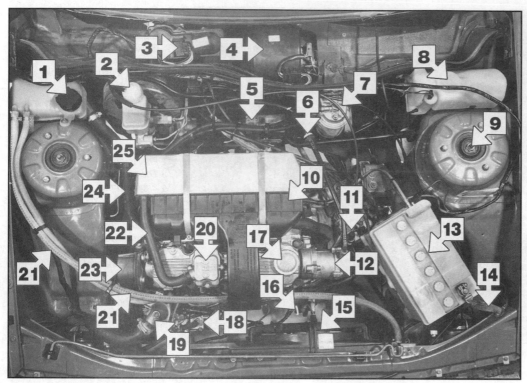

1 Cooling system filler/
  pressure cap
2 Brake fluid reservoir cap
3 Windscreen wiper motor
4 Heater blower motor
5 Fuel hoses
6 Brake servo non-return valve
7 Fuel filter
8 Screen washer reservoir
9 Suspension turret
10 Air cleaner housing
11 Gearbox breather
12 Vacuum pump
13 Battery
14 Earth strap
15 Radiator fan
16 Engine oil dipstick
17 Engine oil filler
18 Fuel injection pump
19 Thermostat elbow
20 Engine breather
21 Cooling system vent hoses
22 Crankcase ventilation hose
23 Camshaft drivebelt cover
24 Coolant hose
   (to expansion tank)
25 Inlet manifold

Underbonnet view of 17D engine in Cavalier

1 Cooling system filler/
  pressure cap
2 Brake fluid reservoir cap
3 Electrical ancillary box
4 Fuel filter
5 Fuel filter heater unit
6 Fuel filter temperature sensor
7 Fuel hoses
8 Brake servo non-return valve
9 Suspension turret
10 Air cleaner housing
11 Gearbox breather
12 Vacuum pump
13 Battery
14 Battery earth strap
15 Radiator fan
16 Engine oil dipstick
17 Engine oil filler
18 Fuel injection pump
19 Thermostat elbow
20 Engine breather
21 Cooling system vent hoses
22 Crankcase ventilation hose
23 Camshaft drivebelt cover
24 Coolant hose
   (to expansion tank)
25 Inlet manifold
26 Clutch cable
27 Screen washer reservoir
28 VIN plate

Underbonnet view of 17DR engine in Astra

1 Cooling system filler/
   pressure cap
2 Brake fluid reservoir cap
3 Relay box
4 Fuel filter
5 EGR valve
6 Screen washer reservoir
7 Suspension turret
8 Air cleaner housing
9 Battery
10 Radiator fan
11 Engine oil dipstick
12 Engine oil filler cap
13 Fuel injector
14 Fuel injection pump
15 Cold start device
16 Thermostat elbow
17 Engine breather
18 Camshaft drivebelt cover
19 Inlet manifold
20 Vacuum pump
21 Relay box
22 Clutch lever

Underbonnet view of 17DTL engine in Astra

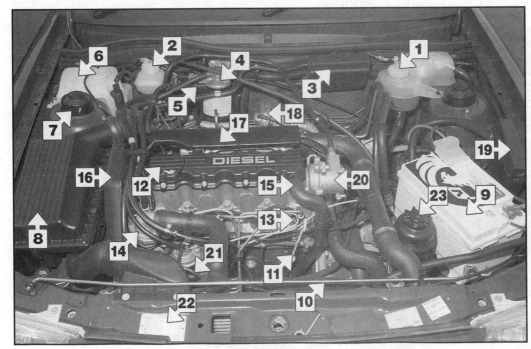

1 Cooling system filler/
   pressure cap
2 Brake fluid reservoir cap
3 Relay box
4 Fuel filter
5 Fuel heater
6 Screen washer reservoir
7 Suspension turret
8 Air cleaner housing
9 Battery
10 Radiator fan
11 Engine oil dipstick
12 Engine oil filler cap
13 Fuel injector
14 Thermostat elbow
15 Engine breather hose
16 Camshaft drivebelt cover
17 Inlet manifold
18 EGR valve
19 Relay box
20 Vacuum pump
21 Fuel injection pump
22 VIN plate
23 Power steering fluid reservoir

2

Underbonnet view of 17DT engine in Astra

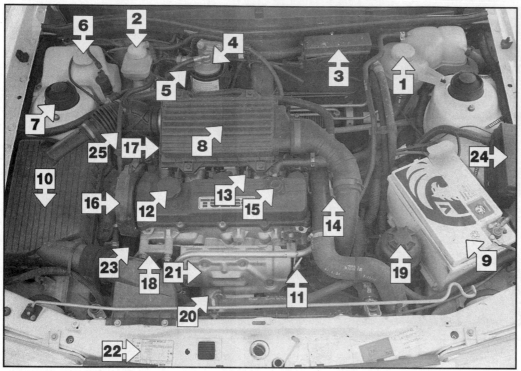

1 Cooling system filler/
  pressure cap
2 Brake fluid reservoir cap
3 Relay box
4 Fuel filter
5 Fuel heater
6 Screen washer reservoir
7 Suspension turret
8 Air cleaner housing
9 Battery
10 Air collector box
11 Engine oil dipstick
12 Engine oil filler cap
13 Fuel injector
14 Thermostat housing
   (beneath hose)
15 Engine breather
16 Camshaft drivebelt cover
17 Inlet manifold
18 Power steering pump bracket
19 Power steering fluid reservoir
20 Turbocharger heat shield
21 Exhaust manifold heat shield
22 VIN plate
23 Coolant pump
24 Relay box
25 Brake servo line

Underbonnet view of 17DT engine in Cavalier

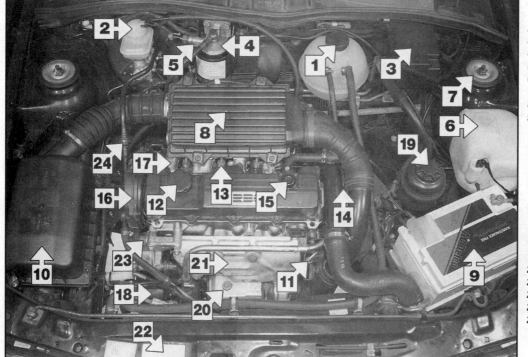

1 Cooling system filler/
  pressure cap
2 Brake fluid reservoir cap
3 Electrical ancillary box
4 Fuel filter
5 Fuel heater
6 Screen washer reservoir
7 Suspension turret
8 Air cleaner housing
9 Battery
10 Air collector box
11 Engine oil dipstick
12 Engine oil filler cap
13 Fuel injector
14 Thermostat housing
   (beneath hose)
15 Engine breather
16 Camshaft drivebelt cover
17 Inlet manifold
18 Power steering pump
19 Power steering fluid reservoir
20 Turbocharger heat shield
21 Exhaust manifold heat shield
22 VIN plate
23 Coolant pump
24 Brake servo line

1 Introduction

1 This Chapter is designed to help the home mechanic maintain his/her engine for economy, long life and peak performance.

2 The Chapter contains a master maintenance schedule, followed by Sections dealing specifically with each task in the schedule. Visual checks, adjustments, component renewal and other helpful items are included. Refer to the accompanying illustrations of the engine compartment and the underside of the vehicle for the locations of the various components.

3 Servicing your engine in accordance with the mileage/time maintenance schedule and the following Sections will provide a planned maintenance programme, which should result in a long and reliable service life. This is a comprehensive plan, so maintaining some items but not others at the specified service intervals, will not produce the same results.

4 As you service your engine, you will discover that many of the procedures can - and should - be grouped together, because of the particular procedure being performed, or because of the close proximity of two otherwise-unrelated components to one another.

5 The first step in this maintenance programme is to prepare yourself before the actual work begins. Read through all the Sections relevant to the work to be carried out, then make a list and gather together all the parts and tools required. If a problem is encountered, seek advice from a parts specialist, or dealer service department.

2 Intensive maintenance

1 If from the time the engine is new, the routine maintenance schedule is followed closely and frequent checks are made of fluid levels and high-wear items, then the engine will be kept in relatively good running condition, and the need for additional work will be minimised.

2 It is possible that there will be times when the engine is running poorly due to the lack of regular maintenance. This is even more likely if a used vehicle, which has not received regular and frequent maintenance checks, is purchased. In such cases, additional work may need to be carried out, outside of the regular maintenance intervals.

3 If engine wear is suspected, a compression test will provide valuable information regarding the overall performance of the main internal components. Such a test can be used as a basis to decide on the extent of the work to be carried out. If, for example, a compression test indicates serious internal engine wear, conventional maintenance as described in this Chapter will not greatly improve the performance of the engine, and may prove a waste of time and money, unless extensive overhaul work is carried out first.

4 The following series of operations are those usually required to improve the performance of a generally poor-running engine:

Primary operations

a) Clean, inspect and test the battery
b) Check all the engine-related fluids
c) Check the condition and tension of the auxiliary drivebelt
d) Check the condition of the air cleaner filter element, and renew if necessary
e) Check the fuel filter
f) Check the condition of all hoses, and check for fluid leaks
g) Check the idle speed settings

5 If the above operations do not prove fully effective, carry out the following secondary operations:

Secondary operations

a) Check the charging system
b) Check the preheating system
c) Check the fuel system

250 mile / 400 km Service

3 Engine oil level check

HAYNES HiNT *If the oil level is checked immediately after driving the vehicle, some of it will remain in the upper engine components, resulting in an inaccurate reading on the dipstick!*

1 Make sure that the vehicle is on level ground. Check the oil level before the vehicle is driven, or at least 5 minutes after the engine has been switched off.

2 The dipstick is located at the front of the engine. Withdraw the dipstick and using a clean rag or paper towel, wipe all the oil from its end **(see illustration)**. Insert the clean dipstick into the tube as far as it will go, then withdraw it again.

3 Note the oil level on the end of the dipstick, which should be between the upper MAX mark and the lower MIN mark **(see illustration)**.

4 Oil is added through the filler cap. A funnel may help to reduce spillage. Add the oil slowly, checking the level on the dipstick often. Do not overfill **(see illustration)**.

4 Coolant level check

Warning: Do not attempt to remove the expansion tank pressure cap when the engine is hot, as there is a very great risk of scalding. Do not leave open containers of coolant about, as it is poisonous.

1 Check the coolant level by inspecting the expansion tank. The tank is translucent, so the level can be verified without removing the cap. The level should be between the MAX

2

3.2 Withdrawing the engine oil level dipstick

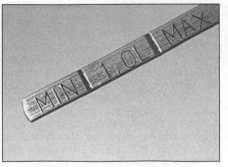

3.3 Oil level dipstick markings

3.4 Topping up the engine oil

4.3 Topping up the engine coolant

5.2 Checking the battery cable clamps

5.4 Topping-up battery with distilled water

(HOT) and MIN (COLD) marks embossed on the side of the tank. If it is below the MIN mark, proceed as follows.

2 Take great care to avoid scalding if the system is hot. Place a thick cloth over the expansion tank cap and turn the cap slowly anti-clockwise, waiting for any pressure to be released. Turn the cap further anti-clockwise and remove it completely.

3 Top up to the MAX mark using antifreeze mixture of the correct type and concentration **(see illustration)**. In an emergency, plain water may be used, but this will dilute the antifreeze remaining in the system. Do not add cold water to an overheated engine, or damage may result.

4 Refit the expansion tank cap when the level is correct. Check for leaks if frequent topping-up is required. Normally loss from this type of system is minimal.

5 Battery check

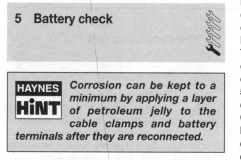

HAYNES HiNT *Corrosion can be kept to a minimum by applying a layer of petroleum jelly to the cable clamps and battery terminals after they are reconnected.*

1 The battery is located on the left-hand side of the engine compartment. Inspect the exterior of the battery for damage such as a cracked case or cover.

2 Check the tightness of the battery cable clamps to ensure good electrical connections. You should not be able to move them. Also check each cable for cracks and frayed conductors **(see illustration)**.

3 If corrosion (white fluffy deposit) is evident, remove the cables from the battery terminals, clean them with a small wire brush, then refit them. Automotive stores sell a useful tool for cleaning the battery post as well as the terminals. Coat the battery terminals with a smear of petroleum jelly, or proprietary anti-corrosion product, when they are clean.

4 The battery fitted as original equipment requires no maintenance, other than that described above. However, other types of battery may be fitted as replacements. Unless otherwise instructed, check the electrolyte level, either by removing the cell covers or by observing the level through the translucent case. The plate separators in each cell should be covered to a depth of approximately 6 mm. Top up if necessary using clean distilled or de-ionised water **(see illustration)**. Refit the cell covers and mop up any spillage.

5 Make sure that the battery tray is in good condition, and that the clamp is tight. Corrosion on the tray, retaining clamp and the battery itself can be removed with a solution of water and baking soda. Thoroughly rinse all cleaned areas with water. Any metal parts damaged by corrosion should be covered with a zinc-based primer, then painted.

6 Exhaust check

Start the engine and visually check the exhaust emissions. Any smoke in the emissions will indicate one of the following faults:

White smoke in exhaust

a) *Injection timing incorrect*
b) *Low compression*
c) *Water entering cylinders*

Black smoke in exhaust

a) *Air cleaner blocked*
b) *Injector(s) defective*

Blue smoke in exhaust

a) *Engine oil entering cylinders*
b) *Injector(s) defective*

If any fault is indicated then take action immediately, referring to the appropriate Chapter.

7 Warning light check

The glow plug warning light in the instrument console should extinguish approximately 4 seconds after the ignition is switched on. If it does not do so, then suspect a fault in the circuit or one of the plugs and take the appropriate action.

3000 mile / 5000 km Service

8 Engine oil and filter renewal

Note: *Always park the vehicle on level ground when replenishing and checking the engine oil level.*

16D and 16DA engines, schedules A and B

Oil draining

1 The engine oil should be drained just after a run, when the contaminants which it carries are still in suspension.

2 Park the vehicle on level ground. Position a drain pan of adequate capacity beneath the sump. Wipe clean around the sump drain plug, then unscrew and remove it **(see illustration)**. Be careful to avoid scalding if the oil is very hot. Do not lose the drain plug washer.

3 Remove the oil filler cap to speed up the draining process. Allow the oil to drain for at least 15 minutes. Inspect the drain plug washer and renew it if necessary.

4 When draining is complete, refit the drain plug with washer and tighten it to the

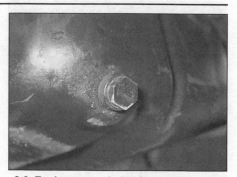

8.2 Engine sump drain plug - 16D engine

8.6 Fitting a new oil filter - 16D engine

9.2 Loosening the fuel filter vent plug - 16D engine

9.3 Fuel filter drain plug (arrowed) - 16D engine

specified torque. Before refilling the engine with oil, renew the oil filter as follows.

Filter renewal

5 Position the drain pan beneath the oil filter. Unscrew the filter and remove it. A chain or strap wrench will probably be needed to undo the filter. Failing this, a screwdriver can be driven through the filter and used as a lever to unscrew it. Be prepared for considerable oil spillage in this case. Some spillage is inevitable as the filter is withdrawn.

6 Wipe clean around the filter seat on the engine and check that no sealing rings have been left behind. Smear the sealing ring on the new filter with engine oil or grease, then screw the filter into position **(see illustration)**. Unless instructed otherwise by the filter maker, tighten the filter by hand only. Usually, tightening by two-thirds of a turn beyond the point where the sealing ring contacts the seat is sufficient.

Oil refilling and engine checks

7 Refill the engine with new oil of the specified type through the filler cap. A funnel may help to reduce spillage. Add the oil slowly, checking the level on the dipstick often. Do not overfill. Ensure that the oil level is at least up to the MIN mark on the dipstick.

8 Refit the filler cap, then start the engine. The oil pressure warning light will take a few seconds to go out as the filter fills with oil. Do not rev the engine until the light has gone out.

9 With the engine running, check for leaks around the filter base and the drain plug. Tighten further if necessary. Stop the engine and check again for leaks.

9.6a Top of heated filter unit, showing vent plug location (arrowed) - later 16DA engine

10 Allow a couple of minutes for the oil to return to the sump, then recheck the level on the dipstick and top-up if necessary to the MAX mark. The new filter will absorb approximately 0.5 litre of oil.

11 Put the old oil into a sealed container and dispose of it safely.

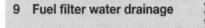

9 Fuel filter water drainage

> ⚠️ *Warning: After draining the fuel filter, dispose of the water/fuel mixture safely*

16D and 16DA engines, schedules A and B

Unheated filter

1 The fuel filter should be drained to remove any water which may have accumulated.

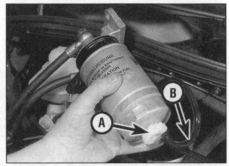

9.6b Fuel filter drain plug (A) and hose (B) - later 16DA engine

2 Position a container underneath the filter drain plug. Loosen the vent plug on top of the filter carrier by one turn **(see illustration)**.

3 Loosen the drain plug at the filter base by one turn and allow the water layer to drain from the filter **(see illustration)**.

4 When clean fuel emerges, tighten both screws and remove the container.

5 Dispose of the water/fuel safely.

Heated filter

6 For most purposes, this filter type can be dealt with as described for the unheated type. It is easier to release the assembly from the bulkhead to carry out the periodic draining operation, as access below the filter is restricted while it is in place, making the operation potentially messy. The main reason for the poor access problem is the adoption of the heat shield around the filter head **(see illustrations)**.

2

4500 mile / 7500 km Service

10 Engine oil and filter renewal

16D and 16DA engines, schedule C. 15D, 15DT, 17D 17DR, 17DTL and 17DT engines

Refer to Section 8 (see illustrations).

11 Fuel filter water drainage

16D and 16DA engines, schedule C

Refer to Section 9.

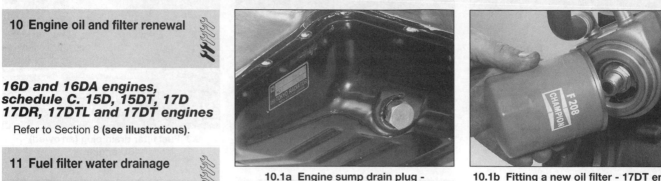

10.1a Engine sump drain plug - 17DT engine

10.1b Fitting a new oil filter - 17DT engine

6000 mile / 10 000 km Service

12 Idle speed check and adjustment

Caution: The usual type of tachometer which works from ignition system pulses cannot be used on diesel engines.

16D and 16DA engines, schedule A

⚠️ *Warning: Keep clear of the cooling fan when making adjustments.*

16D and early 16DA engines

1 The main difficulty in making engine speed adjustments is the measurement of the speed. Conventional tachometers cannot be used because they are triggered by ignition system pulses. Proprietary instruments are available which operate by sensing the passage of a mark on the crankshaft pulley, but they are expensive (see Chapter 8).

2 If the relationship of road speed to engine rpm is known for any gear, the vehicle can be positioned with its front wheels off the ground and the speedometer reading converted to rpm. Apply the handbrake and chock the rear wheels securely if this method is adopted. The accuracy of the speedometer may not be great, especially at the low speeds involved at idle.

3 A third possibility is the use of a dynamic timing light (stroboscope) connected to the ignition system of a petrol-engined vehicle. Make a chalk or paint mark on the crankshaft pulley of the diesel engine and shine the stroboscope at it. Run the petrol engine at the desired speed. When the diesel engine is running at the same speed, the pulley chalk mark will appear stationary. The same applies at half or twice the speed, so some common sense must be used.

4 If adjustment is necessary, remove the air cleaner snorkel to improve access. Slacken the locknut on the idle speed adjusting screw and turn the screw clockwise to increase the speed, anti-clockwise to decrease it. Tighten

the locknut, without altering the screw position, when adjustment is correct (see illustrations). Refit the snorkel.

Later 16DA engine

Bosch VE fuel injection pump
Caution: The manufacturer warns that injection pumps which have had the stop screw tampered with cannot be re-adjusted by a dealer, which suggests that the pump will have to be set up by a Bosch specialist.

5 Later versions of the Bosch VE injection pump require a revised idle speed adjustment procedure to that described above. The later pump can be identified by the vertical idle speed adjustment screw located on the front face of the pump. Where this type of pump is fitted, it is essential that the engine speed control lever stop screw is not disturbed. The positions of the adjustment screws are as shown (see illustration).

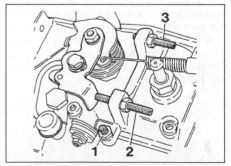

12.5 Bosch VE injection pump adjustment points - later 16DA and 17D engines

1 *Idle speed adjustment screw*
2 *Engine speed control lever stop screw - do not disturb*
3 *Maximum speed adjustment screw*

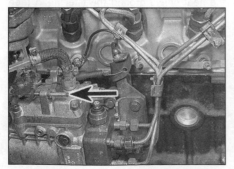

12.4a Idle speed adjusting screw (arrowed) on fuel injection pump - 16D engine

12.4b Adjusting the idle speed - 16D engine

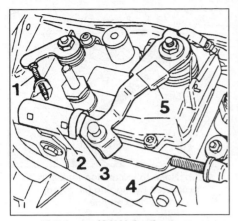

12.8 Lucas/CAV injection pump adjustment points - later 16DA and 17D engines

1 *Idle speed stop screw*
2 *Plastic anti-tamper cap*
3 *Engine speed control lever stop screw - do not disturb*
4 *Cut-off speed stop screw*
5 *Timing value for individual pump (marked on plate)*

6 Refer to paragraphs 1 to 4 for details of various methods of measuring the engine speed. It is recommended that the methods described in paragraph 1 or 3 be adopted for the following adjustments.
7 To adjust the idle speed, slacken the locknut on the idle speed adjustment screw and turn the screw as necessary to obtain the specified speed. Tighten the locknut, without disturbing the screw position, on completion.

Lucas/CAV fuel injection pump

8 The idle speed on engines fitted with the Lucas/CAV injection pump is adjusted using the stop screw shown **(see illustration)**. The engine speed control lever stop screw must not be disturbed and is covered with a plastic anti-tamper cap.
9 Refer to paragraphs 1 to 4 for details of various methods of measuring the engine speed. It is recommended that the methods described in paragraph 1 or 3 of that Section be adopted for the following adjustments.
10 To adjust the idle speed, slacken the locknut on the idle speed stop screw and turn

13.3 Removing the fuel filter element - 16D engine

the screw as necessary to obtain the specified speed. Tighten the locknut, without disturbing the screw position, on completion.

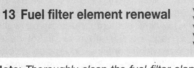

13 Fuel filter element renewal

Note: *Thoroughly clean the fuel filter element and carrier before removing the filter element*

16D and 16DA engines, schedule A

1 Thoroughly clean the filter element and carrier, especially around the joint between the two.
2 Drain the fuel from the filter by opening the vent and drain plugs. Catch the fuel in a container and dispose of it safely. Tighten the vent plugs.
3 Unscrew the filter element with the aid of a chain or strap wrench similar to that used for oil filter removal **(see illustration)**. Discard the old element and make sure that no sealing rings have been left behind on the filter carrier.
4 Place the sealing ring supplied with the new filter over the centre hole in the filter and clip it into place with the retainer **(see illustration)**.
5 Lubricate the outer sealing ring with a smear of clean fuel. Offer the filter to the carrier and tighten it with firm hand pressure

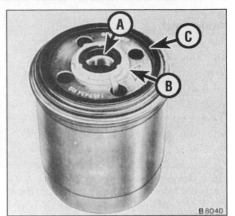

13.4 Fuel filter inner sealing ring (A) retainer (B) and outer sealing ring (C) - 16D engine

or as directed by the filter manufacturer. Tighten the drain plug.
6 Start the engine and run it at a fast idle for a minute or so to vent the system. Check around the filter seal for leaks, tightening a little further if necessary.

14 Air filter element renewal

Note: *Clean inside the air cleaner box before fitting the new element*

16D and 16DA engines, schedule A

1 Remove the air filter snorkel, which is held to the bonnet lock platform by two screws **(see illustration)**.
2 Slacken the screws which tension the two retaining clips **(see illustration)**.
3 Unhook the clips and remove the air cleaner box complete with element.
4 Remove and discard the old element **(see illustration)**. Wipe clean inside the air cleaner box.
5 Fit the new element to the box, engaging the rubber seal round the edge.
6 Engage the clips and tension them by tightening the screws.
7 Refit and secure the snorkel.

2

14.1 Remove the air filter snorkel . . .

14.2 . . . release the air cleaner retaining clips (arrowed) . . .

14.4 . . . and remove the filter element - 16D engine

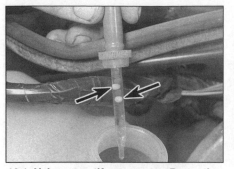

16.1 Using an antifreeze tester. Protection against freezing is shown by the position of the balls (arrowed)

17.3a Secure the heater hoses clear of the exhaust downpipe by plastic ties (arrowed) - 16D engine

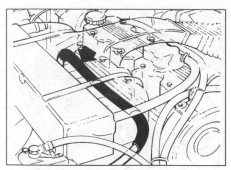

17.3b Hose to expansion tank can be protected by lagging (arrowed) - 16D engine

15 Auxiliary drivebelt check

16D and 16DA engines, schedule A

1 Disconnect the battery earth (negative) lead.

2 Inspect each drivebelt for cracks, fraying or other damage. Ideally the engine should be turned by hand so that the whole length of each belt can be inspected.

3 If the belt is in good condition, check the tension and adjust as necessary.

4 It is worth renewing the drivebelt as a precautionary measure at every fourth major service, even if it appears to be in good condition.

5 For information on belt renewal and adjustment, refer to Chapter 6.

16 Coolant strength check

16D and 16DA engines, schedule A

 Warning: Remember that antifreeze is poisonous and must be handled with due care.

1 The concentration of antifreeze in the system should be checked and made good if necessary. Most garages can do this check, or an instrument similar to a battery hydrometer can be purchased for making the check at home **(see illustration)**.

2 It is essential that an antifreeze mixture is retained in the cooling system at all times to act as a corrosion inhibitor and to protect the engine against freezing in winter months. The mixture should be made up from clean water with a low lime content (preferably rainwater) and a good quality ethylene glycol based antifreeze which contains a corrosion inhibitor and is suitable for use in aluminium engines.

3 The proportions of antifreeze to water required will depend on the manufacturer's recommendations, but the mixture must be adequate to give protection down to approximately -30°C (-22°F).

4 In climates which render frost protection redundant, it is still necessary to use a corrosion inhibitor in the cooling water. Suitable inhibitors should be available from a local GM agent or other reputable specialist.

17 Fluid leakage check

HAYNES HINT *Leaks in the cooling system will usually show up as white or rust-coloured deposits around the area adjoining the leak.*

16D and 16DA engines, schedules A, B and C

1 Visually inspect the engine joint faces, gaskets and seals for any signs of coolant or oil leaks. Pay particular attention to the areas around the cylinder head, oil filter and sump joint faces. Bear in mind that over a period of time some very slight seepage from these areas is to be expected but what you are really looking for is any indication of a serious leak. Should a leak be found, renew the offending gasket or oil seal by referring to the appropriate Chapter of this Manual.

2 Check the security and condition of all engine related pipes and hoses. Ensure that all cable-ties or securing clips are in place and in good condition. Clips which are broken or missing can lead to chafing of the hoses, pipes or wiring which could cause more serious problems in the future. If wire type hose clips are used, it may be a good idea to replace them with screw-type clips.

3 Pay particular attention to the heater hoses where they pass near the exhaust downpipe and to the spur to the expansion tank. When routed as shown, this spur can suffer from chafing. Protect it if necessary by lagging it with suitable adhesive tape **(see illustrations)**.

4 Renew any hose which is cracked, swollen or deteriorated. Cracks will show up better if the hose is squeezed.

5 If any damage or deterioration is discovered, do not drive the vehicle until the necessary repair work has been carried out.

9000 mile / 15 000 km Service

18 Idle speed check and adjustment

16D and 16DA engines, schedules B and C

1 Refer to Section 12.

17D engine

Bosch VE fuel injection pump

2 Refer to the information given for the later 16DA engine in Section 12.

Lucas/CAV fuel injection pump

3 Refer to the information given for the later 16DA engine in Section 12.

17DR and 17DTL engines

Bosch VE fuel injection pump

4 The Bosch injection pump fitted to these engines is equipped with a vacuum-operated cold start device which allows the engine idle speed to increase when the temperature is below 20°C (68°F) **(see illustration)**. Two idle speed adjustments are therefore necessary - one for a cold engine and one for a hot engine.

18.4 Bosch VE injection pump cold start device (arrowed) - 17DR and 17DTL engines

5 Refer to paragraphs 1 to 4 of Section 12 for various methods of measuring the engine speed. It is recommended that the methods described in paragraph 1 or 3 of that Section be adopted for the following adjustments.

6 With the engine cold (ie. below 20°C), check that there is approximately 2 to 3 mm of free play between the clamping sleeve on the end of the cold start device operating cable and the actuating lever **(see illustration)**. Alter the position of the clamping sleeve if necessary.

7 Start the engine, and check that the cold idling speed is as given in the *Specifications* at the start of this Chapter. If adjustment is necessary, turn the cold idling speed adjustment screw as required to achieve the desired speed **(see illustration)**.

8 Warm the engine up by taking the vehicle on a short test drive. With the engine temperature above 20°C, check that the cold start device operating cable has retracted and moved the actuating lever into contact with the hot idling speed adjustment screw. The engine should now be idling at the (lower) hot engine idling speed as given in the *Specifications*. If adjustment is necessary, turn the hot idling adjustment screw as necessary.

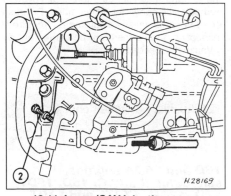

18.11 Lucas/CAV injection pump idle speed adjustment screws - 17DR and 17DTL engines

1 Vacuum unit thrust-rod locknut (cold idle adjustment)
2 Hot idling speed adjustment screw

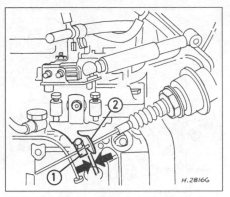

18.6 Checking cold start device free play - Bosch VE injection pump, 17DR and 17DTL engines

1 Clamping sleeve   2 Actuating lever
Arrows indicate free play checking point - engine cold

Lucas/CAV fuel injection pump

9 As with the Bosch pump described earlier, the Lucas/CAV injection pump is also equipped with a vacuum operated cold start device which allows the engine idle speed to increase when the temperature is below 20°C (68°F). Two idle speed adjustments are therefore necessary - one for a cold engine and one for a hot engine.

10 Refer to paragraphs 1 to 4 of Section 12 for various methods of measuring the engine speed. It is recommended that the methods described in paragraph 1 or 3 of that Section be adopted for the following adjustments.

11 With the engine cold (ie. below 20°C), check that the cold idling speed is as given in the *Specifications* at the start of this Chapter. If adjustment is necessary, slacken the locknut on the vacuum unit thrust-rod and turn the thrust-rod as required to achieve the desired speed **(see illustration)**. Tighten the locknut when the setting is correct.

12 Warm the engine up by taking the vehicle on a short drive. With the engine above 20°C, the engine should now be idling at the (lower) hot engine idling speed as given in the *Specifications*. If adjustment is necessary, slacken the locknut and turn the hot idling

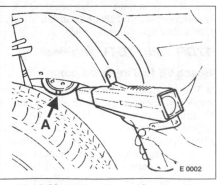

18.14 Measuring the engine speed - 15D and 15DT engines

A   1 to 2 cm wide aluminium foil strip

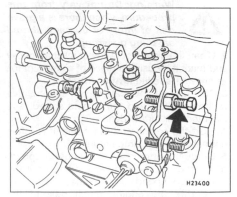

18.7 Bosch VE injection pump idle speed adjustment screws - 17DR and 17DTL engines

1 Cold idling speed adjustment screw
2 Hot idling speed adjustment screw

speed adjustment screw as necessary. Tighten the locknut when the setting is correct.

15D and 15DT engines

Checking

13 Measure the engine speed by using the following method. Do not vary from this procedure, since there is a grave risk of injury or damage should anything go wrong.

14 Clean the outer rim of the crankshaft pulley and mark it by using a piece of aluminium foil as shown **(see illustration)**.

15 Set up an optical or pulse-sensitive tachometer to read the engine speed, see Chapter 8 for further details.

16 Start the engine and run it until it reaches normal operating temperature.

17 With the engine at idle speed, observe the tachometer reading and compare it with the figure given in *Specifications*. If the idle speed is incorrect, adjust it as follows.

Adjustment

18 If adjustment is necessary, slacken the idle speed screw locknut and turn the screw until the desired result is obtained **(see illustration)**.

19 On completion, tighten the locknut without moving the screw.

18.18 Idle speed adjustment screw (arrowed) - 15D and 15DT engines

2

18.21 Adjusting the idle speed -
17DT engine

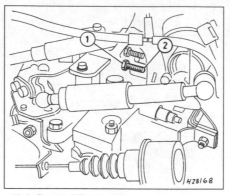

19.9 Bosch VE injection pump maximum
speed adjustment screw location -
17DR and 17DTL engines

1 Locknut
2 Adjustment screw

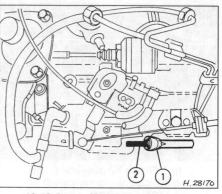

19.10 Lucas/CAV injection pump
maximum speed adjustment screw
location - 17DR and 17DTL engines

1 Lead seal
2 Cut-off speed stop screw

17DT engine

Checking

20 Proceed as detailed for the 15D and 15DT engines, noting the idle speed figure specified for the 17DT engine.

Adjustment

21 If adjustment is necessary, slacken the idle speed adjustment screw locknut and turn the screw until the desired result is obtained (see illustration).
22 On completion, tighten the locknut without moving the screw.

19 Maximum speed check and adjustment
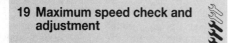

15D, 15DT and 17DT engines

Note: The fuel injection pump fitted to these engines has its maximum speed adjustment screw locked with a lead seal which must be removed for adjustment. As the screw should ideally be resealed after adjustment, it may be beneficial to leave this operation to a Bosch injection specialist.

Checking

1 Measure the engine speed by using the following method.

 Warning: Do not vary from this procedure, since there is a grave risk of injury or damage should anything go wrong.

2 Clean the outer rim of the crankshaft pulley and mark it by using a piece of aluminium foil as shown - see illustration 18.14.
3 Set up an optical or pulse-sensitive tachometer to read the engine speed, see Chapter 8 for further details.
4 Start the engine and run it until it reaches normal operating temperature.
5 Gradually increase the engine speed, observing the tachometer reading until the maximum speed is reached. Do not accelerate the engine much beyond the specified maximum, should maladjustment make this possible.

Adjustment

6 If adjustment is necessary, remove the lead seal from the maximum speed adjustment screw, slacken its locknut and turn the screw until the desired result is obtained. On completion, tighten the locknut without moving the screw.

17D engine

Bosch VE fuel injection pump

7 The procedure for adjustment of the maximum speed is the same as described in Chapter 4B, Section 8. Note that these later injection pumps have their maximum speed adjustment screws locked with a lead seal which must be removed for adjustment. As the screw should ideally be resealed after adjustment, it may be beneficial to leave this operation to a Bosch injection specialist.

Lucas/CAV fuel injection pump

8 Maximum (cut-off) speed is set in production, using the cut-off speed stop screw described in Chapter 4B, Section 8 . The screw is sealed with lead after adjustment has been made. As with all injection pumps it is not normally necessary to disturb the cut-off speed setting in normal circumstances, but if adjustment is necessary, it is recommended that this be carried out by a Lucas/CAV injection specialist.

17DR and 17DTL engines

Bosch VE fuel injection pump

9 The procedure for adjustment of the maximum speed is the same as described in Chapter 4B, Section 8. The location of the adjustment screw is as shown (see illustration). However, these later injection pumps may have their maximum speed adjustment screws locked with a lead seal which must be removed for adjustment. As the screw should ideally be resealed after adjustment, it may be beneficial to leave this operation to a Bosch injection specialist.

Lucas/CAV fuel injection pump

10 Maximum (cut-off) speed is set in production, using the cut-off speed stop screw shown (see illustration). The screw is sealed with lead after adjustment has been made. As with all injection pumps, it is not normally necessary to disturb the cut-off speed setting in normal circumstances; if adjustment is thought necessary, it is recommended that this be carried out by a Lucas/CAV injection specialist.

20 Exhaust emission check
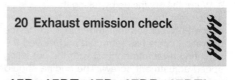

15D, 15DT, 17D, 17DR, 17DTL and 17DT engines

This check includes an inspection of "pollution-relevant" components, including the exhaust gas recirculation (EGR) system and catalytic converter, where fitted. Because of the specialist equipment required, inspection should therefore be carried out by a Vauxhall/Opel dealer.

21 Auxiliary drivebelt check
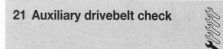

16D and 16DA engines, schedules B and C. 15D, 15DT, 17D, 17DR, 17DTL and 17DT engines

Refer to Section 15.

22 Throttle linkage lubrication

16D and 16DA engines, schedules B and C

Check the security and operation of all throttle linkage components.

Thoroughly clean each component part and lightly lubricate it with a light machine oil.

23 Coolant strength check

16D and 16DA engines, schedules B and C

Refer to Section 16.

24 Fluid leakage check

15D, 15DT, 17D, 17DR, 17DTL and 17DT engines

1 Visually inspect all engine joint faces, gaskets and seals for any signs of coolant or oil leaks. Pay particular attention to the areas around the cylinder head, oil filter and sump joint faces. Bear in mind that over a period of time some very slight seepage from these areas is to be expected but what you are really looking for is any indication of a serious leak. Should a leak be found, renew the offending gasket or oil seal by referring to the appropriate Chapter of this Manual.

2 Check the security and condition of all engine related pipes and hoses. Ensure that all cable-ties or securing clips are in place and in good condition. Clips which are broken or missing can lead to chafing of the hoses, pipes or wiring which could cause more serious problems in the future. If wire type hose clips are used, it may be a good idea to replace them with screw-type clips.

3 Immediately renew any hose which is cracked, swollen or deteriorated. Cracks will show up better if the hose is squeezed.

25 Fuel filter water drainage

15D, 15DT, 17D, 17DR, 17DTL and 17DT engines

Refer to Section 9.

26 Air filter element renewal

17D, 17DR and 17DTL engines

Early models

1 Refer to the information given for the 16D and 16DA engines in Section 14.

Later models

2 A revised inlet system designed to reduce noise has been fitted to these models. The air filter element has been relocated to a rectangular plastic housing which is mounted on the inner wing just behind the right-hand headlight.

3 Access to the filter element is gained after the clips securing the air cleaner lid have been released (see illustration).

26.3 Removing the air filter element - 17D engine

15D and 15DT engines

4 The air filter element on these models is in a rectangular plastic housing, mounted on the inner wing, behind the right-hand headlight.

5 Access to the element is gained by unclipping the housing lid and lifting it clear of the element with the outlet hose still attached (see illustration).

6 Remove and discard the old element (see illustration).

7 Wipe clean inside the element housing and its lid .

8 Fit the new element to the housing, engaging the rubber seal of the element round the housing edge.

9 Refit the housing lid, checking that the outlet hose is properly secured and not split.

17DT engine

10 The air filter element fitted to these models is located in a rectangular plastic housing mounted on top of the inlet manifold.

11 To gain access to the element, first release the filter to turbocharger feed hose from the housing end and then remove the housing retaining bolts to allow it to be lifted clear of the manifold (see illustration).

12 Remove and discard the old element (see illustration).

13 Wipe clean inside the plastic housing and manifold casing.

14 Fit the new element to the housing, engaging the rubber seal of the element round the housing edge.

15 Refitting of the element and housing is a reversal of removal.

26.5 Unclip the housing lid . . .

26.6 . . . to access to the filter element - 15D and 15DT engines

26.11 Lift the housing clear of the manifold . . .

26.12 . . . and remove the filter element - 17DT engine

2

18 000 mile / 30 000 km Service

27 Camshaft drivebelt condition and tension check

16D and 16DA engines, schedules A and B

Inspection

1 Remove the alternator drivebelt.

2 Remove the camshaft drivebelt covers. The large cover is secured by four screws - note the fuel pipe clip under one of them. The injection pump sprocket cover is secured by three screws **(see illustration)**. On 1987 models, the covers completely enclose the drivebelt and additional clamps and gaskets are fitted.

3 Turn the engine using a spanner on the crankshaft pulley bolt, removing the right-hand front wheel for access if necessary. Inspect the belt for damage or contamination. Pay particular attention to the roots of the teeth where cracking may occur. Renew the belt if it is damaged or contaminated. If necessary, attend to the source of contamination.

Tensioning

4 Belt tension can only be adjusted accurately using tension gauge KM-510-A or equivalent **(see illustration)**. If this gauge is not available, an approximation to the correct tension can be achieved by tensioning the belt so that it can just be twisted through 90° by thumb and forefinger in the middle of its longest run. A belt which is too tight will usually hum when running and a belt which is too slack will wear rapidly and may jump teeth. Use of a proper tension gauge is strongly recommended.

5 Settle the belt by rotating the crankshaft through half a turn in the normal direction of rotation. Fit the tension gauge to the slack side of the belt (the alternator side) and read the tension. Desired values are given in the *Specifications*.

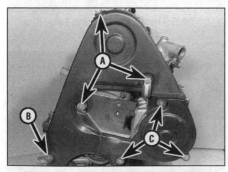

27.2 Camshaft drivebelt cover screw location - 16D engine

A Large cover - short screws
B Large cover - long screw
C Pump sprocket cover screws

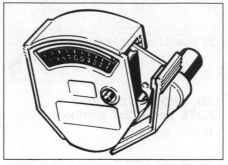

27.4 Camshaft drivebelt tension gauge

6 If adjustment is necessary, slacken the coolant pump bolts and pivot the pump to increase or decrease the tension. Nip up the coolant pump bolts.

7 Turn the crankshaft through one full turn, then recheck the tension. Keep adjusting the belt tension until a stable value is obtained.

8 Tighten the coolant pump bolts to the specified torque.

9 If the drivebelt has been re-tensioned or renewed, check the injection pump timing.

10 Refit the belt covers, clutch/flywheel cover and other disturbed components.

11 Refit the roadwheel, lower the vehicle and tighten the wheel bolts.

17DR and 17DTL engines

Inspection

12 The camshaft drivebelt cover is a two-piece assembly, it being necessary to remove the upper part prior to removal of the lower part.

13 Remove the auxiliary drivebelt(s) and the air cleaner assembly for access to the drivebelt cover. The power steering drivebelt (where applicable) should be removed as described in the relevant petrol-engine Manual.

14 To remove the upper part of the cover, undo the five securing bolts and lift it off the engine **(see illustration)**.

15 From under the front wheel arch, undo the four crankshaft pulley retaining bolts and withdraw the pulley from the drivebelt sprocket.

16 Undo the remaining three bolts and remove the lower part of the cover from the engine **(see illustration)**.

17 Turn the engine using a spanner on the crankshaft pulley bolt, removing the right-hand front wheel for access if necessary. Inspect the belt for damage or contamination. Pay particular attention to the roots of the teeth, where cracking may occur. Renew the belt if it is damaged or contaminated. If necessary, attend to the source of contamination.

27.14 Removing the camshaft drivebelt upper cover - 17DR engine

Tensioning

18 A spring-loaded automatic camshaft drivebelt tensioner is fitted to this engine. The tensioner automatically sets the drivebelt to the correct tension on assembly and maintains that tension for the life of the drivebelt.

19 If required, details of setting the automatic tensioner are contained in Section 4 of Chapter 3C.

28 Fuel filter element renewal

16D and 16DA engines, schedules B and C

Refer to Section 13.

29 Air filter element renewal

16D and 16DA engines, schedules B and C

Refer to Section 14.

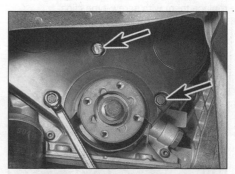

27.16 Removing the camshaft drivebelt lower cover (crankshaft pulley removed) - 17DR engine

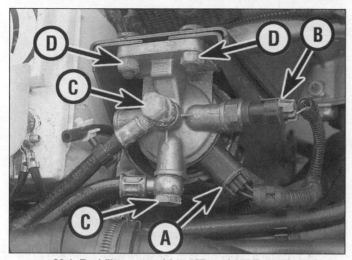

30.1 Fuel filter assembly - 15D and 15DT engines

A Heating element connector
B Temperature sensor connector
C Fuel pipe unions
D Retaining nuts

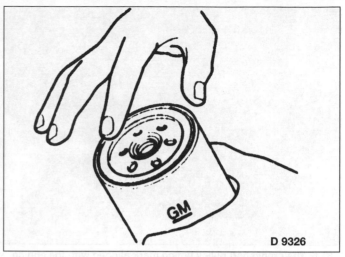

30.9 Lightly smear the sealing ring of a new element with clean diesel fuel before fitting

D 9326

30 Fuel filter element renewal

15D and 15DT engines

Removal

1 Because of its location in the engine bay and the fitting of a heat shield around it, access to the fuel filter element is extremely restricted (see illustration). To facilitate removal of the filter element, it is therefore necessary to withdraw the filter assembly from its heat shield.

2 Commence by disconnecting the battery earth (negative) lead.

3 Where fitted, unplug the wiring connectors from the heating element and temperature sensor.

4 Clean around the pipe unions and disconnect both fuel pipes from the filter element carrier. Renew the union sealing washers.

5 Blank off the exposed pipe connections to prevent any ingress of dirt and moisture.

6 Undo the filter assembly retaining nuts and withdraw the assembly from its heat shield.

7 Drain all water/fuel from the filter and dispose of it safely, whilst observing the usual safety precautions.

8 Grip the filter head carefully between the padded jaws of a vice and unscrew the element by using a chain or strap wrench.

Fitting

9 Fitting a filter element is a reversal of the removal procedure. Lightly smear the sealing ring of the new element with clean diesel fuel before fitting (see illustration).

10 Offer the element to its carrier and tighten it with firm hand pressure or as directed by the manufacturer.

11 Refit the filter assembly to its heat shield.

12 Remove all blanking materials and reconnect both fuel pipes to the filter element carrier, using new sealing washers.

13 Reconnect all electrical connections.

14 Start the engine and run it at a fast idle for a minute or so to vent the fuel system. Check the filter seal for leaks.

17D, 17DR and 17DTL engines

Unheated filter

15 Refer to Section 13.

Heated filter

16 This filter type can be dealt with as described for the unheated type. Depending on accessibility, it may be easier to withdraw the assembly from its heat shield and place it in a vice to facilitate unscrewing of the filter element. Refer to the procedure given for the 15D and 15DT engines.

17DT engine

Removal

17 Drain all water/fuel from the filter and dispose of it safely, whilst observing the usual safety precautions.

18 Unscrew the filter element with the aid of a chain or strap wrench. Discard the old element, making sure that no sealing ring has been left behind on the filter carrier.

Fitting

19 Smear the sealing ring of the new filter element with clean diesel fuel before fitting.

20 Offer the element to its carrier (see illustration) and tighten it with firm hand pressure or as directed by the manufacturer.

21 Start the engine and run it at a fast idle for a minute or so to vent the system. Check around the filter seal for leaks, tightening a little further if necessary.

31 Valve clearance check

15D, 15DT and 17DT engines

Caution: Never attempt to carry out valve clearance adjustment with the pistons at TDC as there is a possibility of the valves striking the piston crown.

1 The importance of having valve clearances correctly adjusted cannot be overstressed, as they vitally affect the performance of the engine. The engine must be cold for any check to be accurate.

2 The engine can be turned over by placing the engine in gear and rocking the vehicle back and forth. It will be easier to turn if the fuel injectors or glow plugs are removed.

3 The following procedure is for the valves of No 1 cylinder and should be repeated for the valves of the other three cylinders in the firing order of 1-3-4-2.

4 Remove the cylinder head cover (with attached baffle plate) to expose the camshaft. Obtain a new cover gasket.

2

30.20 Refitting the fuel filter element - 17DT engine

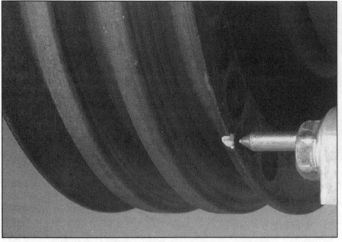

31.6 The crankshaft pulley timing mark aligned with the engine block reference pointer - 17DT engine

31.7 Using a feeler blade to measure valve clearance - 17DT engine

5 The Manufacturers recommend that the camshaft bearing cap retaining nuts are now checked for tightness to the specified torque.
6 Turn the crankshaft in the normal direction of rotation until the timing mark on its pulley aligns with the reference pointer on the engine block **(see illustration)**. In this position No 1 piston is at TDC on the firing stroke and the two cams of that cylinder are positioned with both valves closed.
7 Using feeler blades, measure the clearances between the Inlet and Exhaust cams and their respective shims **(see illustration)**.
The blade should be a stiff sliding fit in the gap. The valve sequence from the timing side of the engine is:

In - Ex - In - Ex - In - Ex - In - Ex

8 Each clearance should be equal to that specified. Should a clearance be incorrect, refer to the procedure for adjusting valve clearances given in Section 6, Chapter 3D.

27 000 mile / 45 000 km Service

32 Camshaft drivebelt condition and tension check

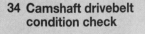

16D and 16DA engines, schedule C for adverse operating conditions

Refer to Section 27.

36 000 mile / 60 000 km Service

33 Camshaft drivebelt condition and tension check

16D and 16DA engines, schedule C for normal operating conditions

1 Refer to Section 27.

34 Camshaft drivebelt condition check

15D and 15DT engines

1 The drivebelt cover is a two-piece assembly, it being necessary to remove the upper part for drivebelt inspection.
2 Gain access to the drivebelt cover by first removing the air cleaner housing from its mounting on the right-hand side of the engine bay. Do this by first detaching the outlet tube retaining clamp at the engine manifold. Release the housing inlet scoop from the vehicle front crossmember and manoeuvre it clear of the housing. Disconnect the front retainer at the housing base and pull the housing forward to release it from its rear retainer.
3 Where necessary, release the brake servo vacuum line retaining clamp from the cover and pull the line from the servo unit, moving it to one side. Move any electrical cables clear of the drivebelt cover after having released their respective retaining clamps.
4 Remove the upper part of the drivebelt cover by undoing its securing bolts (noting their respective lengths) and lifting it from position.
5 With the drivebelt thus exposed, turn the engine and inspect the belt for damage or contamination. Pay particular attention to the roots of the teeth, where cracking may occur. Renew the belt if it is damaged or contaminated. If necessary, attend to the source of contamination.

17DT engine

6 The drivebelt cover is a two-piece assembly, it being necessary to remove the upper part for drivebelt inspection.
7 Gain access to the drivebelt cover by first removing the air inlet collector box from its mounting on the right-hand side of the engine bay. Proceed as follows:

34.8a Release the air intake collector box lid retaining clips, screws (A) and alternator cable ties (B) . . .

34.8b . . . and depress the retaining tangs (arrowed) before releasing the collector box - 17DT engine in Cavalier

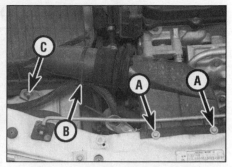

34.9 Remove the air intake collector box inlet scoop securing screws (A) unclip the cable loom (B) and release the box front mounting nut (C) - 17DT engine in Astra

Cavalier

8 Remove the box lid retaining screws and clips and the outlet tube retaining clamp at the engine air filter box. With the lid removed, remove the box retaining nuts and release the box inlet tube to allow the box to be lifted from position, unclipping the alternator cable-ties if necessary. Note that the inlet tube may be a very tight fit on the box stub, ensure that the retaining tangs are fully depressed before attempting to release the tube (see illustrations).

Astra

9 Release the box inlet scoop from the vehicle front crossmember by removing its two securing screws and then pull it clear of the box inlet stub. Unclip the cable loom from the inlet stub (see illustration). Release the outlet tube retaining clamp at the engine air filter box. Release the box mounting nuts at its base and lift the box from the vehicle.

All models

10 Release the brake servo vacuum line retaining clamp and pull the line from the servo unit (see illustrations).

34.10a Release the brake servo vacuum line retaining clamp (arrowed) . . .

11 Remove the upper part of the drivebelt cover by undoing its nine securing bolts (noting their respective lengths) and lifting it from position.
12 With the drivebelt thus exposed, turn the engine and inspect the belt for damage or contamination. Look for contamination caused by oil or coolant leaks, and pay particular attention to the roots of the teeth, where cracking may occur. Renew the belt if it is damaged or contaminated. If necessary, attend to the source of contamination.

34.10b . . . and pull the line from the servo unit - 17DT engine

35 Camshaft drivebelt renewal

16D and 16DA engines, schedules A and B

Refer to Chapter 3B, Section 4.

17D, 17DR and 17DTL engines

Refer to Chapter 3C, Section 4.

2

54 000 mile / 90 000 km Service

36 Camshaft drivebelt renewal

16D and 16DA engines, schedule C for adverse operating conditions

Refer to Chapter 3B, Section 4.

60 000 mile / 100 000 km Service

37 Glow plug renewal

16D and 16DA engines, schedule A

Removal

1 Disconnect the battery earth lead.
2 Remove the air cleaner snorkel.

3 Disconnect the feed wire from the glow plug bus bar **(see illustration)**.
4 Unscrew the retaining nuts and remove the bus bar and link wire from each glow plug **(see illustration)**. Note the position of the washers.
5 Unscrew and remove the glow plugs **(see illustration)**.

Fitting

6 Refit in the reverse order of removal. Tighten the glow plugs to the specified torque and make sure that the electrical connections are clean and tight.

37.3 **Disconnect the glow plug bus bar feed wire . . .**

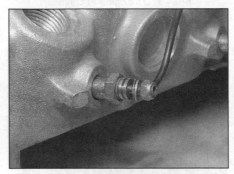

37.4 **. . . unscrew the retaining nuts and remove the bus bar and link wire from each glow plug . . .**

37.5 **. . . then remove the glow plugs - 16D engine**

63 000 mile / 105 000 km Service

38 Glow plug renewal

16D and 16DA engines, schedules B and C. 17D, 17DR and 17DTL engines

1 Refer to Section 37.

15D, 15DT and 17DT engines

Removal

2 Disconnect the battery earth lead.
3 Disconnect the feed wire from the glow plug bus bar **(see illustration)**.
4 Unscrew the retaining nuts and remove the bus bar from each glow plug. Note the position of the washers.
5 Unscrew and remove the glow plugs.

Fitting

6 Refit in the reverse order of removal. Tighten the glow plugs to the specified torque and make sure that the electrical connections are clean and tight.

39 Camshaft drivebelt renewal

16D and 16DA engines, schedule C for normal operating conditions

1 Refer to Chapter 3B, Section 4.

15D and 15DT engines (up to '91)

2 Refer to Chapter 3A, Section 4.

38.3 **Disconnecting the glow plug bus bar feed wire. Glow plug arrowed - 17DT engine**

72 000 mile / 120 000 km Service

40 Camshaft drivebelt renewal

15D and 15DT engines (from '92)

1 Refer to Chapter 3A, Section 4.

17DT engine

2 Refer to Chapter 3D, Section 4.

Every 2 years, regardless of mileage

41 Coolant renewal

⚠️ **Warning: Take care to avoid scalding when removing the cooling system expansion tank cap. Place a thick cloth over the cap before turning it anti-clockwise.**
Caution: Never operate the vehicle with plain water in the cooling system, except in an emergency. Apart from the risk of freezing in winter weather, serious corrosion and rust and scale formation may occur.

16D and 16DA engines, schedules A, B and C. 17D, 17DR and 17DTL engines

⚠️ *Warning: Antifreeze is poisonous and must be handled with due care.*

Draining

1 The system should only be drained when it is cool. If it must be drained hot, take great care to avoid scalding.
2 Remove the expansion tank cap. If the system is hot, place a thick cloth over the cap before turning it anti-clockwise.
3 Place a container underneath the radiator bottom hose. Disconnect the hose from the radiator and allow the system to drain **(see illustration)**.
4 There is no cylinder block drain plug, making it impossible to drain the system completely.

Flushing

5 If coolant has been neglected, or if the antifreeze mixture has become diluted, then in time the cooling system will gradually lose efficiency as the cooling passages become choked with rust, scale deposits and other sediment. To restore cooling system efficiency it is necessary to flush the system clean.
6 First drain the system and then remove the thermostat. Temporarily refit the thermostat housing and reconnect the hose.
7 Insert a garden hose into the disconnected radiator bottom hose and secure it in place with rags. Turn on the supply and allow clean water to flow through the system and out of the radiator bottom outlet. Continue flushing for ten to fifteen minutes or until clean rust-free water emerges from the radiator.
8 If contamination is particularly bad, reverse flush the system by inserting the hose in the radiator bottom outlet and allow the water to flow through the system and out of the radiator bottom hose. This should dislodge deposits that were not moved by conventional flushing. If any doubt exists about the cleanliness of the radiator after flushing, it should be removed so that it can be flushed and agitated at the same time. After severe flushing, carry out a normal flow flush before refitting the thermostat and reconnecting the system hoses.
9 In extreme cases, the use of a proprietary de-scaling compound may be necessary. If such a compound is used, adhere to the manufacturer's instructions and satisfy yourself that no damage will be caused to the engine or cooling system components.
10 If the coolant is renewed regularly, flushing will not normally be required, simply drain the old coolant and refill with a fresh mixture.

Filling

11 Make sure that all hoses and clips are in good condition. Refit any disturbed hoses and see that their clips are tight.
12 Fill the system via the expansion tank cap. If new coolant is being put in, start by pouring in the required quantity of neat antifreeze and follow it up with the water.
13 Massage the large coolant hoses to help displace air pockets during filling.
14 Most vehicles will be fitted with a self-venting cooling system this can be recognised by the two small vent hoses which enter the top of the expansion tank. If the system is not self-venting, open the bleed screw on the thermostat elbow during filling and close it when coolant runs out at the bleed screw **(see illustration)**.
15 When the system appears full, refit the expansion tank cap. Run the engine up to operating temperature, keeping a look-out for coolant leaks, then stop it and allow it to cool. Recheck the coolant level and top-up if necessary.
16 Recheck the tightness of all hose clips when the engine has cooled, and again after a few hundred miles.

Antifreeze mixture

17 The antifreeze mixture should be made up from clean water with a low lime content (preferably rainwater) and a good quality ethylene glycol based antifreeze which contains a corrosion inhibitor and is suitable for use in aluminium engines.
18 The proportions of antifreeze to water required will depend on the manufacturer's recommendations but the mixture must be adequate to give protection down to approximately -30°C (-22°F).

15D, 15DT and 17DT engines

19 Follow the above procedure when renewing the coolant of these engines but note that a cylinder block drain plug is provided, making it possible to drain the cooling system completely **(see illustration)**.
20 Before refitting the drain plug, coat its threads with sealing compound (to GM spec. 15 03 166).

2

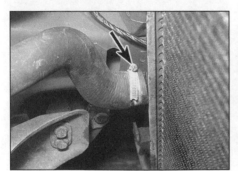

41.3 Release the radiator bottom hose clamp (arrowed) to drain the cooling system - 16D engine

41.14 The thermostat elbow coolant bleed screw (arrowed) - 16D engine

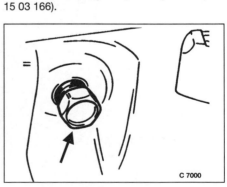

C 7000

41.19 The cylinder block coolant drain plug (arrowed) - 17DT engine

Chapter 3 Part A:
Engine overhaul - 15D and 15DT engines

Contents

Degrees of difficulty

Easy, suitable for novice with little experience	**Fairly easy,** suitable for beginner with some experience	**Fairly difficult,** suitable for competent DIY mechanic	**Difficult,** suitable for experienced DIY mechanic	**Very difficult,** suitable for expert DIY or professional

Specifications

General

Engine type:

15D . . . . Normally aspirated, 4-cylinder, four stroke, overhead camshaft, indirect injection, compression ignition.

15DT . . . . Turbocharged, 4-cylinder, four stroke, overhead camshaft, indirect injection, compression ignition.

Bore . . . . 76.00 mm
Stroke . . . . 82.00 mm
Displacement . . . . 1488 cc
Firing order . . . . 1-3-4-2 (No 1 at pulley end)
Compression ratio:

15D . . . . 23 : 1
15DT . . . . 22 : 1

Maximum power:

15D . . . . 49 bhp @ 4800 rpm
15DT . . . . 66 bhp @ 4600 rpm

Maximum torque:

15D . . . . 90 Nm @ 2400 rpm
15DT . . . . 132 Nm @ 2400 rpm

Camshaft drivebelt

Tension . . . . Automatically tensioned by tension roller

3A

Cylinder head

	Thickness	Identification
Gasket thickness and identification:		
Piston projection 0.58 to 0.64 mm	1.35 mm	One notch
Piston projection 0.65 to 0.70 mm	1.40 mm	Two notches
Piston projection 0.71 to 0.78 mm	1.45 mm	Three notches

Valve clearance adjustment .... By exchanging shims

Valve seat width in head:
  Inlet:
    New seats .... 1.2 to 1.5 mm
    Run-in seats .... 2.0 mm maximum
  Exhaust:
    New seats .... 1.2 to 1.5 mm
    Run-in seats .... 2.0 mm maximum

Valve stem play in guide:
  Inlet .... 0.02 to 0.20 mm
  Exhaust .... 0.03 to 0.25 mm

Recess of valve head when fitted:
  Inlet .... 0.5 to 1.0 mm
  Exhaust .... 0.5 to 1.0 mm

Swirl chamber projection .... 0.00 to 0.03 mm

Sealing surface finish deviation:
  Head to block .... 0.0 to 0.1 mm
  Head to manifold .... 0.00 to 0.20 mm

Overall height of head:
  Maximum .... 131.45 to 131.55 mm
  Minimum .... 131.25 mm

Valves

Clearances:
  Inlet .... 0.15 mm
  Exhaust .... 0.25 mm

Length:
  Inlet .... 104 mm
  Exhaust .... 104 mm

Head diameter:
  Inlet .... 34.6 mm
  Exhaust .... 30.6 mm

Stem diameter (standard):
  Inlet .... 6.88 to 7.0 mm
  Exhaust .... 6.88 to 7.0 mm

Valve guide bore (standard) .... 7.10 mm
Valve sealing face angle .... 44°

Camshaft and bearings

Camshaft radial run-out .... 0.03 to 0.10 mm
Camshaft endfloat .... 0.05 to 0.20 mm
Cam lift:
  Inlet .... 8.70 mm
  Exhaust .... 8.63 mm

Cylinder bores

	Diameter	Identification
Production size:		
A	76.00 to 76.01 mm	Coefficient on crankcase
B	76.01 to 76.02 mm	Coefficient on crankcase
C	76.02 to 76.03 mm	Coefficient on crankcase
D	76.03 to 76.04 mm	Coefficient on crankcase
Service oversize 0.5 mm:		
A	76.50 to 76.51 mm	Coefficient on crankcase
B	76.51 to 76.52 mm	Coefficient on crankcase
C	76.52 to 76.53 mm	Coefficient on crankcase
D	76.53 to 76.54 mm	Coefficient on crankcase
Service oversize 1.0 mm:		
A	77.00 to 77.01 mm	Coefficient on crankcase
B	77.01 to 77.02 mm	Coefficient on crankcase
C	77.02 to 77.03 mm	Coefficient on crankcase
D	77.03 to 77.04 mm	Coefficient on crankcase
Rebore limit	77.04 mm	
Bore out-of-round and taper	0.01 mm max	

Pistons

		Diameter	Identification
Production size:			
A	....	75.97 to 75.98 mm	Coefficient on piston head
B	....	75.98 to 75.99 mm	Coefficient on piston head
C	....	75.99 to 76.00 mm	Coefficient on piston head
D	....	76.00 to 76.01 mm	Coefficient on piston head
Service oversize 0.5 mm:			
A	....	76.47 to 76.48 mm	Coefficient on piston head
B	....	76.48 to 76.49 mm	Coefficient on piston head
C	....	76.49 to 76.50 mm	Coefficient on piston head
D	....	76.50 to 76.51 mm	Coefficient on piston head
Service oversize 1.0 mm:			
A	....	76.97 to 76.98 mm	Coefficient on piston head
B	....	76.98 to 76.99 mm	Coefficient on piston head
C	....	76.99 to 77.00 mm	Coefficient on piston head
D	....	77.00 to 77.01 mm	Coefficient on piston head
Clearance in bore	....	0.015 to 0.035 mm	
Projection at TDC (used to determine head gasket thickness)	....	0.58 to 0.78 mm	

Piston rings

Thickness:	
Top compression	2.0 mm
Centre compression	1.5 mm
Oil scraper	3.0 mm
End gap (fitted):	
Top compression	0.25 to 0.80 mm
Centre compression and oil scraper	0.20 to 0.80 mm
Vertical clearance in groove:	
Top compression	0.09 to 0.15 mm
Centre compression	0.04 to 0.10 mm
Oil scraper	0.025 to 0.10 mm
Gap offset	90°

Gudgeon pins

Length	59.8 to 60.0 mm
Diameter:	
Type 1	21.97 to 22.0 mm
Type 2	24.97 to 25.0 mm
Clearance:	
In piston	0.002 to 0.012 mm
In connecting rod	0.008 to 0.050 mm

Connecting rods

Weight variation (in same engine)	4 g.
Torsion	0.05 mm
Parallelism	0.05 mm
Endfloat on crankshaft	0.20 to 0.40 mm
Bearing running clearance	0.025 to 0.100 mm

Identification - rod marking:	Bearing shell colour code	Bearing clearance
I	Blue	0.025 to 0.054 mm
II	Black	0.027 to 0.056 mm
III	Brown	0.029 to 0.058 mm

Crankshaft and bearings

Bearing journal out-of-round and taper	0.025 mm
Shaft run-out (measured at centre main bearing journal)	0.00 to 0.06 mm
Shaft endfloat	0.06 to 0.30 mm
Main bearing running clearance	0.03 to 0.10 mm

Bearing bore size marking:	Diameter
1	51.992 to 52.000 mm
2	51.984 to 51.991 mm
3	51.976 to 51.983 mm

Main bearing shell size marking:	Journal diameter	Bearing play
Blue	47.918 to 47.928	0.032 to 0.058 mm
Black	47.929 to 47.938	0.030 to 0.056 mm
Black	47.918 to 47.928	0.032 to 0.058 mm
Brown	47.929 to 47.938	0.030 to 0.056 mm
Brown	47.918 to 47.928	0.032 to 0.058 mm
Green	47.929 to 47.938	0.030 to 0.056 mm

3A

Flywheel

Run-out	0.5 mm max
Refacing limit (depth of material removed from clutch wear face)	0.3 mm max

Lubrication system

System type	Wet sump, pressure feed, full flow filter
Lubricant type/specification/capacity	Refer to *"Lubricants, fluids and capacities"*
Filter type	Champion F126
Oil pressure (at idle, engine warm)	1.5 bar
Pump tolerances:	
Pump shaft to cylinder block:	
New shaft	0.032 to 0.074 mm
Run-in shaft	0.20 mm max
Rotors to pump cover:	
New rotors	0.04 to 0.09 mm
Run-in rotors	0.15 mm max
Outer rotor to cylinder block:	
New rotor	0.24 to 0.36 mm
Run-in rotor	0.40 mm max
Outer rotor to inner rotor mesh:	
New rotors	0.13 to 0.15 mm
Run-in rotor	0.20 mm max

Coolant pump

Type	Impeller
Drive	From crankshaft via V-belt

Coolant thermostat

Type	Bypass/twin valve
Identification	88
Opening commences at	88°C
Fully open at	106°C

Torque wrench settings

	Nm	lbf ft
Cylinder head		
Cylinder head bolts:		
Stage 1:		
Up to May 1989	30	22
From May 1989	40	30
Stage 2	Tighten a further 60 to 75°	
Stage 3	Tighten a further 60 to 75°	
Cover bolts	8	6
Camshaft		
Drivebelt sprocket bolts	10	7
Drivebelt cover to cylinder block	8	6
Drivebelt guide roller to cylinder block	80	60
Drivebelt tension roller bolt and nut	19	15
Bearing cap to cylinder head	25	18
Crankshaft		
Pulley-to-sprocket bolts	20	15
Drivebelt sprocket centre bolt	133 to 161	98 to 118
Flywheel to crankshaft:		
Stage 1	30	22
Stage 2	Tighten a further 45 to 60°	
Main bearing caps	88	66
Connecting rod caps:		
Stage 1	25	18
Stage 2	Tighten a further 45 to 60°	
Rear seal bracket to cylinder block	10	7
Lubrication system		
Pump cover to cylinder block	10	7
Pump inlet pipe to cylinder block	15	11
Drivebelt pulley to pump	50	38
Pressure regulator valve	45	33
Pressure switch	20	15
Cooler to cylinder block central hollow screw	50	38

Torque wrench settings

	Nm	lbf ft
Lubrication system (continued)		
Cooler to cylinder block securing bolt	26	20
Cooler thermostat housing to cylinder head	19	15
Cooler thermostat cover to cylinder head	30	22
Cooler banjo bolt to cylinder block	49	37
Filter to cylinder block	15	11
Return hose connection to turbocharger	10	7
Pressure line to turbocharger	15	11
Pressure line connection - turbocharger	41	30
Pressure line to cylinder block pipe connection (cap nut)	28	21
Pressure line to cylinder block pipe connection	20	15
Line to vacuum pump	25	18
Line to vacuum pump banjo bolt	22	16
Line to cylinder block	15	11
Sump to cylinder block	10	7
Drain plug	78	56
Baffle plate to cylinder block	19	15
Cooling system		
Pump to cylinder block	20	15
Drivebelt pulley to pump	10	7
Temperature sensor to thermostat housing	8	6
Thermostat housing to cylinder head	30	22
Thermostat housing cover to housing	30	22
Drain plug to cylinder block	39	30
Line to turbocharger	8	6
Pipe to cylinder block	95	70
Power steering system (where fitted)		
Pump mounting bracket to cylinder block	60	44
Mountings		
Right-hand mounting bracket:		
To cylinder block	45	33
To damping block	45	33
Engine rear suspension bracket:		
To damping block	65	47
To gearbox	90	66
To underbody	75	55
Tension strut to crossmember	60	44
Other components		
Alternator mounting bracket to cylinder block	40	30
Vacuum pump to alternator	7	5
Starter motor to cylinder block	40	30
Turbocharger support to cylinder block	50	38
Transmission to cylinder block	60	44

3A

1 General information

Installed in the Nova and Corsa, this engine appears in turbocharged (15DT) and non turbocharged (15D) versions and is of four-cylinder overhead camshaft design. The cylinder head is of light alloy construction and the block is of iron. The crankshaft runs in five main bearings.

The camshaft is belt-driven from the crankshaft sprocket. The same belt drives the oil pump and the fuel injection pump. Belt tension is automatically adjusted by means of a spring and pulley adjuster.

The coolant pump is driven by a V-belt which runs from the crankshaft pulley, as is the power steering pump (where fitted) and alternator (which has the vacuum pump attached).

Lubrication is by means of the crankshaft driven pump, oil being drawn from the sump and pumped through a full flow filter before entering the main oil galleries in the block and crankshaft. The oil is cooled by passing through a cooler unit located between the oil filter and cylinder block.

Valve clearance adjustment is by means of exchanging shims. Maintenance tasks are mostly straightforward but operations which involve disturbing or checking the valve timing should not be undertaken unless the necessary equipment is available.

2 Major operations possible with the engine in the vehicle

1 Since the cylinder head, sump and camshaft drivebelt covers can all be removed with the engine in the vehicle, most dismantling can be carried out without removing the engine. However, access to some areas is difficult and if much work is to be done, it may be quicker in the long run to remove the engine.

2 Removal of the oil pump and crankshaft front and rear oil seals entails removal of the sump, due to the sump end holding studs passing through the seal retaining plates.

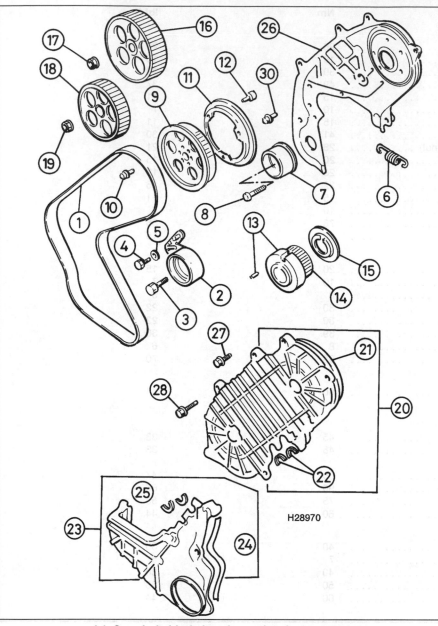

4.1 Camshaft drivebelt and associated components

1 Camshaft drivebelt	11 Sprocket flange
2 Tensioner pulley	12 Screw
3 Bolt	13 Crankshaft sprocket
4 Bolt	14 Locating pin
5 Washer	15 Flange disc
6 Tensioner spring	16 Fuel injection pump sprocket
7 Guide roller	17 Nut
8 Bolt	18 Oil pump sprocket
9 Camshaft sprocket	19 Nut
10 Bolt	20 Drivebelt upper front cover

21 Cover seal
22 Cover seal
23 Drivebelt lower front cover
24 Cover seal
25 Cover seal
26 Drivebelt rear cover
27 Bolt
28 Screw
29 Screw
30 Screw

3 In theory, even the crankshaft and main bearings can be removed with the engine installed but this is not recommended unless there is some compelling reason for not removing the engine.

3 Engine oil and oil filter - renewal

Refer to the appropriate Section of Chapter 2.

4 Camshaft drivebelt - inspection, removal, refitting and tensioning

Caution: A camshaft drivebelt which is damaged, oil-soaked or fuel soaked must be renewed or it will fail, resulting in serious engine damage.

1 The camshaft drivebelt (sometimes called the timing belt) also drives the oil pump and fuel injection pump **(see illustration)**.

Inspection

2 Refer to the appropriate Section of Chapter 2.

Removal

3 Disconnect the battery earth lead.
4 Remove the drivebelt upper cover as explained in drivebelt inspection.
5 Gain access to the side of the engine through the right-hand wheel arch.
6 Support the engine by positioning a jack beneath its sump and raising it slightly. Protect the sump by placing a piece of thick wood between it and the jack.
7 Remove the engine right-hand mounting assembly, see Section 19.
8 Where applicable, slacken the power steering pump upper and lower retaining bolts to allow the pump to be moved towards the engine, see Chapter 6. With the V-belt slackened, detach it from the crankshaft, coolant pump and power steering pump pulleys.
9 Slacken the alternator pivot and retaining bolts and move it towards the engine. With the V-belt slackened, detach it from the crankshaft, coolant pump and alternator pulleys.
10 Turn the crankshaft in the normal direction of rotation until the timing mark on its pulley aligns with the reference pointer on the engine block **(see illustration)**. In this position No 1 piston is at TDC on the firing stroke.
11 Now check that the locking bolt holes in the camshaft and fuel injection pump sprockets are aligned with their respective threaded holes in the engine casing before

4.10 Align the timing mark on the crankshaft pulley with the reference pointer on the engine block to bring No 1 piston to TDC on the firing stroke

4.11a Insert the locking bolt (arrowed) through the camshaft sprocket . . .

4.11b . . . and insert the locking bolt through the injection pump sprocket

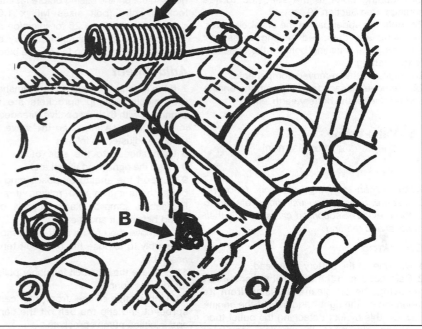

4.14 Release the camshaft drivebelt tensioner pulley securing bolts (A and B) and remove the spring (C)

inserting the locking bolts (bolt sizes M6 x 1.00 for camshaft and M8 x 1.25 for injection pump) **(see illustrations)**.

12 Mark the fitted position of the crankshaft pulley. Remove the pulley bolts and detach the pulley, tapping its rim to free it if necessary.

13 Remove the lower part of the drivebelt cover to fully expose the belt.

14 Release the drivebelt tensioner pulley and remove the spring **(see illustration)**.

15 Mark the running direction of the drivebelt if it is to be reused. Also take care not to kink the belt, nor get oil, grease etc. on it.

16 Unbolt the flange from the camshaft sprocket **(see illustration)**. Slip the belt off the sprocket and then the remaining sprockets to remove it from the engine .

Refitting and tensioning

17 Commence refitting by first placing the drivebelt over the camshaft sprocket and then the injection pump sprocket etc. until it is correctly routed **(see illustration)**. The crankshaft must not be disturbed and the camshaft and fuel injection pump sprockets should still be locked in alignment. Refit the flange to the camshaft sprocket.

18 Remove the camshaft and fuel injection pump sprocket alignment bolts.

19 Refit the drivebelt tensioner spring and check that the tensioner assembly moves freely before tightening the tensioner securing bolts to the specified torque setting **(see illustration)**.

20 Refit the lower part of the drivebelt cover to the engine, renewing any damaged sealing strips and tightening the retaining bolts to the specified torque setting.

21 Refit the crankshaft pulley in its previously noted position, tightening its retaining bolts to the specified torque setting.

22 Refit and tension each auxiliary drivebelt, referring to the appropriate Section of Chapter 2.

3A

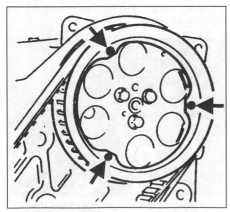

4.16 Remove the camshaft sprocket flange securing screws (arrowed)

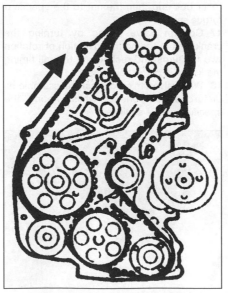

4.17 Ensure the camshaft drivebelt is correctly routed
Arrow denotes direction of belt travel

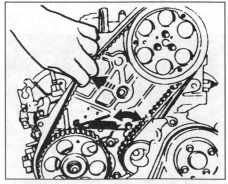

4.19 Refit the drivebelt tensioner spring and check that the tensioner assembly moves freely before tightening the tensioner securing bolts

23 Refit the engine right-hand mounting in the reverse sequence to removal, tightening all retaining bolts to the specified torque settings. See Section 19.

24 Refit the upper part of the drivebelt cover, renewing any damaged sealing strips and tightening the retaining bolts to the specified torque setting.

25 Refit all other removed components.

26 Remove the jack from beneath the engine and reconnect the battery earth lead.

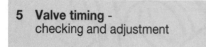

5 Valve timing - checking and adjustment

Note: *When carrying out the following procedure, refer to the illustrations referred to in the previous Section on camshaft drivebelt removal and refitting.*

Checking

1 Disconnect the battery earth lead.

2 Gain access to the drivebelt cover by first removing the air cleaner housing from its mounting on the right-hand side of the engine bay. Do this by first detaching the outlet tube retaining clamp at the engine manifold. Release the box inlet scoop from the vehicle front crossmember and manoeuvre it clear of the housing. Disconnect the front retainer at the housing base and pull the housing forward to release it from its rear retainer.

3 Where necessary, release the brake servo vacuum line retaining clamp from the cover and pull the line from the servo unit, moving it to one side. Move any electrical cables clear of the drivebelt cover after having released their respective retaining clamps.

4 Remove the upper part of the drivebelt cover by undoing its securing bolts (noting their respective lengths) and lifting it from position.

5 Turn the crankshaft in the normal direction of rotation until the timing mark on its pulley aligns with the reference pointer on the engine block. In this position No 1 piston is at TDC on the firing stroke.

6 Now check that the valve timing is correct by ensuring that the locking bolt holes in the camshaft and fuel injection pump sprockets are aligned with their respective threaded holes in the engine casing before inserting the locking bolts (bolt sizes M6 x 1.00 for camshaft and M8 x 1.25 for injection pump). The mark on the crankshaft pulley should align with the pointer on the engine block.

Adjustment

7 If the locking bolt holes in the camshaft and fuel injection pump sprockets are not in alignment with their respective threaded holes in the engine casing, then the valve timing must be adjusted as follows.

8 Gain access to the side of the engine through the right-hand wheel arch.

9 Support the engine by positioning a jack beneath its sump and raising it slightly. Protect the sump by placing a piece of thick wood between it and the jack.

10 Remove the engine right-hand mounting assembly to expose the drivebelt tensioner assembly.

11 Release the drivebelt tensioner pulley and remove the spring.

12 Unbolt the flange from the camshaft sprocket and slip the belt off the camshaft and injection pump sprockets.

13 Rotate the camshaft and fuel injection pump sprockets by the least amount until the locking bolt holes are aligned with their respective threaded holes in the engine casing. Insert the locking bolts. The mark on the crankshaft pulley should still align with the pointer on the engine block.

14 Place the drivebelt over the injection pump and camshaft sprockets.

15 Remove the sprocket locking bolts.

16 Refit the drivebelt tensioner spring and check that the tensioner assembly moves freely before first tightening the tensioner roller bolt and then the nut to the specified torque setting.

17 Confirm valve timing by turning the crankshaft in the normal direction of rotation two full turns and rechecking that all timing marks are in correct alignment.

18 With valve timing correct, reassemble all disturbed components whilst noting the specified torque settings.

6 Valve clearances - checking and adjustment

Refer to Section 6, Chapter 3D.

7 Cylinder head - removal and refitting

Caution: Wait until the engine is cold before removing the cylinder head bolts

Removal

1 Disconnect the battery earth lead.

2 Drain the cooling system, recovering the coolant if it is fit for re-use.

3 Remove the camshaft drivebelt (Section 4).

15D engine

4 Detach the air resonator box from the plenum chamber by removing the lower hose clamp and the box securing bolts **(see illustration)**.

5 Remove the EGR valve and pipe assembly from the inlet and exhaust manifolds by disconnecting the following:

a) *The pipe flange to exhaust manifold bolts (see illustration)*

b) *The pipe to cylinder head support*

c) *The vacuum pipe from the EGR valve (see illustration)*

d) *The EGR valve to inlet manifold bolts*

15DT engine

6 Remove the plenum chamber to turbocharger feed hose by disconnecting the following **(see illustration)**:

a) *The hose to cylinder head cover breather pipe clip*

b) *The hose centre section support*

c) *The hose to turbocharger securing clamp*

d) *The hose to plenum chamber securing clamp*

7 Remove the turbocharger to inlet manifold hose located beneath the above by unbolting it from the inlet manifold, unclipping it from the turbocharger and then releasing it from the cylinder head.

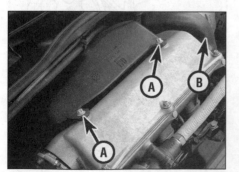

7.4 Detach the air resonator box from the plenum chamber by removing its securing bolts (A) and hose clamp (B)

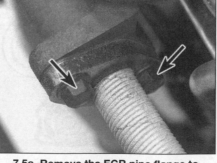

7.5a Remove the EGR pipe flange to exhaust manifold bolts (arrowed) . . .

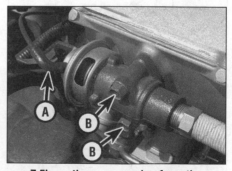

7.5b . . . the vacuum pipe from the EGR valve (A) and the EGR valve to inlet manifold bolts (B)

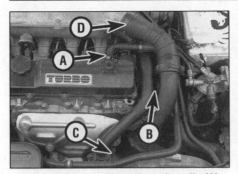

7.6 Cylinder head breather pipe clip (A), hose centre section support (B), hose to turbocharger clamp (C) and hose to plenum chamber clamp (D)

7.12 Remove the exhaust manifold heat shield securing bolts (arrowed)

7.18 Remove the camshaft drivebelt rear cover securing bolts (arrowed)
A Camshaft sprocket locating pin

Both engines

8 To facilitate removal of the inlet manifold, proceed as follows:

a) *Where necessary, loosen the pipe union of No 1 fuel injector to allow movement of the pipe and access to the manifold securing bolt obscured by it*

b) *Release all cable-ties from the manifold*

c) *Where fitted, disconnect the manifold heater*

d) *Disconnect any remaining hoses from beneath the manifold*

9 Remove the inlet manifold to cylinder head securing bolts and nuts, working in a diagonal sequence. Withdraw the manifold and recover the gasket.

10 Where necessary, detach the power steering pump mounting bracket by removing its three securing bolts and move the pump assembly clear of the engine.

15D engine

11 From beneath the vehicle, disconnect the exhaust pipe from the manifold.

15DT engine

12 Remove the exhaust manifold heat shield. Note that the special insulating washers are retained on each of the shield securing bolts by a retaining plate which should stay in place as long as the bolts are unscrewed only enough for them to disengage from the manifold **(see illustration)**.

7.19 Remove the thermostat housing retaining bolts (arrowed)

13 From beneath the vehicle, disconnect the exhaust pipe from the turbocharger.

14 Release the turbocharger from the cylinder block, see Chapter 4.

Both engines

15 Remove the oil level dipstick tube securing bolt from the cylinder head.

16 Remove the exhaust manifold securing bolts and studs, working in a diagonal sequence. Pull the manifold forwards to detach it from the cylinder head and recover the gasket.

17 Remove the camshaft sprocket by removing its three retaining bolts and pulling it from position.

18 Detach the drivebelt rear cover from the cylinder head by first removing its two securing bolts and then easing it clear of the camshaft end **(see illustration)**.

19 Remove the thermostat housing retaining bolts and move the housing clear of the cylinder head with the hoses still attached **(see illustration)**.

20 Detach the coolant hose from the oil cooler thermostat housing, see Section 13.

21 Disconnect the electrical wire from the glow plug bus bar.

22 Disconnect the fuel return line from the No 3 injector. Be prepared for fuel spillage.

23 Clean around the injection pipe unions, then unscrew them from the injectors and from the injection pump. Unscrewing the unions from the pump can prove difficult and should be carried out in the following sequence:

a) *Unscrew No 1 union and ease the pipe away from the pump to expose No 2 union*

b) *Unscrew No 2 union and remove pipes 1 and 2 as an assembly*

c) *Repeat the above procedure with unions Nos 3 and 4*

24 Blank off all exposed pipe connections to prevent the ingress of dirt and moisture.

25 Remove the cylinder head cover (with attached baffle plate) and discard its gasket.

26 Slacken the cylinder head bolts a little at a time, working in the reverse sequence to that

used for tightening. Remove the bolts with washers and discard them. Obtain new bolts for reassembly.

27 Lift off the cylinder head. Do not prise between the mating faces to free a stuck head but if necessary, tap around the mating faces with a soft-faced mallet to break the gasket seal. Recover the gasket.

28 Clean and examine the cylinder head and engine block mating faces.

Refitting

29 Commence refitting by selecting the correct cylinder head gasket. Three thicknesses of gasket are available and they are identified by the presence or absence of notches in the position shown **(see illustration)**. It is essential if the pistons have been disturbed, to measure piston projection as described in the Section for complete reassembly and then select the correct gasket. See *Specifications* for piston projection and gasket thickness figures.

30 Fit the new cylinder head gasket to the block, positioning it over the locating dowels. It can only be fitted the right way up. Do not use jointing compound.

31 Bring the pistons to mid-stroke (90° BTDC) and place the head on the block, making sure that the dowels engage in their recesses.

32 Fit the new cylinder head retaining bolts with their washers. Nip up the bolts in a spiral

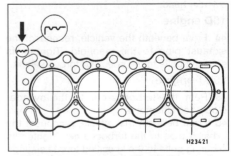

7.29 Cylinder head gasket thickness is identified by notches in the gasket edge (arrowed)

3A

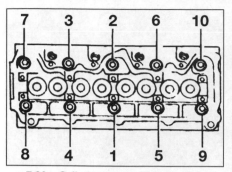

7.32a Cylinder head bolt tightening sequence

7.32b Measuring the angular rotation of each cylinder head bolt

7.33 Fitting a new gasket to the cylinder head cover

sequence, working from the centre outwards in the order shown **(see illustration)** and in the tightening sequence specified. Use a protractor or a marked card to indicate the angular rotation of each bolt **(see illustration)**.

33 Refit the cylinder head cover with a new gasket, tightening its securing bolts to the specified torque setting **(see illustration)**.

34 Remove all blanking materials from the pipe connections.

35 Reconnect the injection pipe unions to the injectors and pump, working in the reverse sequence to removal.

36 Reconnect the fuel return line to the No 3 injector.

37 Reconnect the electrical wire to the glow plug bus bar.

38 Reattach the coolant hose to the oil cooler thermostat housing.

39 Refit the thermostat housing to the cylinder head, using a new gasket and tightening its securing bolts to the specified torque setting.

40 Refit the drivebelt rear cover to the cylinder head, ensuring that it is correctly aligned over the camshaft end before tightening its two securing bolts to the specified torque setting.

41 Refit the camshaft sprocket over its alignment pin on the camshaft end. Refit its three retaining bolts and tighten them to the specified torque setting.

42 Refer to Chapter 4 and refit the exhaust manifold.

43 Refit the oil level dipstick tube to the cylinder head.

15D engine

44 From beneath the vehicle, reconnect the exhaust pipe to the manifold. Tighten its securing bolts to the specified torque setting.

15DT engine

45 Refit the turbocharger to the cylinder block, see Chapter 4.

46 From beneath the vehicle, reconnect the exhaust pipe to the turbocharger. Tighten its securing bolts to the specified torque setting.

47 Refit the exhaust manifold heat shield, taking care not to displace the special insulating washers.

Both engines

48 Reattach the power steering pump mounting bracket to the engine, tightening its securing bolts to the specified torque setting.

49 Refer to Chapter 4 and refit the inlet manifold to the cylinder head.

50 Ensure that the following components associated with the inlet manifold are reconnected:

a) The hoses beneath the manifold
b) The manifold heater (where fitted)
c) All cable-ties
d) The pipe union of No 1 fuel injector (if loosened)

15D engine

51 Refit the EGR valve and pipe assembly to the inlet and exhaust manifolds using a reversal of the removal procedure. Renew all gaskets and tighten bolts to the specified torque.

52 Reattach the air resonator box to the plenum chamber and reconnect its hose.

15DT engine

53 Refit the turbocharger to inlet manifold hose, fitting a new gasket before bolting it to the manifold.

54 Refit the plenum chamber to turbocharger feed hose.

Both engines

55 Refit the camshaft drivebelt as detailed in Section 4.

56 Refill the cooling system.

57 Check that nothing has been overlooked, then reconnect the battery and start the engine.

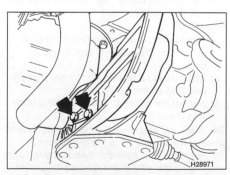

9.4 Remove the lower cover plate to bellhousing securing bolts (arrowed)

8 Camshaft - removal and refitting

Refer to Section 8, Chapter 3D.

9 Sump - removal and refitting

Removal

1 Raise and securely support the front of the vehicle, or place it over a pit.

2 Remove the sump drain plug and drain the engine oil into a suitable container. Refit the plug when draining is complete, tightening it to the specified torque setting.

3 Depending on engine type, detach the front section of exhaust pipe so that enough clearance is gained to allow the sump to be removed from the cylinder block.

4 Remove the cover plate from the bottom of the bellhousing to facilitate access to the two left-hand securing nuts **(see illustration)**.

5 Remove the sump by first unscrewing its bolts and nuts **(see illustration)**. The sump

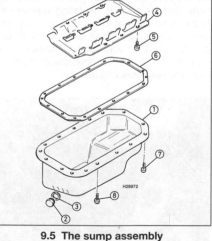

9.5 The sump assembly

1 Sump pan	4 Baffle	6 Gasket
2 Drain plug	plate	7 Nut
3 Washer	5 Screw	8 Bolt

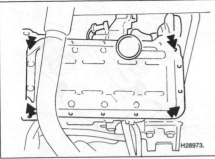

9.8 Before fitting the sump, apply RTV sealant to the cylinder block mating surface at the points arrowed

mating face is sealed with a liquid sealant at certain points and may be stuck fast. To separate the sump mating faces, use a thin, wide blade such as that of a paint stripping tool to break the seal and ease the faces apart.

6 Ease the sump away from the block, taking care to avoid damaging the studs at either end, and discard the gasket.

Refitting

7 Before refitting, clean the inside of the sump. Remove all traces of sealant from the sump and block faces.

8 Commence refitting by applying RTV sealant (to GM spec 15 03 294) to the points shown (see illustration).

9 Fit a new gasket and locate the sump on the cylinder block. Fit and tighten the nuts and bolts in an even sequence to the specified torque.

10 Refit the cover plate to the bottom of the bellhousing and reconnect any disturbed exhaust system connections.

11 With the drain plug fitted and tightened, refill the engine with oil.

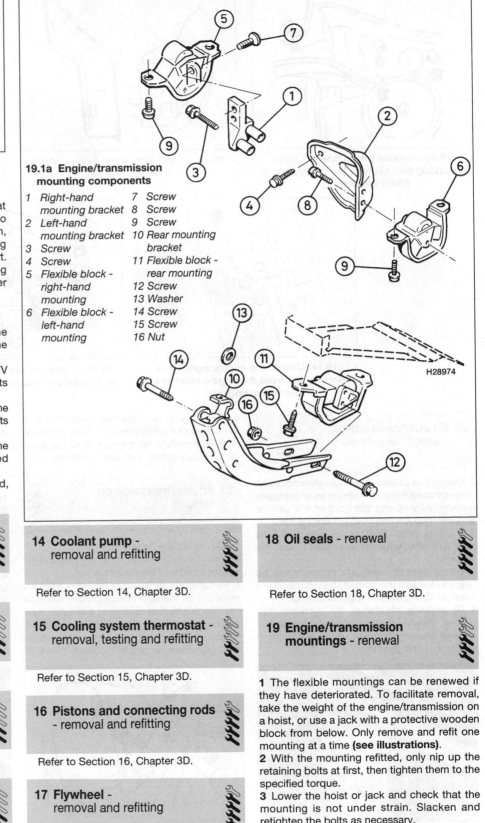

19.1a Engine/transmission mounting components

1	Right-hand mounting bracket	7	Screw
2	Left-hand mounting bracket	8	Screw
3	Screw	9	Screw
4	Screw	10	Rear mounting bracket
5	Flexible block - right-hand mounting	11	Flexible block - rear mounting
6	Flexible block - left-hand mounting	12	Screw
		13	Washer
		14	Screw
		15	Screw
		16	Nut

---

10 Oil pump - removal and refitting

Refer to Section 10, Chapter 3D.

11 Oil pressure regulating valve - removal, testing and refitting

Refer to Section 11, Chapter 3D.

12 Oil cooler - removal and refitting

Refer to Section 12, Chapter 3D.

13 Oil cooler thermostat - removal, testing and refitting

Refer to Section 13, Chapter 3D.

14 Coolant pump - removal and refitting

Refer to Section 14, Chapter 3D.

15 Cooling system thermostat - removal, testing and refitting

Refer to Section 15, Chapter 3D.

16 Pistons and connecting rods - removal and refitting

Refer to Section 16, Chapter 3D.

17 Flywheel - removal and refitting

Refer to Section 17, Chapter 3D.

18 Oil seals - renewal

Refer to Section 18, Chapter 3D.

19 Engine/transmission mountings - renewal

1 The flexible mountings can be renewed if they have deteriorated. To facilitate removal, take the weight of the engine/transmission on a hoist, or use a jack with a protective wooden block from below. Only remove and refit one mounting at a time (see illustrations).

2 With the mounting refitted, only nip up the retaining bolts at first, then tighten them to the specified torque.

3 Lower the hoist or jack and check that the mounting is not under strain. Slacken and retighten the bolts as necessary.

3A

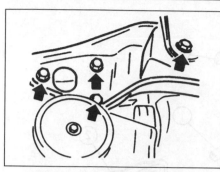

19.1b Remove the engine left-hand mounting bracket with the flexible block (bolts arrowed) . . .

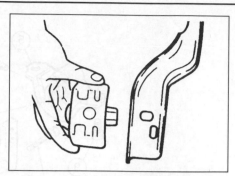

19.1c . . . and detach the flexible block from the bracket

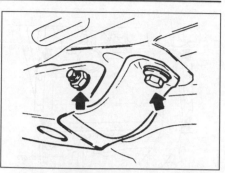

19.1d Remove the engine rear mounting flexible block securing bolts (arrowed)

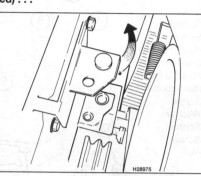

19.1e Detach the engine right-hand flexible block from the engine bracket and lower the engine . . .

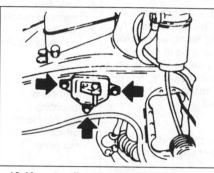

19.1f . . . to allow the right-hand flexible block to be unbolted from the vehicle body

20 Engine/transmission - methods of removal

1 During this project, the engine/transmission was removed from the vehicle as a complete assembly by raising the front of the vehicle and lowering the unit from the engine bay.
2 A lifting hoist and tackle with which to suspend the engine/transmission will be required.
3 Lifting gear of adequate capacity will be required to raise the front of the vehicle as will a pair of strong vehicle support stands.
4 To provide clearance for working, the bonnet should be raised as far as possible without causing damage to the windscreen and then tied in position.

5 The procedures in the next Section and in the Section for refitting relate to one particular vehicle, therefore allowances must be made for individual model and year variations.

21 Engine/transmission - removal

1 Disconnect the battery earth lead.
2 Drain the cooling system, taking precautions against scalding if the coolant is hot.
3 Remove the air cleaner housing from its mounting on the right-hand side of the engine bay. Do this by first detaching the outlet tube retaining clamp at the engine manifold. Release the box inlet scoop from the vehicle front crossmember and manoeuvre it clear of

the housing. Disconnect the front retainer at the housing base and pull the housing forward to release it from its rear retainer.
4 Protect the exposed section of radiator matrix with a piece of wood or similar to obviate the risk of it being damaged during engine removal **(see illustration)**.
5 Remove the brake servo to vacuum pump line by pulling the line from the servo unit, unscrewing it from the pump and then releasing the line retaining clamps to allow the line to be removed from the vehicle **(see illustration)**.
6 Where a power steering pump is fitted, release tension on the pump drivebelt. Detach the pump mounting bracket from the engine by removing its three securing bolts then move the pump assembly clear of the engine, taking care not to place any strain on the hoses **(see illustration)**.

21.4 Protect the exposed section of radiator matrix

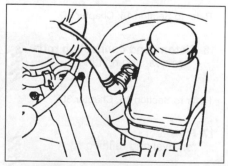

21.5 Pull the brake servo to vacuum pump line from the servo unit

21.6 Detach the power steering pump mounting bracket from the engine

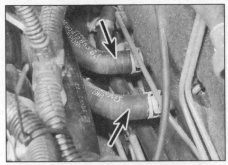

21.8 Disconnect the two heater hoses (arrowed) from their connectors on the engine bay bulkhead

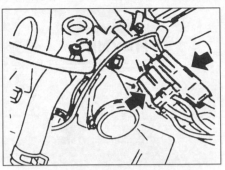

21.9 Disconnect the electrical wiring harness connectors (arrowed) adjacent to the thermostat housing

21.10 Detaching the vent hose from the thermostat housing

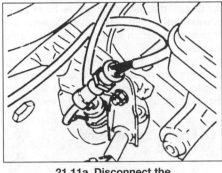

21.11a Disconnect the odometer pick-up . . .

21.11b . . . and then disconnect the speedometer cable from the gearbox

21.13 Disconnecting the clutch cable inner from the operating lever

7 Remove the coolant hose connecting the thermostat housing to the radiator, cutting any cable clips.

8 Disconnect the two heater hoses from their connectors on the bulkhead of the engine bay **(see illustration)**.

9 Disconnect the electrical wiring harness connectors adjacent to the thermostat housing, attaching labels if there is any possibility of confusion later **(see illustration)**.

10 Detach the vent hose from the thermostat housing **(see illustration)**.

11 Disconnect the odometer pick-up and then disconnect the speedometer cable adjacent to it from the gearbox by unscrewing its retaining cap **(see illustrations)**.

12 On 15D engines, detach the air resonator box from the plenum chamber by removing the lower hose clamp and the box securing bolts - **see illustration 7.4**.

13 Disconnect the clutch cable outer from the gearbox casing bracket and its inner from the operating lever **(see illustration)**.

14 Disconnect the cable connector from the reversing lamp switch adjacent to the clutch operating lever **(see illustration)**.

15 Disconnect the throttle cable from the fuel injection pump by unclipping its inner from the pump lever and then releasing its outer from the retaining bracket, see Chapter 4.

16 Disconnect the gearchange linkage by releasing the securing clamp and separating the linkage from the shaft **(see illustration)**. Push the linkage in towards the engine and secure it in position.

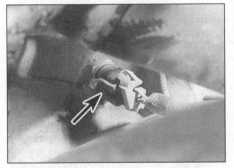

21.14 Disconnect the cable connector from the reversing lamp switch (arrowed)

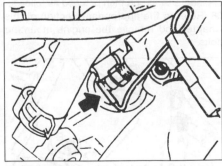

21.17a Disconnect the coolant temperature sensor cable connector (arrowed)

17 Disconnect the electrical cables from the coolant temperature sensor and oil pressure switch **(see illustrations)**.

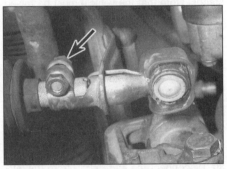

21.16 Release the gearchange linkage securing clamp (arrowed)

21.17b . . . and the oil pressure switch connector

18 Where the fuel filter is equipped with a heater, disconnect the electrical connectors from it **(see illustration)**.

3A

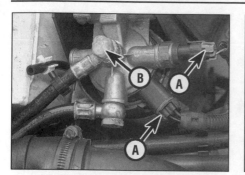

21.18 Disconnect the electrical connectors (A) from the fuel filter heater. Note the filter feed line connection (B)

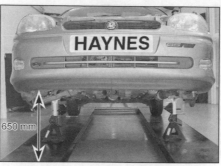

21.25 The vehicle must be raised approximately 650 mm to enable the engine/transmission unit to be removed

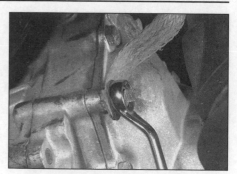

21.30 Disconnecting the engine/transmission unit earth strap

19 Disconnect the feed line from the fuel filter.
20 Disconnect the return line from the fuel injection pump.
21 Remove the alternator and mounting bracket assembly.
22 Detach all pipes and cables from the camshaft drivebelt cover.
23 Release any cable-ties from the rear of the inlet manifold.
24 Check that no cables or hoses have been left connected and secure them to one side, away from the engine.
25 Apply the handbrake, then jack up the front of the vehicle and support it securely on axle stands. Note that the vehicle must be raised sufficiently high (approximately 650 mm) to enable the engine/transmission to be withdrawn from under the front of the vehicle **(see illustration)**. Remove the front roadwheels.
26 Attach a suitable hoist and lifting tackle to the engine lifting brackets on the cylinder head, and support the weight of the engine.
27 Working beneath the vehicle, carry out the following tasks:
28 Remove the complete lower coolant hose.
29 Disconnect the wiring from the starter motor, referring to Chapter 5.
30 Disconnect the earth strap from the left-hand side of the engine/transmission **(see illustration)**.
31 Unbolt and remove the horn.
32 Disconnect the cable connector from the fuel injection pump solenoid and its retaining clip **(see illustration)**.

33 On 15D engines, unbolt the exhaust pipe from the engine manifold. Release the pipe mounting bracket **(see illustration)** and remove the front section of exhaust pipe from the vehicle. Recover the flange gasket. Now unbolt the pipe mounting bracket from the cylinder block **(see illustration)**.
34 On 15DT engines, disconnect the exhaust pipe from the turbocharger and recover the flange gasket. Remove the front section of exhaust pipe from the vehicle.
35 Remove the front suspension lower arms, tie-bars, and anti-roll bar, referring to the appropriate Manual for petrol-engined vehicles.
36 Disconnect the driveshafts from the gearbox, referring to the appropriate Manual for petrol-engined vehicles. There is no need to disconnect the driveshafts from the swivel hubs. Be prepared for oil spillage and plug the openings in the gearbox to prevent dirt ingress and further oil loss. Do not allow the driveshafts to hang down under their own weight as the joints may be damaged. Support the driveshafts with wire or string.
37 To stabilise the engine/transmission as it is removed, it is advisable to support the unit from underneath using a jack and interposed block of wood, in addition to the engine hoist and lifting tackle. Take the weight of the engine/transmission then proceed as follows:
38 Refer to the appropriate Section of this Chapter and remove the engine mounting bolts.

39 Check that no attachments have been overlooked, then carefully lower the engine/transmission from the engine bay onto a suitable trolley.
40 Ensure that the unit is adequately supported on the trolley, then disconnect the engine hoist and lifting tackle and withdraw the unit from under the front of the vehicle.

22 Engine/transmission - separation

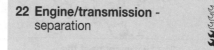

Refer to Section 22, Chapter 3D.

23 Engine dismantling - general information

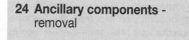

Refer to Section 19, Chapter 3B.

24 Ancillary components - removal

Refer to Section 24, Chapter 3D, whilst noting the following:

a) Any reference to a turbocharger applies to the 15DT engine only.
b) Disregard any reference to the wiring loom.

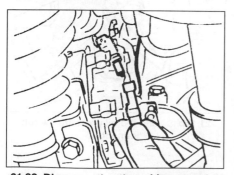

21.32 Disconnecting the cable connector from the fuel injection pump solenoid and its retaining clip

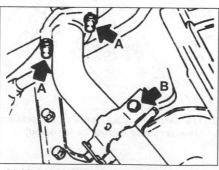

21.33a Unbolt the exhaust pipe from the engine manifold (A) and release the pipe mounting bracket (B)

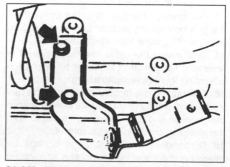

21.33b Remove the exhaust pipe mounting bracket to cylinder block securing bolts (arrowed)

25 Engine - complete dismantling

Refer to Section 25, Chapter 3D, whilst noting that any reference to a turbocharger applies to the 15DT engine only.

26 Oil pump - dismantling, overhaul and reassembly

Refer to Section 26, Chapter 3D.

27 Cylinder head - dismantling and reassembly

Refer to Section 27, Chapter 3D.

28 Cylinder head - examination and overhaul

Refer to the information given in Section 24, Chapter 3B, whilst noting the *Specifications* of this Chapter and disregarding any references to hydraulic valve lifters.

29 Cylinder head and pistons - decarbonising

Refer to Section 25, Chapter 3B.

30 Examination and renovation - general information

Refer to Section 30, Chapter 3D.

31 Engine components - examination and renovation

Refer to Section 31, Chapter 3D.

32 Engine reassembly - general information

Refer to the information given in Section 28, Chapter 3B, whilst noting that no dial test indicator or any special tools other than the locking bolts mentioned in Section 5 will be needed to set valve timing.

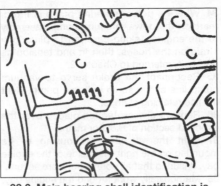

33.2 Main bearing shell identification is stamped into the cylinder block

33 Engine - complete reassembly

Note illustrations: *Where necessary, refer to the appropriate Sections of this Chapter for illustrations relating to component assembly.*
1 Refer to Section 33, Chapter 3D, whilst noting the following:

Crankshaft and main bearings

2 Main bearing shell identification is stamped into the cylinder block **(see illustration).**

Sump and oil inlet pipe

3 A one-part sump pan is fitted to these engines.

Camshaft drivebelt and associated components

4 Refer to Sections 4 and 5 of this Chapter for details of camshaft drivebelt tensioner assembly and valve timing respectively.

All other removed components

5 All references to a turbocharger appertain to the 15DT engine only. Disregard all references to the crankshaft pulley.

34 Engine/transmission - reconnection

Refer to Section 34, Chapter 3D.

35 Engine/transmission - refitting

Caution: Do not attempt to fit the engine/transmission on your own, a minimum of two people will be required
Note illustrations: *When carrying out the procedures detailed in this Section, refer to the illustrations shown for removal of the engine/transmission.*
1 A minimum of two people will be required to carry out this operation. One person should

operate the lifting tackle whilst the other guides the engine/transmission into place and keeps watch for fouling.
2 With the front of the vehicle raised and securely supported on axle stands to a height of approximately 650 mm, move the engine/transmission into position underneath the vehicle, ensuring that the unit is adequately supported on its trolley.
3 Reconnect the hoist and lifting tackle to the engine lifting brackets.
4 Carefully raise the engine/transmission into the engine bay and align its mountings. Fit the mounting bolts. Some lifting and lowering of the unit will be necessary before all the bolts will go in. Do not tighten the bolts fully until all the mountings are fitted and then tighten to the specified torque settings.
5 Remove the engine lifting tackle and trolley.
6 Reconnect the driveshafts to the gearbox, referring to the appropriate Manual for petrol-engined vehicles.
7 Reconnect the front suspension lower arms, tie-bars, and anti-roll bar, referring to the appropriate Manual for petrol-engined vehicles.
8 On 15DT engines, refit the front section of exhaust pipe to the vehicle, using a new pipe flange to turbocharger gasket and tightening all bolts to the specified torque settings.
9 On 15D engines, refit the exhaust pipe mounting bracket to the cylinder block, then refit the front section of exhaust pipe to the vehicle, using a new pipe flange to manifold gasket and tightening all bolts to the specified torque settings.
10 Reconnect the cable connector to the fuel injection pump solenoid and retaining clip.
11 Refit the horn.
12 Reconnect the earth strap to the left-hand side of the engine/transmission.
13 Reconnect the wiring to the starter motor.
14 Refit the complete lower coolant hose.
15 Refit both roadwheels and lower the vehicle to the ground.
16 Reconnect any cable-ties to the rear of the inlet manifold.
17 Reattach all pipes and cables to the camshaft drivebelt cover.
18 Refit the alternator and mounting bracket assembly.
19 Reconnect the return line to the fuel injection pump.
20 Reconnect the feed line to the fuel filter.
21 Where the fuel filter is equipped with a heater, reconnect its electrical connectors.
22 Reconnect the electrical cables to the coolant temperature sensor and oil pressure switch.
23 Reconnect and adjust the gearchange linkage. Refer to the appropriate Manual for petrol-engined vehicles for adjustment procedures and tighten the linkage securing clamp on completion.
24 Reconnect the throttle cable inner and outer to the fuel injection pump, see Chapter 4.
25 Reconnect the cable connector to the reversing lamp switch.

3A

26 Reconnect the clutch cable inner to the operating lever and its outer to the gearbox casing bracket.

27 On 15D engines, reattach the air resonator box to the plenum chamber.

28 Reconnect the speedometer cable to the gearbox, tightening its retaining cap fully.

29 Reconnect the odometer pick-up.

30 Connect the vent hose to the thermostat housing.

31 Reconnect the electrical wiring harness connectors adjacent to the thermostat housing.

32 Reconnect the two heater hoses to their connectors on the bulkhead of the engine bay.

33 Reconnect the coolant hose which connects the thermostat housing to the radiator.

34 Where a power steering pump is fitted, reattach the power steering pump assembly to the engine, taking care not to place any strain on the hoses, then fit and tension its drivebelt, referring to Chapter 2.

35 Reconnect the brake servo to vacuum pump line at the servo unit and pump. Refit the line retaining clamps.

36 Remove any protection placed over the exposed section of radiator matrix.

37 Refit the air cleaner housing to its mounting on the right-hand side of the engine bay, ensuring that all connections are secure.

38 Methodically work around the engine bay, ensuring that all hoses, cables, etc. are correctly routed, clear of hot or moving parts and free of any strain. Replace any cable-ties cut during removal. Check that nothing has been overlooked

39 Refill the cooling system (see Chapter 2).

40 Refer to Chapter 2 and refill the engine with oil.

41 Check the gearbox oil level and top-up if necessary.

42 Reconnect the battery earth lead.

43 Run the engine, referring first to the following Section.

36 Engine - initial start-up after overhaul

Refer to Section 36, Chapter 3D.

Chapter 3 Part B:
Engine overhaul - 16D and 16DA engines

Contents

Degrees of difficulty

Easy, suitable for novice with little experience	**Fairly easy,** suitable for beginner with some experience	**Fairly difficult,** suitable for competent DIY mechanic	**Difficult,** suitable for experienced DIY mechanic	**Very difficult,** suitable for expert DIY or professional

Specifications

General

Engine type .... Four-cylinder, four stroke, overhead camshaft, indirect injection, compression ignition

Designation:
   1982 to 1985 .... 16D
   1986 on 16DA
Bore .... 80.00 mm nominal
Stroke .... 79.50 mm
Displacement .... 1598 cc
Firing order .... 1-3-4-2 (No 1 at pulley end)
Compression ratio .... 23 : 1
Maximum power .... 54 bhp @ 4600 rpm
Maximum torque:
   16D .... 96 Nm @ 2400 rpm
   16DA .... 95 Nm @ 2400 rpm

Camshaft drivebelt

Tension (using gauge KM-510-A):
   New belt, warm 9.0
   New belt, cold 6.5
   Run-in belt, warm 8.0
   Run-in belt, cold 4.0

3B

Cylinder head

	Thickness (fitted)	Identification
Gasket thickness and identification:		
Piston projection up to 0.75 mm	1.3 mm	None
Piston projection 0.75 to 0.85 mm	1.4 mm	One notch
Piston projection above 0.85 mm	1.5 mm	Two notches
Valve clearance adjustment	Automatic by hydraulic tappets	
Valve seat width in head:		
Inlet	1.3 to 2.0 mm	
Exhaust	1.3 to 2.6 mm	
Valve stem play in guide:		
Inlet	0.015 to 0.047 mm	
Exhaust	0.030 to 0.062 mm	
Recess of valve head when fitted	0.25 to 0.75 mm	
Swirl chamber projection	0.00 to 0.04 mm	
Sealing surface finish - peak-to-valley height	0.025 mm max	
Overall height of head:		
Maximum	106.10 mm	
Minimum	105.75 mm	
Deviation of sealing surface from true	0.15 mm max	

Valves

Length 123.25 mm	
Head diameter:	
Inlet	36 mm
Exhaust	32 mm
Stem diameter (standard):	
Inlet	7.970 to 7.985 mm
Exhaust	7.955 to 7.970 mm
Valve guide bore (standard)	8.000 to 8.017 mm
Valve stem oversizes:	
Marked 1	+ 0.075 mm
Marked 2	+ 0.150 mm
Marked A (inlet) or K (exhaust)	+ 0.250 mm
Valve sealing face angle	44°

Camshaft and bearings

Journal diameters (standard):	
No 1	42.455 to 42.470 mm
No 2	42.705 to 42.720 mm
No 3	42.955 to 42.970 mm
No 4	43.205 to 43.220 mm
No 5	43.455 to 43.470 mm
Bearing diameters (standard):	
No 1	42.500 to 42.525 mm
No 2	42.750 to 42.775 mm
No 3	43.000 to 42.025 mm
No 4	43.250 to 43.275 mm
No 5	43.500 to 43.525 mm
Camshaft and bearing undersize	- 0.1mm
Camshaft identification marks:	
Letter	B
Colour - standard	None
Colour - undersize	Violet
Camshaft run-out	0.03 mm max
Camshaft endfloat	0.04 to 0.14 mm
Cam lift (inlet and exhaust)	6.12 mm

Cylinder bores

	Diameter (± 0.005 mm)	Identification
Production grade 1	79.95 mm	5
. . . .	79.96 mm	6
. . . .	79.97 mm	7
Production grade 2	79.98 mm	8
. . . .	79.99 mm	99
. . . .	80.00 mm	00
. . . .	80.01 mm	01
. . . .	80.02 mm	02
. . . .	80.03 mm	03

Cylinder bores (continued)

	Diameter (± 0.005 mm)	Identification
Production grade 3	80.04 mm	04
....	80.05 mm	05
....	80.06 mm	06
....	80.07 mm	07
....	80.08 mm	08
....	80.09 mm	09
....	80.10 mm	1
Oversize (0.5 mm)	80.47 mm	7 + 0.5
....	80.48 mm	8 + 0.5
....	80.49 mm	9 + 0.5
....	80.50 mm	0 + 0.5
Oversize (1.0 mm)	80.97 mm	7 + 1.0
....	80.98 mm	8 + 1.0
....	80.99 mm	9 + 1.0
....	81.00 mm	0 + 1.0
Bore out-of-round and taper	0.013 mm max	

Pistons

Make	Mahle or Alcan
Marking (maker's identity):	
Mahle	m
Alcan	D
Diameter:	
Mahle	0.030 mm less than bore diameter
Alcan	0.020 mm less than bore diameter
Grade marking	As for cylinder bore
Projection at TDC (used to determine head gasket thickness)	0.65 to 0.95 mm
Clearance in bore:	
Mahle	0.020 to 0.040 mm
Alcan	0.015 to 0.035 mm

Piston rings

Thickness:	
Compression rings	1.978 to 1.990 mm
Oil scraper ring	2.975 to 3.010 mm
End gap (fitted)	0.2 to 0.4 mm
Vertical clearance in groove	Not stated
Gap offset	180°

Gudgeon pins

Length	64.7 to 65.0 mm
Diameter	25.995 to 26.000 mm
Clearance in piston	0.007 to 0.011 mm
Clearance in connecting rod	0.014 to 0.025 mm

Connecting rods

Weight variation (in same engine)	4 g. max
Identification of weight class:	
785 g. nominal	Black/1
789 g. nominal	Blue/2
793 g. nominal	Green/3
797 g. nominal	Yellow/4
807 g. nominal	White/5
805 g. nominal	Grey/6
Endfloat on crankshaft	0.07 to 0.24 mm

Crankshaft and bearings

Main bearing journal diameter:	
Standard	57.982 to 57.995 mm
0.25 undersize (production and service)	57.732 to 57.745 mm
0.50 undersize (service only)	57.482 to 57.495 mm
Big-end bearing journal diameter:	
Standard	48.971 to 48.987 mm
0.25 undersize	48.721 to 48.737 mm
0.50 undersize	48.471 to 48.487 mm

3B

Crankshaft and bearings (continued)

Bearing shell identification - standard:	Colour	Marking
Main, except centre, top	Brown	413 N or 403 N
Main, centre, top	Brown	400 N or 410 N
Main, except centre, bottom	Green	414 N or 404 N
Main, centre, bottom	Green	401 N or 411 N
Big-end	None	419 N
Bearing shells identification - 0.25 undersize:		
Main, except centre, top	Brown-blue	415 A or 405 A
Main, centre, top	Brown-blue	402 A or 412 A
Main, except centre, bottom	Green-blue	416 A or 406 A
Main, centre, bottom	Green-blue	403 A or 413 A
Big-end	Blue	420 A
Bearing shell identification - 0.50 undersize:		
Main, except centre, top	Brown-white	236 B or 407
Main, centre, top	Brown-white	238 B or 414 B
Main, except centre, bottom	Green-white	237 B or 408
Main, centre, bottom	Green-white	239 B or 415 B
Big-end	White	421 B
Crankshaft bearing out-of-round and taper	0.004 mm max	
Crankshaft run-out (measured at centre main bearing journal)	0.03 mm max	
Crankshaft endfloat	0.07 to 0.30 mm	
Main bearing running clearance	0.015 to 0.040 mm	
Big-end bearing running clearance	0.019 to 0.063 mm	

Flywheel

Run-out	0.5 mm max
Refacing limit (depth of material removed from clutch wear face)	0.3 mm max

Lubrication system

System type	Wet sump, pressure feed, full flow filter
Lubricant type/specification/capacity	Refer to *"Lubricants, fluids and capacities"*
Oil filter type	Champion G105
Oil pressure (at idle, engine warm)	1.5 bar (22 lbf/in2)
Oil pump tolerances:	
Gear backlash	0.1 to 0.2 mm
Outer gear-to-housing clearance	0.03 to 0.10 mm
Gear recess below body	0.03 to 0.10 mm

Coolant pump

Type	Impeller
Drive	From camshaft drivebelt

Thermostat

Opening commences at	91°C (196°F)
Fully open at	106°C (223°F)
Marking	91

Torque wrench settings

16D engine	Nm	lbf ft
Crankshaft pulley-to-sprocket	20	15
Crankshaft pulley/sprocket centre bolt	155	114
Starter motor to block	45	33
Camshaft sprocket bolt:*		
Stage 1	75	55
Stage 2	Tighten a further 60°	
Oil pump housing to block	6	4
Flywheel to crankshaft:*		
Stage 1	60	44
Stage 2	Tighten a further 30°	
Main bearing caps	80	59
Connecting rod caps	50	37
Oil pump pressure regulator valve	30	22
Sump bolts	5	4

Torque wrench settings

16D engine (conditioned)

	Nm	lbf ft
Cylinder head bolts:*		
Stage 1	25	18
Stage 2	Tighten a further 90°	
Stage 3	Tighten a further 90°	
Stage 4	Tighten a further 45°	
Stage 5 (after warm-up)	Tighten a further 30°	
Stage 6 (after 600 miles/1000 km)	Tighten a further 45°	
Vacuum pump to camshaft housing	28	21
Oil pressure switch	30	22
Crankcase ventilation oil separator to block	15	11
Engine mounting bracket (RH) to block	50	37
Other engine mountings	40	30
Oil drain plug	45	33
Coolant pump to block	25	18
Thermostat housing to head	15	11
Coolant temperature sensor to thermostat housing	8	6

Bolts tightened by the angular method must be renewed every time.

16DA engine

The torque wrench settings shown below are only those which have been revised or amended by the manufacturer since the original publication of this Manual. Where no figure is quoted below, refer to the above torque wrench settings for the 16D engine).

	Nm	lbf ft
Crankshaft pulley/sprocket centre bolt*:		
Stage 1	130	96
Stage 2	Angle-tighten a further 45°	
Flywheel to crankshaft*:		
Stage 1	50	37
Stage 2	Angle-tighten a further 30°	
Main bearing caps*:		
Stage 1	50	37
Stage 2	Angle-tighten a further 45°	
Connecting rod caps*:		
Stage 1	35	26
Stage 2	Angle-tighten a further 30°	
Cylinder head bolts*:		
Stage 1	25	18
Stage 2	Angle-tighten a further 90°	
Stage 3	Angle-tighten a further 90°	
Stage 4	Angle-tighten a further 45°	
Stage 5 (after warm-up)	Angle-tighten a further 30°	
Stage 6 (after 650 miles/1000 km)	Angle-tighten a further 45°	
Glow plugs	20	15

Bolts tightened by the angular method must be renewed every time.

1 General information

The engine is of four-cylinder overhead camshaft design and bears many similarities to the family of petrol engines from which it is derived (see illustration). The cylinder head is of light alloy construction and the block is of iron. The crankshaft runs in five main bearings. Both main and big-end journals are hardened to withstand the greater loads imposed by compression ignition.

The camshaft is belt-driven from the crankshaft sprocket. The same belt drives the coolant pump and the fuel injection pump. Belt tension is adjusted by moving the coolant pump, which has its sprocket eccentrically mounted.

Lubrication is by means of a pump driven directly from the nose of the crankshaft. Oil is drawn from the sump and pumped through a full flow filter before entering the main oil galleries in the block and the crankshaft. Two pressure regulating valves, one in the pump and one in the cylinder head, open when the oil pressure exceeds a certain value. A bypass valve in the oil filter housing ensures a continued supply of oil, albeit unfiltered, should the filter element become clogged.

Valve clearance adjustment is automatic by means of the hydraulic lifters which support the cam followers. Both inlet and exhaust valve springs sit on rotators.

Crankcase ventilation is achieved by two hoses. One connects the lower crankcase to the camshaft carrier and runs between the carrier and the dipstick tube whilst the other runs from a filter in the camshaft cover to the inlet manifold side of the air cleaner.

Maintenance tasks are mostly straight-forward, but operations which involve disturbing or checking the valve timing should not be undertaken unless the necessary equipment is available.

2 Major operations possible with the engine in the vehicle

1 Since the cylinder head, sump and (when applicable) clutch can all be removed with the engine in place, most dismantling can be carried out without removing the engine. However, access to some areas is difficult and if much work is to be done, it may be quicker in the long run to remove the engine.

3B

2 Unless various special tools can be hired or borrowed, renewal of the crankshaft rear oil seal entails engine or transmission removal. This is unavoidable on automatic transmission models, since the torque converter cannot be removed with the engine and transmission installed.

3 In theory, even the crankshaft and main bearings can be removed with the engine installed (again, only on manual gearbox models) but this is not recommended unless there is some compelling reason for not removing the engine.

3 Engine oil and oil filter - renewal

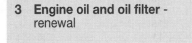

Refer to the appropriate Section of Chapter 2.

4 Camshaft drivebelt - inspection, removal, refitting and tensioning

Caution: A camshaft drivebelt which is damaged, oil-soaked or fuel soaked must be renewed or it will fail, resulting in serious engine damage.

1 The camshaft drivebelt (sometimes called the timing belt) also drives the coolant pump and the fuel injection pump. If it breaks in service, the pistons are likely to hit the valves.

Inspection

2 Refer to the appropriate Section of Chapter 2.

Removal

3 With the drivebelt covers removed (see inspection), to remove the belt begin by removing the crankshaft pulley - it is secured to the sprocket by four Allen screws.

4 Disconnect the battery earth lead.

5 Remove the clutch/flywheel access cover from the bottom of the gearbox bellhousing **(see illustration)**.

6 Turn the crankshaft in the normal direction of rotation, using a spanner on the sprocket bolt, until the timing mark on the injection pump sprocket aligns with the reference mark

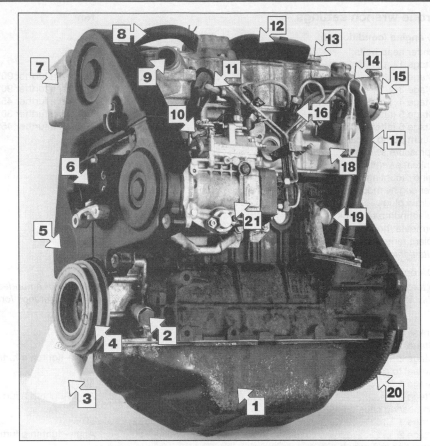

1.0 Front three-quarter view of 16D diesel engine

1 Sump	8 Breather hose	15 Vacuum pump
2 Oil pressure regulator valve	9 Thermostat elbow	16 Fuel injector
3 Oil filter	10 Fuel inlet union	17 Breather hose
4 Crankshaft pulley	11 Fuel return union	18 Glow plug bus bar
5 Camshaft drivebelt cover	12 Air cleaner intake	19 Core plug
6 Engine mounting	13 Oil filler cap	20 Flywheel
7 Intake manifold	14 Oil dipstick	21 Fuel injection pump

on the pump bracket. In this position No 1 piston is at TDC on the firing stroke **(see illustration 5.5)**.

7 Check that the TDC mark on the flywheel and the pointer on the clutch housing are aligned **(see illustration)**.

8 If tool KM-537 or equivalent is available, remove the vacuum pump and lock the

camshaft in position by fitting the tool. If the tool is not available or cannot be fitted, make alignment marks between the camshaft sprocket and its backplate for use when refitting. See Section 5 for more details.

9 Slacken the three bolts which secure the coolant pump to the block **(see illustration)**. Using a large open-ended spanner on the flats

4.5 Removing the clutch/flywheel access cover

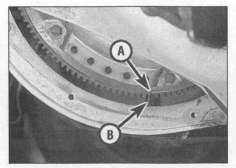

4.7 TDC mark on flywheel (A) and pointer on clutch housing (B)

4.9 Undoing a coolant pump bolt - other two arrowed (engine removed)

4.14 Camshaft drivebelt correctly fitted

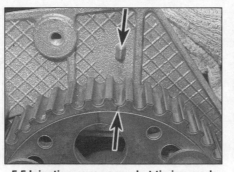

5.5 Injection pump sprocket timing mark aligned with mark on pump bracket

5.6 Removing the camshaft cover

of the pump, pivot it to release the tension on the belt.

10 Separate the right-hand front engine mounting by undoing the two bolts which are accessible from the top.

11 Mark the running direction of the belt if it is to be reused. Also take care not to kink the belt, nor get oil, grease etc. on it.

12 Slip the belt off the sprockets and jockey wheel. Remove the belt by feeding it through the engine mounting.

Refitting

13 Commence refitting by threading the belt through the engine mounting. Refit and tighten the engine mounting bolts.

14 Place the belt over the sprockets and the jockey wheel **(see illustration)**. Make sure that No 1 piston is still at TDC, the injection pump sprocket mark is aligned and the camshaft position is still correct.

15 Move the coolant pump so as to put some tension on the drivebelt. Nip up the pump securing bolts, but do not tighten them fully yet.

16 Remove the camshaft locking tool, if used, and refit and secure the crankshaft pulley.

Tensioning

17 Refer to the appropriate Section of Chapter 2.

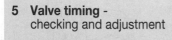
5 Valve timing -
checking and adjustment

16D and 16DA engines up to May 1989

1 Valve timing on these engines is more complicated than on the petrol equivalents because there are no timing marks as such on the camshaft or sprocket, neither is the sprocket keyed or pegged to the camshaft. This makes the use of special tools unavoidable, although one can be home-made.

2 Note that the camshaft sprocket bolt should be renewed whenever it has been slackened.

3 If the valve timing has been lost completely, be careful when turning the crankshaft or camshaft in case piston/valve contact occurs.

4 Two methods of checking the valve timing are described. For either method, begin by checking the camshaft drivebelt tension.

5 Bring the engine to TDC, No 1 firing, by turning the crankshaft in the normal direction of rotation, using a spanner on the sprocket bolt, until the timing mark on the injection pump sprocket aligns with the reference mark on the pump bracket **(see illustration)**. Check that the TDC mark on the flywheel and the pointer on the clutch housing are aligned **(see illustration 4.7)**.

6 Remove the air cleaner. Disconnect the breather hose and remove the camshaft cover **(see illustration)**. If necessary, also remove the vacuum pump.

Using tool KM-537 or equivalent

7 The maker's tool KM-537 consists of a plate which bolts onto the camshaft carrier in place of the vacuum pump. When the peg on the plate will enter the hole in the tail of the camshaft, the camshaft is correctly positioned for TDC, No 1 piston firing.

Making the tool

8 It is possible to make a substitute for tool KM-537 **(see illustration)**, but the valve timing must be known to be correct first - thereafter the tool can be used to check the timing. As can be seen, the home-made tool is simply a metal bar with three holes drilled in it **(see illustration)**. The accuracy of the tool

5.8a Fitting the camshaft alignment tool KM-537

depends on the precision with which the holes are drilled, and the snug fit of the screws or bolts in their holes. The crankshaft must be at TDC, No 1 firing, before marking up and constructing the tool.

9 Drill one of the end holes in the metal bar. Insert a short stud or dowel into the camshaft peg hole, marking the end with chalk or paint. The stud should be just long enough to touch the metal bar in its fitted position.

10 Secure the bar, using one of the vacuum pump screws, so that it is just free to move. Swing the bar past the stud or dowel so that an arc is marked on the bar. Remove the bar and drill a hole in the centre of the arc to accept a bolt or screw which will fit snugly into the camshaft peg hole. Fit this bolt or screw and clamp it with a couple of nuts.

11 Mark around the other vacuum pump screw hole with paint or chalk. Offer the tool to the camshaft and carrier so that the peg hole bolt and first fixing screw are snug and the position of the second fixing screw hole is marked. Remove the tool and drill the second fixing screw hole.

12 Offer up the tool again and make sure that it fits without strain or slack; repeat the construction exercise if necessary.

Using the tool

13 With the crankshaft and injection pump timing marks correctly positioned, offer the tool to the camshaft carrier in place of the vacuum pump. If the tool can be located and secured so that the peg enters the hole in the camshaft, valve timing is correct. In fact, a tolerance of 1.0 mm in either direction at the flywheel TDC mark is allowed.

3B

5.8b Home-made tool for locking the camshaft in a set position

5.18 Dial test indicator zeroed on base circle of second cam . . .

5.19 . . . another reading is taken towards the top of the cam

14 If the tool will not enter, remove it. Hold the camshaft using a spanner on the flats provided and slacken the camshaft sprocket bolt. Break the taper between the sprocket and camshaft if necessary by tapping the sprocket with a wooden or plastic mallet. Turn the camshaft until the alignment tool enters snugly. Remove the old camshaft sprocket bolt and insert a new bolt. Nip the bolt up until the sprocket taper bites, then remove the alignment tool. Hold the camshaft again and tighten the sprocket bolt to the specified torque.

15 Back off the crankshaft a quarter turn, then regain TDC and check that the alignment tool still fits snugly.

Using a dial test indicator

16 Tool KM-537 cannot be used on later models (mid-1984 on) because the holes into which it screws have been deleted. The home-made tool which screws into the vacuum pump holes is not affected. Instead of tool KM-537, the makers specify the use of a dial test indicator (DTI or clock gauge) and suitable support. The support must allow the DTI to move across the camshaft carrier without changing height relative to the carrier top surface. The DTI foot (the part which will rest on the cam lobe) should have a flat bottom and be 7 to 10 mm in diameter.

17 To check the valve timing, position the timing marks as specified in paragraph 5, then place the DTI and support over the second cam from the sprocket end (No 1 cylinder inlet cam).

18 Zero the DTI on the base circle of the cam **(see illustration)**.

19 Carefully move the DTI, and its support if applicable, exactly 10 mm towards the top of the cam. In this position the DTI should show a lift of 0.55 ± 0.05 mm. If so, the valve timing is correct **(see illustration)**.

20 If adjustment is necessary, proceed as described in paragraph 14, but working towards a correct DTI reading instead of a correct fit of the tool.

All methods

21 Check the injection pump timing, then refit the belt covers, flywheel/clutch cover, cam cover and other disturbed components.

16DA engines from May 1989

22 The valve timing on this engine is adjusted using the dial test indicator method described above but modified as follows. Before starting work, it is necessary to make sure that the drivebelt tension is set correctly.

23 You will need a dial test indicator (DTI) with a 10 mm diameter measuring foot. Special tool KM-661-1 should ideally be available. This is a support bar which rests on the top face of the camshaft carrier and positions the DTI above the camshaft. A home-made equivalent (such as that described above) can be used if tool KM-661-1 is not available.

24 An additional tool (KM-661-2) is prescribed by the manufacturer. This comprises a slotted steel plate with a stop screw which is secured by bolts to the camshaft carrier, immediately above the flats on the camshaft. The second part of the tool is effectively an open-jawed spanner which fits over the flats on the camshaft and passes up through the slotted plate. The stop screw bears on the spanner handle, allowing precise positioning of the camshaft. In the absence of the manufacturer's tool, it should not prove difficult to make up an equivalent device at

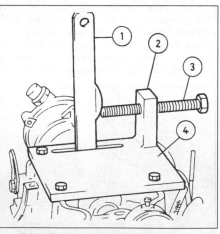

5.24a Service tool KM-661-1 in use

1   *Open-jawed spanner*
2   *Stop screw bracket welded to baseplate*
3   *Stop screw*
4   *Baseplate located by camshaft cover bolts*

home. Both these tools are depicted in the accompanying illustrations **(see illustrations)**.

Checking

25 To check the valve timing, turn the crankshaft in the normal direction of rotation and stop when the crankshaft is approximately 90° BTDC, with No 1 cylinder on the compression stroke. Fit the DTI to the support bar and position the foot of the gauge over the base circle of the second cam from the sprocket end (No 1 cylinder inlet cam). Set the DTI to zero.

26 Carefully move the DTI and the support bar (without disturbing the position of the DTI in the support bar) exactly 10 mm to the left, as viewed from the camshaft sprocket end of the engine (ie. towards the peak of the cam lobe). Turn the crankshaft to the TDC position for No 1 cylinder (see Section 4). In this position, the DTI should show a lift of 0.55 ± 0.03 mm. If so, the valve timing is correct.

Adjustment

27 If adjustment is necessary, slacken the camshaft sprocket bolt, noting that since this must be renewed each time it is disturbed. It is as well to fit a new bolt loosely at this stage. Release the taper between the sprocket and the camshaft, if necessary by tapping the sprocket with a wooden or plastic mallet.

28 Using the flats on the camshaft, turn it until the DTI reads approximately 0.80 mm of lift. Check that the crankshaft is still set to TDC.

29 Assemble and fit the holding tool, KM-661-2 or equivalent. Using the stop screw, gradually set the cam lift to 0.60 to 0.64 mm. Tighten the camshaft sprocket bolt tight enough for the camshaft taper to lock the sprocket, then remove the holding tool.

30 Carefully lift away the DTI and its support bar, taking care not to disturb the DTI position in the bar. Turn the crankshaft through two complete revolutions, then position the DTI once more and check that a lift figure of 0.55 ± 0.03 mm is shown at TDC. If the correct figure is not shown, repeat the adjustment sequence. If the figure is correct, tighten the

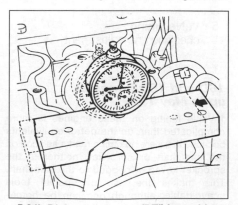

5.24b Dial test indicator (DTI) in position above camshaft
Note dotted lines indicating the two base positions during the test procedure

6.16a Remove the cam follower . . .

6.16b . . . the thrust pad (arrowed) . . .

6.16c . . . and the hydraulic lifter

(new) camshaft sprocket bolt to the specified torque, check the valve timing once more, then remove the tools.

31 Remember that the injection pump timing must be checked after any change in the valve timing setting. Refit the various covers removed during the checking operation.

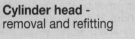

6 Cylinder head - removal and refitting

Caution: Wait until the engine is cold before removing the cylinder head bolts

Removal

1 Disconnect the battery earth lead.
2 Drain the cooling system, recovering the coolant if it is fit for re-use.
3 Remove the air cleaner.
4 Disconnect the breather hose then unbolt and remove the camshaft cover. Also disconnect the breather hose from the camshaft carrier.
5 Remove the vacuum pump.
6 Disconnect the radiator top hose, the heater hose and the coolant bleed hose from the cylinder head. On models where the expansion tank main hose obstructs head removal, disconnect the hose and move it aside.
7 Disconnect the coolant temperature sender lead from the thermostat housing.
8 Clean around the injection pipe unions, then unscrew them from the injectors and from the injection pump. Be prepared for fuel spillage. Disconnect the fuel return line.
9 Disconnect the glow plug wire from the bus bar.
10 Remove the alternator drivebelt and (when fitted) the steering pump drivebelt.
11 Remove the camshaft drivebelt covers and the clutch/flywheel cover, position the engine at TDC (No 1 firing) and remove the camshaft drivebelt from the camshaft sprocket. Refer to Section 4 for fuller details. If the valve timing has been satisfactory so far, make sure that the camshaft is locked or that marks are made so that the timing is not lost.
12 Unbolt the exhaust downpipe from the exhaust manifold and the flexible coupling.

Release the pipe from its mounting bracket and remove it. Recover the manifold flange gasket.
13 Slacken the cylinder head bolts a quarter turn each, working in a spiral sequence from outside to inside. Follow the same sequence and slacken the bolts another half turn, then remove the bolts and washers. Obtain new bolts for reassembly.
14 Unbolt and remove the thermostat housing, disengaging it from the coolant distribution pipe.
15 Remove the camshaft carrier and camshaft.
16 Recover the loose valve gear (cam followers, thrust pads and hydraulic lifters) from the top of the head (see illustrations). Immerse the hydraulic lifters in a container of clean engine oil to avoid any possibility of draining. Keep all of the components in order if they are to be reused.
17 Lift off the cylinder head and manifolds, using the manifolds as handles to rock it free if necessary. Do not prise between the mating faces if the cylinder head sticks. A couple of lugs are provided at the ends of the block and head for prising. Recover the gasket.
18 Clean and examine the cylinder head and engine block mating faces.

Refitting

19 Commence refitting by selecting the correct gasket. Three thicknesses of gasket are available and they are identified by the presence or absence of notches in the

6.19 Head gasket thickness is shown by notches (circled)

position shown (see illustration). You may choose to fit a new gasket of the same thickness as that removed, provided that no work has been carried out on the pistons and there is no evidence of piston/valve contact. It is certainly wise, and essential if the pistons have been disturbed, to measure piston projection as described in the Section for complete reassembly and then select the correct gasket. See the *Specifications* for piston projection and gasket thickness figures.
20 Fit the new head gasket to the block. Make sure the gasket is the right way up - it is marked OBEN/TOP (see illustration). Do not use any jointing compound.
21 Place the head on the block, making sure that the dowels engage in their recesses.
22 Refit the valve lifters, thrust pads and cam followers to their original locations (if applicable), lubricating them generously with clean engine oil. If new hydraulic lifters are being used, initially immerse each one in a container of clean engine oil and compress it (by hand) several times to charge it.
23 Wipe clean the camshaft carrier and head mating faces and coat them with jointing compound to GM spec 15 03 166. Fit the camshaft and carrier to the head.
24 Fit the new head bolts with their washers. Nip up the bolts in a spiral sequence, working from the centre outwards. Make sure that the camshaft carrier is pulled down evenly.
25 In the same sequence, tighten the bolts to the Stage 1 specified torque. Subsequent tightening is by angular rotation rather than torque. Use a protractor or a marked card if

3B

6.20 Head gasket OBEN/TOP marking

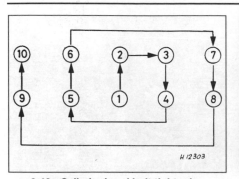

6.40a Cylinder head bolt tightening sequence

6.40b Tightening a cylinder head bolt through a set angle

necessary to indicate the angles. Tighten the bolts in the same sequence through the angles specified for Stages 2, 3 and 4.

26 Refit the thermostat housing, using new O-rings on the head face and on the coolant distribution pipe.

27 Refit and tension the camshaft drivebelt, then check the valve timing.

28 Refit and connect the vacuum pump, using new sealing rings.

29 Refit the camshaft cover, using a new gasket, and tighten its securing bolts.

30 Refit and secure the camshaft drivebelt covers.

31 Refit and tension the alternator drivebelt and (when applicable) the steering pump drivebelt.

32 Reconnect the breather hoses and coolant hoses.

33 Reconnect the coolant temperature sender and glow plug leads.

34 Refit and secure the fuel injection pipework. Also reconnect the fuel return line.

35 Refit the air cleaner.

36 Refit the clutch/flywheel cover

37 Refit and secure the exhaust pipe, using a new gasket and a new sealing ring if necessary.

38 Refill the cooling system.

39 Check that nothing has been overlooked, then reconnect the battery and start the engine.

40 Run the engine to operating temperature, then stop it and tighten the head bolts in the sequence shown through the angle specified for Stage 5 **(see illustrations)**.

41 After approximately 600 miles (1000 km)

have been covered, tighten the bolts through the angle specified for Stage 6. This should be done with the engine cold or warm (not hot).

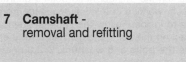

7 **Camshaft -**
removal and refitting

Removal

1 There is a special tool available (KM 2068) by means of which the camshaft can be removed without disturbing the camshaft

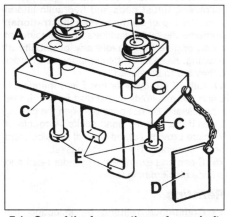

7.1a One of the four sections of camshaft removal tool KM-2068

A Plate   D Spacer (not used)
B Nuts   E Feet
C Bolts

carrier. The tool consists of a series of plates carrying adjustable feet which bolt to the camshaft carrier so that the feet depress the cam followers **(see illustrations)**. The camshaft can then be withdrawn after removal of the drivebelt, sprocket and thrust plate. The pistons must be placed at mid-stroke (90° BTDC) for this operation.

2 In the absence of the special tool, the camshaft must be removed with the camshaft carrier. Since this entails the removal of the cylinder head bolts, strictly speaking the cylinder head should be removed and the gasket renewed. Bearing in mind the greater compression pressures in this type of engine, it is most unwise not to renew the gasket.

3 With the camshaft and carrier removed as described in the previous Section, restrain the camshaft from turning and unbolt the sprocket. Strike the sprocket lightly, if need be, to force it from its taper.

4 Unbolt and remove the camshaft thrust plate **(see illustrations)**.

5 Withdraw the camshaft, being careful not to catch the cam lobes on the carrier bearings **(see illustration)**. Be careful also not to be injured by any sharp edges which may be present.

6 Refer to the Section for general examination and renovation when examining the camshaft and carrier .

Refitting

7 Lubricate all bearing surfaces with clean engine oil before commencing refitting.

7.1b Camshaft removal tool KM-2068 in use

7.4a Undoing the camshaft thrust plate Allen screws

7.4b Removing the camshaft thrust plate

7.5 Removing the camshaft from the carrier

7.9 Measuring camshaft endfloat

8 Fit a new oil seal to the sprocket end of the carrier.

9 Insert the camshaft, again being careful of the bearing surfaces. Fit and secure the thrust plate, then check the camshaft endfloat **(see illustration)**. Renew the thrust plate if endfloat is excessive.

10 Loosely fit the camshaft sprocket, using a new bolt, but do not tighten it yet.

11 Position the camshaft in roughly the correct position for TDC, No 1 firing - ie both cam lobes for No 1 cylinder inclined upwards, and those for No 4 cylinder inclined downwards.

12 Refit the camshaft and carrier as described in the previous Section.

13 If a new camshaft has been fitted, coat the lobes and cam followers with molybdenum disulphide paste, or with special cam lube if this was supplied with the new camshaft.

14 Unless otherwise instructed by the camshaft maker, observe the following running-in schedule immediately after start-up:

  a) 1 minute at 2000 rpm
  b) 1 minute at 1500 rpm
  c) 1 minute at 3000 rpm
  d) 1 minute at 2000 rpm

Precise speeds are not important, the main thing is that the engine should not be left to idle until this initial running-in has taken place.

15 Change the engine oil (but not the filter) approximately 600 miles (1000 km) after fitting a new camshaft.

8 Sump - removal and refitting

Removal

1 Raise and securely support the front of the vehicle, or place it over a pit.

2 Remove the sump drain plug and drain the engine oil into a suitable container. Refit the plug when draining is complete.

3 Remove the sump securing bolts and their special washers.

4 Pull the sump off the cylinder block. If it is stuck, strike it on the sides with a wooden or plastic mallet. Only lever between the sump and block as a last resort as damage may be caused to the sealing faces.

5 Clean the inside of the sump. Remove all traces of gasket from the sump and block faces.

Refitting

6 Commence refitting by applying RTV sealant (to GM spec 15 03 294) to the joints between the rear main bearing cap and the block, and the oil pump and the block.

7 Smear the new sump gasket with grease to improve its adhesion and position it on the block or sump.

8 Offer the sump to the block, making sure that the gasket is not displaced. Secure with the bolts and washers, using thread locking compound on the bolt threads.

9 Tighten the bolts in an even sequence to the specified torque.

10 Make sure that the drain plug is fitted and tightened, then refill the engine with oil.

9 Oil pump - removal and refitting

Removal

1 Remove the sump as described in the previous Section.

2 Remove the oil filter and disconnect the oil pressure warning light switch.

3 Bring the engine to TDC, No 1 firing, then slacken the camshaft drivebelt as described in Section 4.

4 Jam the starter ring gear and unscrew the crankshaft pulley/sprocket centre bolt. This bolt is extremely tight. Remove the bolt and the pulley/sprocket assembly; recover the Woodruff key.

5 Remove the drivebelt idler pulley, which is secured by a large Allen screw through its hub.

6 Remove the drivebelt backplate which is secured by some of the drivebelt cover screws.

7 Remove the six Allen screws which secure the oil pump to the block, and the single bolt which secures the oil pump pick-up tube to the block lower face. Note that this latter bolt appears identical to the sump bolts, so keep it separate or it may be considered "lost" until after the sump has been refitted.

8 Pull the pump off its dowels and remove it with the pick-up tube. Recover the gasket and unbolt the pick-up tube.

Refitting

9 Commence refitting by lubricating the lips of the oil seal.

10 Fit the pump to the block, using a new gasket. Be careful not to damage the oil seal on the step on the crankshaft nose. Fit and tighten the securing screws.

11 Refit and secure the pick-up tube, using a new O-ring at the pump flange.

12 Refit the drivebelt backplate and the idler pulleys. Tighten the idler pulley Allen screw.

13 Refit the Woodruff key to the crankshaft nose.

14 Engage the sprocket with the drivebelt and fit the sprocket/pulley assembly to the crankshaft nose.

15 Fit the sprocket/pulley centre bolt. Jam the ring gear teeth and tighten the bolt to the specified torque.

16 Tension the camshaft drivebelt, then check the valve timing.

17 Refit the sump.

10 Coolant pump - removal and refitting

Removal

1 Drain the cooling system, saving the coolant if it is fit for re-use.

2 Remove the camshaft drivebelt, the drivebelt idler pulley and backplate.

3 Remove the three bolts which retain the coolant pump. Lift out the pump - some coolant will be released. It may be necessary to remove the alternator to provide sufficient clearance to remove the pump completely.

4 Pump overhaul is not a practical proposition.

Refitting

5 Use a new O-ring when refitting the pump. In order to prevent corrosion and the resultant impossibility of moving the coolant pump to tension the timing belt, apply silicone grease to the pump O-ring and cylinder block mating surface. Insert but do not tighten the retaining bolts **(see illustrations)**.

10.5a Fitting a new O-ring to the coolant pump

10.5b Fitting the coolant pump (engine removed)

3B

11.2 Removing the thermostat from its housing

6 Refit the drivebelt backplate and the idler pulley.
7 Refit and tension the camshaft drivebelt.
8 Refit the other disturbed components, then refill the cooling system.

11 Thermostat -
removal, testing and refitting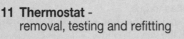

Removal

1 Drain the cooling system, saving the coolant if it is fit for re-use.
2 Unbolt the thermostat elbow from the thermostat housing. Remove the elbow and lift out the thermostat **(see illustration)**.

Testing

3 Test the thermostat by suspending it in a saucepan of cold water and bringing the water to the boil. The thermostat should not contact the saucepan. The thermostat should be closed until the water is nearly boiling, when it should start to open. The precise opening temperature is given in the *Specifications*. It is not so easy to check the fully open temperature, since this is above the boiling point of water in an open pan.
4 Renew the thermostat if it does not open and close as described, or if it is damaged.

Refitting

5 Refit the thermostat in the reverse order of removal. Always use a new sealing ring **(see illustration)**.
6 Refill the cooling system.

11.5 Fitting a new sealing ring to the thermostat

12 Pistons and connecting rods -
removal and refitting

Removal

1 Remove the cylinder head.
2 Remove the sump.
3 Examine the connecting rods and caps for identification and match marks. If none are present, make paint or punch marks to identify the rods and caps and to make sure that the caps are refitted the right way round.
4 Bring two pistons to BDC. Remove the connecting rod cap nuts, take off the caps and push the pistons up through the top of the block. Recover the bearing shells, keeping them with their original rods if they are to be reused.
5 If there is a pronounced wear ridge at the top of the bore, the piston or its rings may be damaged during removal. This can be avoided by removing the ridge with a tool known as a ridge reamer. Such a degree of bore wear would probably mean that a rebore was necessary, which would also entail the fitting of new pistons in any case.
6 Bring the other two pistons to BDC and remove them.
7 If it is proposed to separate the pistons from the connecting rods, make identifying marks on the piston crowns first so that they can be refitted to their original rods and the right way round.
8 Remove the circlip from the gudgeon pin bore on one side of the piston. From the other

side, press out the gudgeon pin by hand. No great force should be required **(see illustrations)**.

Refitting

9 When refitting the pistons to the connecting rods, oil the gudgeon pins liberally first. Push the pins home and secure them with the circlips. Some patience may be needed when fitting the circlips as they are liable to spring out.
10 If new pistons or rings are to be fitted to old bores, it is essential to deglaze the bores to allow the new rings to bed in. Do this using medium grit emery paper, or a flap wheel in an electric drill, with a circular up-and-down action. The aim is to produce a criss-cross pattern on the bores. Protect the bearing journals on the crankshaft by covering them with masking tape during this operation. Clean the bores thoroughly with a paraffin-soaked rag and dry them with a clean cloth. Then remove the masking tape from the journals and clean them.
11 Commence refitting by laying out the pistons, connecting rods, caps and shells in order **(see illustration)**. If the piston rings have been removed, refit them and stagger the gaps as described in the Section for engine reassembly.
12 Make sure that the seats for the bearing shells are absolutely clean, then press the shells into their seats in the rods and caps, aligning the locating tangs correctly.
13 Lubricate the bores and the piston rings with clean engine oil. Fit a piston ring compressor to the first piston to be fitted. Turn the crankshaft to bring the journal for that piston to BDC.
14 Insert the rod and piston into the block so that the base of the ring compressor rests on the block. Make sure that the piston is the right way round (arrow on crown pointing towards the pulley end) and that the connecting rod is also the right way round - refer to the marks made when dismantling **(see illustrations)**.
15 Drive the piston into the bore by tapping the piston crown with, for example, the wooden handle of a hammer. If the piston does not want to go in, do not use more force, but release the compressor and see if a ring has jammed. Remove the compressor as the piston enters the bore.

12.8a Removing a gudgeon pin circlip

12.8b Removing a gudgeon pin

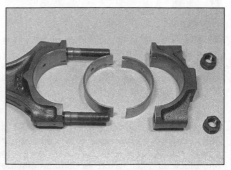

12.11 Connecting rod bearing assembly

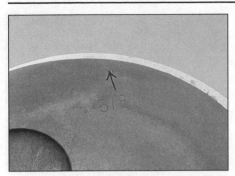

12.14a Arrow on piston crown points to pulley end

16 Lubricate the crankpin and guide the connecting rod onto it, pushing the piston down the bore. Take care that the protruding studs do not scratch the crankpin and check that the bearing shell is not displaced.

17 Fit the connecting rod cap, again making sure that the shell is not displaced. Fit the nuts and tighten them to the specified torque.

18 Repeat the operations on the other pistons and rods.

19 Refit the sump and the cylinder head.

13 Flywheel -
removal and refitting

Note: *This procedure applies to vehicles with a manual gearbox. To gain access to the driveplate on automatic transmission vehicles, the engine and transmission must first be separated when the procedure is then similar.*

Removal

1 Remove the clutch as described in the appropriate Manual for petrol-engined vehicles.

2 Jam the flywheel ring gear and slacken the flywheel bolts. The bolts are tight and their heads are shallow - a socket spanner without any chamfer at the business end will give the best purchase. Mark the location of the shouldered bolt relative to the flywheel and to the crankshaft flange **(see illustration)**.

3 Remove the bolts and lift away the flywheel. Do not drop it, it is heavy. Obtain new bolts for reassembly.

13.2 Shouldered bolt (arrowed) determines flywheel fitted position

12.14b Correct relationship between piston and connecting rod

A Arrow
B Combustion recess
C Oil squirt hole

Refitting

4 When refitting the flywheel, line up the bolt hole for the shouldered bolt in the crankshaft flange and in the flywheel. There is no locating dowel.

5 Apply thread locking compound to the threads of the new bolts. Fit the bolts, making sure that the shouldered bolt is fitted to the correct hole. Tighten the bolts progressively to the specified torque.

6 Refit the clutch.

14 Oil seals - renewal

Camshaft front seal

1 Slacken the camshaft drivebelt and remove it from the camshaft sprocket.

2 Remove the air cleaner. Disconnect the breather hose and remove the camshaft cover.

3 Hold the camshaft with an open-ended spanner on the flats provided. Unscrew and remove the camshaft sprocket bolt. Obtain a new bolt for use when refitting.

4 Remove the camshaft sprocket. Tap it lightly if necessary to break the taper.

5 Carefully drill or punch a hole in the oil seal face. Screw in a self-tapping screw and use this to pull out the seal using pincers, a claw hammer or a nail bar.

6 Fill the lips of the new seal with grease. Clean out the seal seat, then press the seal into position, lips inwards. Take care not to damage the seal lips. Use a piece of tube or a socket to seat the seal.

7 Refit the camshaft sprocket and secure it with a new bolt, tightened to the specified torque.

8 Refit and tension the camshaft drivebelt, then check the valve timing.

9 Refit the camshaft cover and reconnect the breather hose. Refit the air cleaner.

Crankshaft front seal

10 Remove the crankshaft pulley, sprocket and Woodruff key.

11 Carefully drill or punch a hole in the oil seal face. Screw in a self-tapping screw and use this to pull out the seal using pincers, a claw hammer or a nail bar **(see illustration)**.

12 Fill the lips of the new seal with grease and clean out the seal seat. Cover the step on the crankshaft nose with adhesive tape, then press the seal into position, lips inwards. Use a piece of tube or a socket to seat the seal, then remove the adhesive tape.

13 Refit the Woodruff key. Engage the sprocket with the drivebelt, fit the pulley/sprocket assembly to the crankshaft and tighten the centre bolt to the specified torque.

14 Tension the camshaft drivebelt, then check the valve timing.

Crankshaft rear seal

15 Unless various specials tools are available, the engine must be removed and separated from the gearbox for this operation.

16 Remove the clutch and flywheel (or driveplate, on automatic transmission models). Obtain new bolts for reassembly.

17 Carefully drill or punch a hole in the oil seal face. Screw in a self-tapping screw and use this to pull out the seal using pincers, a claw hammer or a nail bar.

18 Fill the lips of the new seal with grease and clean out the seal seat. Cut a piece of thin flexible plastic to fit around the crankshaft flange and slide the seal into place over this **(see illustration)**. The seal lips face inwards.

19 Seat the seal by tapping it carefully with a wooden or plastic hammer. Make sure it seats evenly. Withdraw the plastic collar.

20 Refit the flywheel or driveplate and secure with new bolts. Refer to Section 13 for further details.

3B

14.11 Self-tapping screw (arrowed) screwed into crankshaft front oil seal

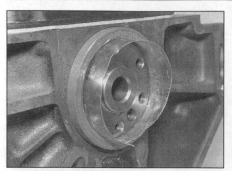

14.18 Using a plastic collar as an aid to fitting the crankshaft rear oil seal

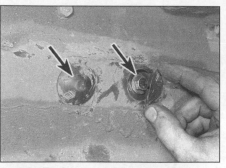

15.2a Engine mounting bolt locations - RH front (arrowed) under wheel arch

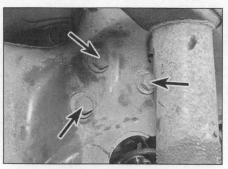

15.2b Engine mounting bolt locations - RH rear (arrowed) under wheel arch

15.2c Engine right-hand rear mounting seen from below. Alternator is normally mounted on top lug (arrowed)

15.2d Transmission mounting - LH rear seen from above

15.2e Transmission mounting - LH front seen from below

21 Refit the clutch (when applicable) and refit the engine and/or gearbox to the vehicle.

Valve stem seals

22 Refer to the Section for cylinder head dismantling and reassembly.

15 Engine/transmission mountings - renewal

Ascona/Cavalier

1 The flexible mountings can be renewed if they have deteriorated. Take the weight of the engine/transmission on a hoist, or use a jack and a wooden block from below. Only remove and refit one mounting at a time.
2 Unbolt the mounting brackets from the engine or transmission and from the bodyframe **(see illustrations)**. Separate the flexible component from the brackets.
3 Fit the new flexible component and refit the mounting. Only nip up the bolts at first, then tighten them to the specified torque.
4 Lower the hoist or jack and check that the mounting is not under strain. Slacken and retighten the bolts if necessary.

Astra/Kadett/Belmont

5 The engine/transmission must be removed in order to renew the right-hand mounting. The left-hand mountings can be renewed as outlined above **(see illustration)**.

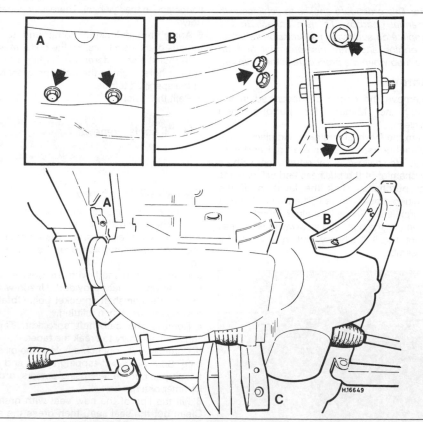

15.5 Engine/transmission mountings - Astra/Kadett

A Right-hand front   B Left-hand front   C Rear

17.4a Coolant temperature sender lead (arrowed) next to thermostat housing

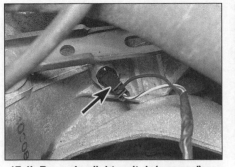

17.4b Reversing light switch (arrowed) on gearbox case

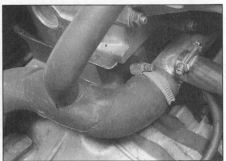

17.6 Heater hose and radiator bottom hose connections to large coolant pipe

17.11 Clutch cable attachment to release lever

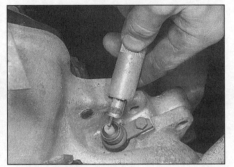

17.14 Disconnecting the speedometer cable (manual gearbox)

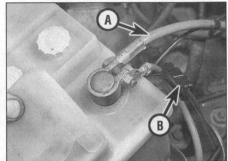

17.15 Starter motor supply lead (A) and command lead connector (B)

16 Engine/transmission - methods of removal

1 The engine/transmission must be removed from below, as the engine cannot be detached from the gearbox in situ.
2 Engine lifting gear will be required. To provide clearance to remove the engine/ transmission from under the vehicle, the use of a pit or a vehicle lift is desirable. Failing this, high-lift ramps or axle stands may suffice, or the front of the vehicle may be lifted after the power unit has been lowered to the ground.
3 The procedures described in the next Section and in Section 31 (refitting) relate to one particular vehicle; allowances must be made for individual model and year variations.

17 Engine/transmission - removal

1 Disconnect the battery earth lead.
2 Remove the bonnet, if wished.
3 Remove the air cleaner and its snorkel.
4 Disconnect the following electrical services, making notes or attaching labels if there is any possibility of confusion later:
 a) Oil pressure switch (next to the oil filter)
 b) Alternator (large and small leads)
 c) Temperature sender (see illustration)
 d) Idle stop solenoid (on injection pump)

17.16a Exhaust system flexible joint

 e) Glow plug feed to bus bar
 f) Reversing light switch (manual gearbox) (see illustration)
 g) Radiator fan and thermoswitch
5 Drain the cooling system, taking precautions against scalding if the coolant is hot.
6 Remove the radiator top and bottom hoses completely. Disconnect the heater and coolant bleed hoses and secure them out of the way (see illustration).
7 On automatic transmission models, disconnect and plug the fluid cooler lines. Be prepared for fluid spillage and take care to keep dirt out of the system.
8 Removal of the radiator and cooling fan is recommended, both to improve access and to reduce the risk of damage. See Chapter 6A.
9 Clean around the fuel inlet and return unions at the pump then disconnect them. Be prepared for fuel spillage. Cap the open unions with polythene and rubber bands to keep fuel in and dirt out.

17.16b Downpipe-to-transmission bracket

10 Disconnect the throttle and cold start cables from the fuel injection pump.
11 On manual gearbox models, disconnect the clutch cable from the release lever (see illustration). Unclip the cable from the bracket at the rear of the engine, noting the insulating material which protects the cable from exhaust system heat.
12 On manual gearbox models, disconnect the gearshift linkage behind the universal joint.
13 On automatic transmission models, disconnect the gearshift and kickdown cables.
14 On all models, disconnect the speedometer cable (see illustration).
15 Disconnect the starter motor supply lead from the battery positive terminal. Separate the starter command lead connector at the same point (see illustration).
16 Unbolt the exhaust downpipe from the manifold flange and the flexible joint. Free the pipe from any brackets and remove it. Recover the flange gasket (see illustrations).

3B

17.21 Front suspension bottom balljoint separated

17.23 Gearbox earth strap attachment (arrowed)

17 Release the clip which secures the fuel hoses to the camshaft drivebelt cover. Tie the hoses out of the way.

18 Remove the power steering pump, when fitted, and secure its pipes out of the way.

19 Disconnect the servo vacuum pipe from the vacuum pump.

20 Raise and support the front of the vehicle and remove the front wheels.

21 Separate the front suspension bottom balljoints **(see illustration)**.

22 Release the driveshafts from the transmission, referring to the appropriate Manual for petrol-engined vehicles. Be prepared for oil spillage. Secure the driveshafts out of the way.

23 Disconnect the earth strap from the transmission end cover **(see illustration)**.

24 Take the weight of the engine/transmission on the lifting gear, using the lifting eyes provided.

25 Unbolt the right-hand engine mounting from the top (two bolts) and side (two bolts accessible through the wheel arch).

26 Unbolt and remove the other engine/transmission mounting brackets.

27 On models where the alternator mounting forms part of an engine mounting bracket, either remove the alternator or secure it so that it cannot fall off.

28 If there is limited side-to-side clearance for lowering the engine/transmission, removing the oil filter and the crankshaft pulley will improve matters slightly.

29 Check that no attachments have been overlooked, then lower the engine/transmission to the ground. Withdraw the unit from under the vehicle and take it to the bench.

18 Engine/transmission - separation

1 Clean the outside of the engine/transmission.

2 Unbolt and remove the starter motor and its heat shield.

3 Unbolt and remove the clutch or torque converter cover plate from the bottom of the bellhousing.

4 On automatic transmission models, unbolt the torque converter from the driveplate **(see illustration)**. Turn the crankshaft to gain access to the bolts through the cover plate aperture. Obtain new bolts for reassembly.

5 On all models, bring the engine to TDC, No 1 firing. With the transmission removed there will be no TDC indicated.

6 Support the transmission and remove the engine-to-transmission bolts.

7 Withdraw the transmission from the engine. Do not allow the weight of the transmission to hang on the input shaft. With automatic transmission, make sure that the torque converter stays in its housing.

8 Make alternative TDC marks between the flywheel and the engine block for use during dismantling and reassembly.

19 Engine dismantling - general information

1 If the engine has been removed from the vehicle for major overhaul or if individual components have been removed for repair or renewal, observe the following general hints on dismantling and reassembly.

2 Drain the engine oil into a suitable container and then thoroughly clean the exterior of the engine using a degreasing solvent or paraffin. Clean away as much external dirt and grease as possible before dismantling.

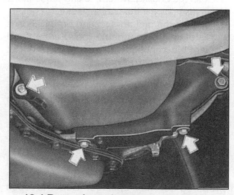

18.4 Removing a torque converter-to-driveplate bolt

3 As parts are removed, clean them in a paraffin bath. However, do not immerse parts with internal oilways in paraffin as it is difficult to remove, usually requiring a high pressure hose. Clean oilways with nylon pipe cleaners.

4 Avoid working with the engine or any of its components directly on a concrete floor, as grit presents a real source of trouble.

5 Wherever possible, work should be carried out with the engine or individual components on a strong bench. If the work must be done on the floor, then cover the floor with a board or sheets of newspaper.

6 Have plenty of clean, lint-free rags available and also some containers or trays to hold small items. This will help during reassembly and also prevent possible losses.

7 Always obtain a complete set of new gaskets if the engine is being completely dismantled, or all those necessary for the individual component or assembly being worked on. Keep the old gaskets with a view to using them as a pattern to make a replacement if a new one is not available.

8 When possible refit nuts, bolts and washers in their locations after removal as this helps to protect the threads and avoids confusion or loss.

20 Ancillary components - removal

If the engine is to be completely dismantled, then remove the following ancillary components (if not already done) whilst referring to the appropriate Chapter:

a) Alternator and drivebelt
b) Inlet and exhaust manifolds
c) Camshaft drivebelt
d) Coolant pump and thermostat
e) Fuel injection pump and bracket
f) Vacuum pump
g) Clutch assembly
h) Fuel injectors
I) Glow plugs
j) Oil filter
k) EGR assembly
l) Dipstick, dipstick tube and cable bracket **(see illustration)**

20.1 Dipstick tube and cable bracket securing bolts (arrowed)

20.2 Two bolts (arrowed) securing the large coolant pipe

Also remove the large coolant pipe which runs along the rear face of the engine, and the hose which connects it to the coolant pump **(see illustration)**.

21 Engine - complete dismantling

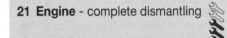

1 Remove the following items as described in the appropriate Sections, disregarding those instructions which have already been carried out in removing the engine:
  a) *Cylinder head*
  b) *Sump - if possible, without inverting the engine, so that any sludge does not enter the crankcase*
  c) *Oil pump*
  d) *Pistons and connecting rods*
  e) *Flywheel or driveplate*

21.4 Removing a main bearing cap bolt

2 Invert the engine so that it is standing on the top face of the block.
3 Check that the main bearing caps are numbered 1 to 4 from the pulley end. The fifth cap is not numbered but it is different from the rest. The numbers are on the rear (coolant pump) halves of the caps. Make identification marks if no numbers are present.
4 Remove the bolts which secure the main bearing caps **(see illustration)**.
5 Lift off the main bearing caps, tapping them lightly to free them if they are stuck. Keep the bearing shells with their caps if they are to be reused. Clean any sealant from the rear cap.
6 Lift out the crankshaft and put it somewhere safe. Do not drop it, it is heavy.
7 Extract the upper half main bearing shells. Keep them in order if they are to be reused.
8 With the exception of semi-permanent items such as dowels and core plugs, dismantling of the engine is complete.

22 Oil pump - dismantling, overhaul and reassembly

Dismantling
1 With the oil pump removed from the vehicle, withdraw the rear cover. The cross-head fixing screws are very tight and an impact driver will be required to remove them **(see illustration)**.

Overhaul
2 Check the clearance between the inner and outer gear teeth and the outer gear and the pump body **(see illustrations)**.
3 Using a straight-edge across the pump cover flange, measure the gear endfloat **(see illustration)**.
4 If any of the clearances are outside the specified tolerance, renew the components as necessary. Note that the outer gear face is marked for position **(see illustration)**.
5 The pressure regulator valve can be unscrewed from the oil pump housing and the components cleaned and examined **(see illustration)**.
6 The oil pressure warning light switch is screwed into the rear of the pump. If it is suspected of being defective it should be renewed, see Chapter 5.
7 The oil filter bypass valve can be removed from the filter carrier by screwing an M10 tap into it **(see illustration)**. Drive the new valve into position up to its stop.

22.1 Removing the oil pump rear cover screws

22.2a Oil pump clearance check - inner-to-outer teeth

22.2b Oil pump clearance check - outer gear-to-body

22.3 Oil pump gear endfloat check

22.4 Oil pump outer gear position marking (arrowed) must face rearwards

22.5 Oil pump pressure regulator valve components

3B

22.7 Oil filter bypass valve (arrowed)

8 Before reassembling the pump, take the opportunity to renew the front oil seal.

Reassembly

9 Refit the gears, lubricating them with clean engine oil.

10 Refit the rear cover (no gasket is used). Insert and tighten the retaining screws.

11 Lubricate the pressure regulator valve plunger with clean engine oil. Refit the plunger and spring and secure them with the plug and washer. Tighten the plug to the specified torque.

12 Refit and tighten the oil pressure warning light switch, if it was removed.

23 Cylinder head - dismantling and reassembly

Note: *Renewal of the oil pressure relief valve is best left to a GM dealer, since special tools are required to extract the valve cage and seat*

Dismantling

1 If not already done, remove the fuel injectors and the glow plugs.

2 A valve spring compressor will be needed to remove each valve and spring assembly. Fit the compressor foot to the head of a valve with the forked end over the valve spring cap. Operate the compressor so that the cap is depressed a little way and extract the split collets **(see illustration)**. If the cap seems to be stuck, remove the compressor and strike the cap smartly with a mallet, then try again.

3 With the collets removed, release the compressor and remove the spring cap, spring and valve rotator. Withdraw the valve from the other side of the head.

4 Remove the valve stem oil seal from the top of the valve guide. New seals will be needed for reassembly.

5 Repeat these operations to remove the remaining valves. Keep each valve and its associated components separate, in a segmented box.

6 The swirl chambers can be driven out if necessary using a non-ferrous drift through

the injector hole **(see illustration)**. The injector insulating sleeves can then be driven out in the opposite direction, using a non-ferrous drift of 10 mm diameter **(see illustration)**. Recover the sleeve sealing rings.

7 There is an oil pressure relief valve in the cylinder head to protect the valve hydraulic lifters **(see illustration)**. Renewal of this valve is best left to a GM dealer, since various special tools are required to extract the valve cage and seat. With the old valve removed, it is simple enough to drive a new one into place through the core plug aperture. Seal with a new plug on completion of fitting.

8 Thoroughly clean the cylinder head and examine it and its components as described in the Section relating to head examination and overhaul.

Reassembly

9 If the swirl chambers and insulating sleeves were removed, the swirl chambers should be refitted first. Make sure that the locating ball is correctly positioned as shown **(see illustration)**. From the other side of the head fit new sealing rings for the insulating sleeves, then drive them into position.

10 After refitting the swirl chambers, check their projection as described in the Section relating to cylinder head examination and overhaul.

11 Lubricate a valve stem with clean engine oil and fit the valve into its guide **(see illustration)**.

23.2 Compress the valve spring and remove the collets (arrowed)

23.6a Driving out a swirl chamber

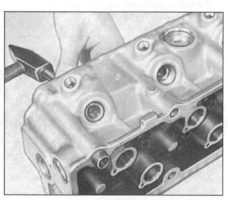

23.6b Driving out an injector insulating sleeve

23.7 Oil pressure relief valve (arrowed) in cylinder head

23.9 Fitting a swirl chamber. Note locating ball and recess (arrowed)

23.11 Inserting a valve into its guide

23.12 Valve rotator in position

23.13 Fitting a valve stem oil seal over the protective sleeve

23.14a Fit the valve spring . . .

23.14b . . . and the valve spring cap

12 From the other side of the head, fit the valve rotator **(see illustration)**.

13 A temporary protective sleeve should have been supplied with the new valve stem oil seals. Fit the sleeve over the valve stem and lubricate it, then press the seal into position over the sleeve **(see illustration)**. Use a piece of tube or a small box spanner if necessary to push the seal onto its seat. The outer part of the seal engages with the groove on the valve guide. Remove the sleeve.

14 Fit the valve spring (either way up) and the spring cap **(see illustrations)**.

15 Fit the valve spring compressor and depress the spring cap far enough to allow the collets to be fitted. A smear of grease on the valve stem will keep them in position. Carefully release the compressor, making sure that the collets are not displaced. Tap the spring cap with a mallet to settle the components.

16 Refit the other valves, springs and associated components in a similar fashion.

17 Check the valve head recess as described in Section 24.

18 Refit the fuel injectors and the glow plugs.

24 Cylinder head - examination and overhaul

Note: *It is advisable to dismantle and clean the hydraulic valve lifters whenever the cylinder head is overhauled. Refer to Section 27.*

1 Check the head visually for cracks or other obvious signs of damage. Small cracks between the inlet and exhaust valve seats are not serious and may be ignored.

2 Examine the valve sealing faces and the valve seats in the head for pitting, burning or other damage. Light pitting may be rectified by grinding but anything more serious means the valve and/or seat must be refaced or renewed. Consult a GM dealer or other specialist if work of this nature appears necessary.

3 Check the fit of the valves in their guides. Worn guides must be reamed out to the next oversize (another specialist job) and valves with oversize stems fitted. Permissible oversizes are listed in the *Specifications*. Note that oversize valves may already have been fitted so look for grade markings on the valve guide and valve stem. Check also that the valve stems are not bent.

4 Valve grinding is carried out as follows. Smear a little coarse grinding paste onto the sealing area of the valve head. Insert the valve into its guide and using a suitable tool, typically a stick with a rubber sucker on it, grind the valve to its seat with a semi-rotary motion **(see illustration)**. Lift the valve

24.4 Grinding a valve to its seat

occasionally to redistribute the grinding paste. Do not use an electric drill or other tool with a continuous circular motion.

5 When an unbroken ring of grinding paste is present on the valve head and its seat, wipe off the coarse paste and repeat the process with fine paste. If the valve seats have been recut accurately, and new or refaced valves are being fitted, only fine paste need be used from the outset.

6 When valve grinding is complete, clean away all traces of grinding paste using first a paraffin-soaked rag, then a clean dry rag, then (if available) an air line. Any grinding paste remaining may cause rapid wear.

7 Renew valve springs if they are obviously distorted or weak, or if they have seen much service. Springs do fatigue in time and it is better to renew them now than to have one break in use.

8 Check the head mating faces, both block and camshaft carrier, for freedom from distortion. Use a straight-edge and feeler blades. Do not be deceived by the (permitted) projection of the swirl chambers. Distortion limits are given in the *Specifications*. An out-of-limit head may be reclaimed by specialist machining, provided that the overall height of the head is not reduced below that specified, and that valve recess and swirl chamber projection stay within limits.

9 Check the projection of the swirl chambers from the head-to-block face, using a straight-edge and feeler blades or (preferably, for such a small measurement) a dial test indicator **(see illustrations)**. The allowable projection is given in the *Specifications*.

24.9a Checking swirl chamber projection with a straight-edge and feeler blades

3B

24.9b Checking swirl chamber projection with a dial test indicator

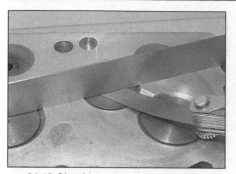

24.10 Checking a valve head recess

10 After refitting the valves, check the recess of their heads. This is a much coarser measurement and feeler blades will suffice **(see illustration)**. The desired recess is given in the *Specifications*. It may be possible to correct out-of-limit valves by machining of the valve and/or seat. Seek specialist advice in this case.

11 Do not overlook the condition of core plugs, studs and dowels.

25 Cylinder head and pistons - decarbonising

1 Bearing in mind that the cylinder head is of light alloy construction and is easily damaged, use a blunt scraper or rotary wire brush to clean all traces of carbon deposits from the combustion spaces and the ports. The valve heads, stems and valve guides should also be freed from any carbon deposits. Wash the combustion spaces and ports down with paraffin and scrape the cylinder head surface free of any foreign matter with the side of a steel rule, or similar item.

2 If the engine is installed in the car, clean the pistons and the top of the cylinder bores. If the pistons are still in the block, then it is essential that great care is taken to ensure that no carbon gets into the cylinder bores as this could scratch the cylinder walls or cause damage to the piston and rings. To ensure this does not happen, first turn the crankshaft so that two of the pistons are at the top of their bores. Stuff rag into the other two bores or seal them off with paper and masking tape. The waterways should also be covered with small pieces of masking tape to prevent particles of carbon entering the cooling system.

3 Press a little grease into the gap between the cylinder walls and the two pistons which are to be worked on. With a blunt scraper, carefully scrape away the carbon from the piston crown, taking great care not to scratch the aluminium. Also scrape away the carbon from the surrounding lip of the cylinder wall. When all carbon has been removed, scrape away the grease which will now be contaminated with carbon particles, taking care not to press any into the bores. To assist prevention of carbon

build-up the piston crown can be polished with a metal polish. Remove the rags or masking tape from the other two cylinders and turn the crankshaft so that the two pistons which were at the bottom are now at the top. Place rag or masking tape in the cylinders which have been decarbonised, and proceed as just described.

26 Examination and renovation - general information

1 With the engine stripped and all parts thoroughly cleaned, every component should be examined for wear. The items listed in the following Sections should receive particular attention and where necessary be renewed or renovated.

2 So many measurements of engine components require great accuracy. It is advisable therefore to check your micrometer against a standard gauge occasionally to ensure that the instrument zero is set correctly.

3 If in doubt as to whether or not a particular component must be renewed, take into account not only the cost of the component but the time and effort which will be required to renew it if it subsequently fails at an early date. With this in mind, Astra/Kadett/Belmont owners may wish to renew the right-hand engine mounting as a precautionary measure.

27 Engine components - examination and renovation

Crankshaft

1 Examine the crankpin and main journal surfaces for signs of scoring or scratches and check the ovality and taper of the crankpins and main journals. If the bearing surface dimensions do not fall within the tolerance ranges given in the *Specifications* at the beginning of this Chapter, the crankpins and/or main journals will have to be reground.

2 In the absence of a micrometer, the crankshaft bearing running clearances can be determined by the use of Plastigage. This is a calibrated plastic filament which is placed between the bearing journal and shell. No oil

must be present. The main bearing or connecting rod cap is fitted and its fastenings tightened to the specified torque, then the cap and shell are removed again. The width of the squashed filament is compared with the chart on the packet to determine the clearance **(see illustration)**. This method is good for detecting taper but it will not detect out-of-round unless several measurements are taken at different points.

3 Big-end and crankpin wear is accompanied by distinct metallic knocking, particularly noticeable when the engine is pulling from low revs, and some loss of oil pressure. Main bearing and main journal wear is accompanied by severe engine vibration and rumble (getting progressively worse as engine revs increase) and again by loss of oil pressure.

4 If the crankshaft requires regrinding, take it to an engine reconditioning specialist who will machine it for you and supply the correct undersize bearing shells. Note that the bearing journals must be hardened (by the process known as "nitriding", or equivalent) after grinding. It is wise to check the clearances on the reground crankshaft (as described in paragraph 2) during reassembly.

Big-end and main bearing shells

Note: *You are strongly advised to renew bearings - regardless of their condition - at time of major overhaul. Refitting used bearings is a false economy.*

5 Inspect the big-end and main bearing shells for signs of general wear, scoring, pitting and scratches. The bearings should be matt grey in colour. With lead-indium bearings, should a trace of copper colour be noticed, the bearings are badly worn as the lead bearing material has worn away to expose the indium underlay. Renew the bearings if they are in this condition or if there are any signs of scoring or pitting.

6 The undersizes available are designed to correspond with crankshaft regrind sizes. The bearings are in fact, slightly more than the stated undersize as running clearances have been allowed for during their manufacture.

7 Main and big-end bearing shells can be identified as to size by the marking on the back of the shell **(see illustration)**. Typical markings are given in the *Specifications*. If other markings

27.2 Using Plastigage to determine bearing clearance

27.7 Identification markings on the back of a crankshaft bearing shell

are encountered, consult a GM dealer for interpretation. Remember that undersize shells may have been fitted in production. As well as numbers, original equipment shells are colour coded on their edges.

Cylinder bores

Note: *Vauxhall/Opel have announced the availability of cylinder liners for certain engine types. The fitting of these liners requires full engine reconditioning facilities and the work must therefore be entrusted to a Vauxhall/Opel dealer or engine reconditioning specialist. The introduction of liners does offer a new lease of life to an engine with worn cylinder bores which has already been rebored to the maximum permissible oversize. Note, however, that it is not permissible to fit oversize pistons to an engine which has been fitted with liners. The makers state that the wall thickness is such that boring them oversize will weaken them too much. It follows that once liners have been fitted, the only way to reclaim the block subsequently would be to fit new liners and bore these back to the standard diameter again.*

8 Cylinder bores must be examined for taper, ovality, scoring and scratches. Start by carefully examining the top of the bores. If they are at all worn, a very slight ridge will be found on the thrust side. This marks the top of the piston travel. The owner will have a good indication of the bore wear prior to dismantling the engine, or removing the cylinder head. Excessive oil consumption accompanied by blue smoke from the exhaust can be caused by worn cylinder bores and piston rings.

9 Measure the bore diameter across the block and just below any ridge. This can be done with an internal micrometer or a dial gauge. Compare this with the diameter of the bottom of the bore, which is not subject to wear. If no measuring instruments are available, use a piston from which the rings have been removed and measure the gap between it and the cylinder wall with a feeler blade.

10 Refer to the *Specifications*. If cylinder wear exceeds the permitted tolerances then

27.15 Using three feeler blades for piston ring removal

the cylinders will need reboring. If the wear is marginal and within the tolerances given, proprietary piston rings which are claimed to offset the effects of bore wear can be fitted. The improvement made by such rings may be short-lived, however.

Connecting rods

11 Examine the mating faces of the big-end caps to see if they have ever been filed in a mistaken attempt to take up wear. If so, the offending rods must be renewed.

12 Check the alignment of the rods visually, and if all is not well, take the rods to your local agent for checking on a special jig.

13 The weight of the connecting rod is indicated by a number or colour mark on the rod cap - see *Specifications*. Replacement rods should be of the same weight class.

14 Separation of the pistons from the rods is described in the Section relating to connecting rod removal and refitting. Wear of the gudgeon pin or the small-end bush in the rod means that the components must be renewed. New gudgeon pins are not sold separately from new pistons.

Pistons and piston rings

15 If the pistons and/or rings are to be reused, remove the rings from the pistons. Prepare three feeler blades or similar strips of thin metal, then spring the top ring open just far enough to insert the blades. The ring can then be slid off the piston without scratching or scoring **(see illustration)**.

16 Repeat the process for the second and third rings.

17 Keep the rings with their original piston if they are to be reused. The top ring carries a very small step on its upper face. The second ring has a "TOP" marking which must be uppermost. The third (oil scraper) ring may be fitted either way up **(see illustration)**.

18 Inspect the pistons to ensure that they are suitable for re-use. Check for cracks, damage to the ring grooves and lands and scores or signs of picking-up on the piston walls. If a micrometer is available, check the diameter of the piston around the base of the skirt.

19 Clean the ring grooves in the piston using a piece of old piston ring **(see illustration)**. Take care not to remove any metal or scratch the ring lands. Protect your fingers as piston rings are sharp!

20 Check the ring end gaps in the bores. Push the ring to the unworn lower section of the bore, using a piston to do this so that the ring stays square. Measure the end gap with feeler blades and compare it with that specified **(see illustration)**. If the gap is too big (and the bore is unworn) the rings must be renewed.

21 It is worth checking the vertical clearance of the compression rings in their grooves. No limit is specified by the makers but experience suggests that a gap of up to 0.075 mm is satisfactory, although much more than this may lead to oil pumping and rapid groove wear in service. New rings will only be effective here if the grooves are relatively unworn.

22 If buying new standard rings of GM manufacture, note that two grades are available, the smaller being for piston production grades 1 and 2 and the larger for grade 3.

23 Check the end gap of new rings at both top and bottom of the bores. If the gap is too small, the ends of the ring can be ground carefully until the correct gap is achieved.

24 If new pistons are to be fitted without reboring, they should be selected from the grades available (see *Specifications*) after accurate measurement of the bores. If a rebore is undertaken, it is normal for the

3B

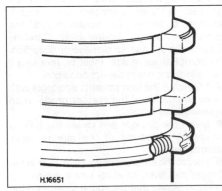

27.17 Piston ring profiles

27.19 Cleaning out a piston ring groove

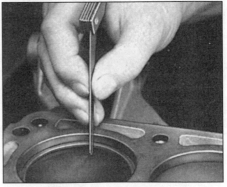

27.20 Checking a piston ring end gap

27.24 Manufacturer's identity and bore grade markings on piston crown

27.37 Fitting a camshaft front oil seal

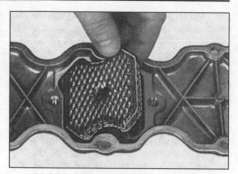

27.38 Removing the filter from the camshaft cover

repairer to obtain the correct oversize pistons at the same time. The piston size and the maker's identity are marked on the crown **(see illustration)**.

25 Remember to deglaze old bores if new rings are fitted.

Flywheel

26 If the teeth on the flywheel starter ring are badly worn, or if some are missing, then it will be necessary to remove the ring and fit a new one.

27 Either split the ring with a cold chisel after making a cut with a hacksaw blade between two teeth, or use a soft-headed hammer (not steel) to knock the ring off, striking it evenly and alternately, at equally spaced points. Take great care not to damage the flywheel during this process and protect your eyes from flying fragments.

28 The new ring gear must be heated to 180° to 230°C (356° to 446°F). Unless facilities for heating by oven or flame are available, leave the fitting to your dealer or motor engineering works. The new ring gear must not be overheated during this work or the temper of the metal will be altered.

29 The ring should be tapped gently down onto its register and left to cool naturally when the contraction of the metal on cooling will ensure that it is a secure and permanent fit.

30 If the driven plate contact surface of the flywheel is scored or on close inspection

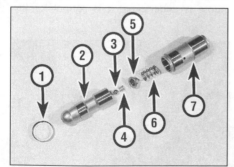

27.41 Hydraulic valve lifter components

1	Collar	5	Plunger cap
2	Plunger	6	Large spring
3	Ball	7	Cylinder
4	Small spring		

shows evidence of small hairline cracks caused by overheating, it may be possible to have the flywheel surface ground provided the overall thickness of the flywheel is not reduced too much. Consult your specialist engine repairer and if it is not possible, renew the flywheel complete.

Driveplate (automatic transmission)

31 Should the starter ring gear on the driveplate require renewal, renew the driveplate complete.

Crankshaft spigot bearing

32 If the needle bearing in the centre of the crankshaft flange is worn, fill it with grease and tap in a close-fitting rod. Hydraulic pressure will remove it. Alternatively, a very small extractor having a claw type leg may be used. When tapping the new bearing into position, make sure that the chamfered side of the bearing enters first.

33 Later engines (from mid-1984) are not fitted with a spigot bearing.

Camshaft and carrier

34 With the camshaft removed, examine the bearings for signs of obvious wear and pitting. If evident, a new camshaft carrier will probably be required.

35 The camshaft itself should show no marks or scoring on the journal or cam lobe surfaces. If evident, renew the camshaft.

36 The camshaft thrust plate should appear unworn and without grooves. Renew it if not, or if the camshaft endfloat is excessive.

37 Always renew the camshaft front oil seal **(see illustration)**.

38 Clean the filter in the camshaft cover in petrol or other solvent and allow it to dry **(see illustration)**.

39 If a new camshaft is being fitted, pay attention to the running-in schedule given in the Section relating to camshaft removal and refitting.

Valve lifters, cam followers and thrust pads

Valve lifters

40 The valve hydraulic lifters must be

renewed if worn or if there is a history of noisy operation.

41 On engines which have covered a high mileage, or for which the service history (particularly oil changes) is suspect, it is possible for the valve lifters to suffer internal contamination, which in extreme cases may result in increased engine top end noise and wear. To minimise the possibility of problems occurring later in the life of the engine, it is advisable to dismantle and clean the hydraulic valve lifters as follows whenever the cylinder head is overhauled. Note that no spare parts are available for the valve lifters, and if any of the components are unserviceable, the complete assembly must be renewed **(see illustration)**.

42 Inspect the valve lifter bores in the cylinder head for wear. If excessive wear is evident, the cylinder head must be renewed. Also check the valve lifter oil holes in the cylinder head for obstructions.

43 Starting with No 1 valve lifter, carefully pull the collar from the top of the valve lifter cylinder. It should be possible to remove the collar by hand. If a tool is used, take care not to distort the collar.

44 Withdraw the plunger from the cylinder, and recover the spring.

45 Using a small screwdriver, carefully prise the cap from the base of the plunger. Recover the spring and ball from under the cap, taking care not to lose them as the cap is removed.

46 Carefully clean all the components using paraffin or a suitable solvent, paying particular attention to the machined surfaces of the cylinder (internal surfaces) and piston (external surfaces). Thoroughly dry all the components using a lint-free cloth. Carefully examine the springs for damage or distortion. The complete valve lifter must be renewed if the springs are not in perfect condition.

47 Lubricate the components sparingly with clean engine oil of the correct grade, then reassemble as follows.

48 Invert the plunger and locate the ball on its seat in the base of the plunger **(see illustration)**.

49 Locate the smaller spring on its seat in the plunger cap then carefully refit the cap and spring, ensuring that the spring locates on the ball. Carefully press around the flange of the

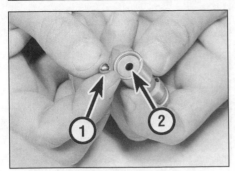

27.48 Locate the ball (1) on its seat (2) in the base of the plunger

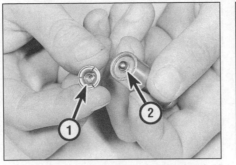

27.49a Spring (1) located in plunger cap and ball (2) located on seat in plunger

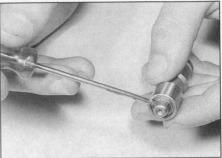

27.49b Locate the cap flange in the plunger groove

27.50a Locate the spring over the plunger cap . . .

27.50b . . . then slide the plunger and spring assembly into the cylinder

28 Engine reassembly - general information

1 All engine components must be clean before starting reassembly. The working area should also be clean and well-lit.

2 Obtain a set of new gaskets, oil seals etc. Also obtain new bolts where these are specified. Renew any other bolts, studs or nuts with damaged threads.

3 Besides the usual hand tools, a torque wrench will be required, as will some means of measuring angular rotation (eg. a protractor and some card).

4 Have handy a squirt type oil can full of clean engine oil, plenty of clean rag, non-setting and RTV jointing compound and thread locking compound.

5 Refer to Section 5 and obtain one of the tools needed to set the valve timing. The dial test indicator is recommended since it will also be used for timing the fuel injection pump and can be used for several other checks during engine rebuilding.

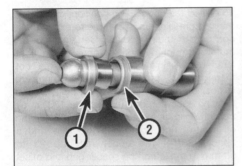

27.51 Slide the collar (1) over the top of the plunger, and engage with the groove (2) in the cylinder

27.55 Removing a core plug

29 Engine - complete reassembly

cap, using a small screwdriver if necessary, until the flange is securely located in the groove in the base of the plunger **(see illustrations)**.

50 Locate the larger spring over the plunger cap, ensuring that the spring is correctly seated, and slide the plunger and spring assembly into the cylinder **(see illustrations)**.

51 Slide the collar over the top of the plunger, and carefully compress the plunger by hand, until the collar can be pushed down to engage securely with the groove in the cylinder **(see illustration)**.

52 Repeat the above procedures on the remaining valve lifters.

Cam followers and thrust pads

53 Inspect the cam followers and thrust pads for signs of wear or grooving and renew if

evident. It is wise to renew the cam followers if the camshaft is being renewed.

Core plugs

54 Check the condition of the core plugs in the block and cylinder head. Those which close oily areas are unlikely to deteriorate but those which close the water jacket may suffer from rust, especially if plain water has been used as coolant. Obviously it is much better to renew the plugs while they are accessible.

55 To remove a core plug, punch or drill a small hole in the middle of the plug. Screw in a large self-tapping screw and use a suitable lever on the screw head to extract the plug **(see illustration)**.

56 Clean out the plug seat. Coat the sides of the new plug with sealant, then drive it into place.

Crankshaft and main bearings

1 Blow out the oilways in the crankcase and crankshaft with an air line, if available, then inject clean engine oil into them.

2 Clean the main bearing shell seats in the crankcase and the shells themselves. New shells may have a protective coating which should be carefully removed.

3 Fit the upper half main bearing shells to their seats. Make sure that the oil holes and the locating tangs are correctly positioned. All the shells are the same except for the centre one, which has thrust flanges **(see illustration)**.

4 Apply oil to the bearing shells, then lower the crankshaft into position **(see illustration)**. Turn it once or twice to make sure it is seated.

5 Clean the shell seats in the main bearing caps and fit the shells to the caps, again making sure that they are the right way round.

3B

29.3 Fitting the centre main bearing upper half shell - note thrust flanges

29.4 Lubricate the bearing shells and lower the crankshaft into position

29.7 Applying jointing compound to the mating faces of the rear main bearing cap

29.8 Applying sealant to the rear main bearing cap side grooves

29.9 Injecting sealant into the bearing cap grooves from the exposed end

29.10 Front cap-to-block joint (arrowed) must be flush

As with the upper half shells, they are all the same except for the flanged centre shell.

6 Oil the shells and fit all the main bearing caps except the rear one. Observe the identification marks or numbers on the caps both to ensure correct numerical position and to ensure that the caps are the right way round. It may be necessary to strike the caps with a mallet to seat them but take care not to displace the shells if doing so. Do not tighten the cap bolts yet.

7 Coat the mating faces of the rear main bearing cap with non-setting jointing compound (to GM spec 15 04 200 or equivalent) **(see illustration)**.

8 Lay a bead of RTV jointing compound (to GM spec 15 03 294, or equivalent) into the grooves on the sides of the rear main bearing cap. The bead should be approximately 6.0 mm in diameter **(see illustration)**.

9 Fit the rear main bearing cap and shell. When the cap is home, inject further RTV sealant into the grooves from the exposed end **(see illustration)**.

10 Fit the main bearing cap bolts and nip them up. Make sure that the front main bearing cap is flush with the block face **(see illustration)**.

11 Tighten the bearing cap bolts progressively to the specified torque.

12 Make sure that the crankshaft is still free to turn. Some stiffness is to be expected with new shells but obvious tight spots or binding should be investigated. See the Section relating to component examination and renovation for measurement of bearing clearances.

29.13 Measuring crankshaft endfloat

13 Measure the crankshaft endfloat, either with a dial test indicator on the flywheel flange or by using feeler blades at the centre bearing thrust flange **(see illustration)**. Strike the shaft with a mallet at one end or the other to take up the endfloat. Out-of-limit endfloat must be due to wear, or to incorrect regrinding.

Piston rings

14 The easiest method of fitting piston rings is to use feeler blades (or similar) around the top of the piston and move the rings into position over the feelers. This is a reversal of the removal procedure detailed earlier in this Chapter.

15 Follow the manufacturer's instructions carefully when fitting rings to ensure that they are correctly fitted. Several variations of compression and oil control rings are available and it is of the utmost importance that they be located correctly in their grooves.

16 When the rings are in position, check that the compression rings are free to expand and contract in their grooves. Certain types of multi-segment oil control rings are a light interference fit in their grooves and this may not therefore apply to them. When all the rings are in position on the pistons, move them around to bring each ring gap to be some 180° away from the gap on the adjacent ring(s). When the oil control ring comprises two rails and a spacer, offset the upper rail gap 25 to 50 mm to the left of the spacer gap and offset the lower rail gap a similar distance to the right.

Pistons and connecting rods

17 Reassemble the pistons and rods if they have been separated, making sure that they are the right way round. Insert the gudgeon pin circlips.

18 Lay out the pistons and rods in order with the rod caps, bearing shells and cap nuts.

19 Clean the bearing shells and their seats. Press the shells into their positions, making sure that the locating tangs are the right way round.

20 Oil the piston rings and the cylinder bores. Make sure that the ring gaps are correctly spaced then fit a piston ring compressor to one of the pistons.

21 Turn the crankshaft to bring the crankpin for the piston being fitted to BDC.

22 Offer the piston/rod assembly to the block, making sure that it is the right way round (arrow on piston crown pointing to pulley end) and that it is being fitted to the correct bore **(see illustration)**.

29.22 Offering the piston to the cylinder bore - ring compressor fitted

29.23 Driving a piston into its bore

29.25a Fitting a connecting rod bearing cap

29.25b Tightening a connecting rod bearing cap nut

29.29 Fitting the oil pump - note new gasket on block

using thread locking compound on the bolt threads. Tighten the bolts evenly to the specified torque.

Rear oil seal and flywheel

35 Lubricate the lips of a new rear oil seal and fit it to the crankshaft, using a plastic collar as described in the Section relating to seal renewal. There is a temptation to fit this seal to the crankshaft before fitting the main bearing caps but there is then a risk of distorting or pinching the seal as the rear main bearing cap is tightened.

36 Fit the flywheel (or driveplate) to the crankshaft flange, lining up the bolt holes for the shouldered bolt.

37 Apply thread locking compound to the threads of the new flywheel bolts. Fit the bolts, making sure the shouldered bolt is correctly located, and tighten them evenly to the Stage 1 specified torque.

23 Drive the piston into the bore by tapping the piston crown with, for example, the wooden handle of a hammer **(see illustration)**. If resistance is encountered, release the compressor and see if a ring has jammed. Remove the compressor as the piston enters the bore.

24 Lubricate the crankpin and guide the connecting rod onto it by pushing the piston down the bore. Take care that the protruding studs do not scratch the crankpin, and check that the bearing shell is not displaced.

25 Fit the connecting rod cap, making sure that it is the right way round and that the shell is not displaced. Fit the securing nuts and tighten them to the specified torque **(see illustrations)**.

26 Repeat the operations to fit the other three pistons. Check after fitting each piston that the crankshaft can still be rotated.

Oil pump and sump

27 Lubricate the lips of the oil pump seal.

28 Fit a new pump gasket to the block, using a smear of grease to hold it in position.

29 Offer the pump to the block so that it fits onto the dowels **(see illustration)**.

30 Fit and tighten the pump securing screws.

31 Fit the pump pick-up tube, using a new O-ring between the tube flange and the pump. Secure the tube with two bolts at the flange and a single bolt at the block **(see illustrations)**.

32 Apply RTV jointing compound (to GM spec 15 03 294) to the joints between the rear main bearing cap and the block, and the oil pump and the block.

33 Smear a new sump gasket with grease and position it on the block. Fit the sump, taking care not to displace the gasket **(see illustration)**.

34 Fit the sump retaining bolts and washers,

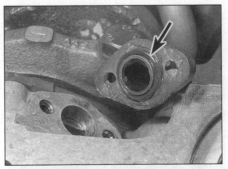

29.31a Fitting the oil pump pick-up tube - O-ring arrowed

29.31c Oil pump pick-up tube securing bolt (arrowed) on block

29.31b Oil pump pick-up flange bolts (arrowed)

29.33 Fitting the sump

3B

29.38a Tightening a flywheel bolt through a specified angle

29.38b Scrap bolt used to lock flywheel

29.43 Using a dial test indicator to measure piston projection

38 Arrange some means of measuring the angular rotation of the bolts, then tighten them through the angle specified for Stage 2. It will be necessary to lock the flywheel as this is done - an old clutch cover bolt can be inserted from the starter motor side, but it is sure to be bent under the strain **(see illustrations)**.

Head gasket selection

39 There are three thicknesses of head gasket and selection of the correct gasket is determined by measuring piston protrusion above the block face at TDC. Precise figures are given in the *Specifications*.

40 The projection could be measured with a straight-edge and feeler blades, but it is more accurate (and much easier to find TDC) to use a dial test indicator.

41 Invert the engine so that it is standing on its sump. Chock it with wooden blocks if necessary to ensure stability.

42 Rotate the crankshaft to bring two pistons to TDC. Take care to determine, either with the dial test indicator or by eye, that the pistons are truly at the very top of their stroke.

43 If a dial test indicator is being used, zero it on the block face next to the piston, then measure the height of the piston crown above the block face **(see illustration)**. If a straight-edge is being used, rest it on the two piston crowns and determine the thickness of feeler blades(s) which will just pass between the straight-edge and the block.

44 Bring the other two pistons to TDC and repeat the measurement, then select the head gasket.

Cylinder head and valve gear

45 Make sure that the block and head mating faces are clean and that the locating dowels are in position in the block. Bring the pistons to mid-stroke (90° BTDC).

46 Fit the head gasket to the block with the OBEN/TOP mark uppermost. It will only fit one way. Do not use any grease or jointing compound.

47 Lower the assembled cylinder head onto the block, making sure that the dowels engage **(see illustration)**.

48 Lubricate and fit the valve lifters, thrust pads and cam followers. If new valve lifters

are being used, initially immerse each one in a container of clean engine oil and compress it (by hand) several times to charge it.

49 Apply a little non-setting jointing compound to the mating faces, then fit the assembled cam carrier and camshaft **(see illustration)**.

50 Insert the new cylinder head bolts, not forgetting the washers. Nip up the bolts in spiral sequence from the centre outwards, being careful to pull down the cam carrier evenly.

51 In the same sequence tighten the bolts to the Stage 1 specified torque, then through the angles specified for Stages 2, 3 and 4. It becomes increasingly difficult to hold the engine still if it is on the bench, so if preferred the later tightening stages can be left until the engine is back in the vehicle. Attach a label or some other reminder where it will be seen before the engine is started.

29.47 Fitting the cylinder head

29.52a Fit a new O-ring (arrowed) to the thermostat housing recess

Camshaft drivebelt and associated components

52 Fit the thermostat housing and thermostat, using new seals **(see illustrations)**.

53 Refit the Woodruff key to the crankshaft nose. Fit the crankshaft sprocket and its securing bolt. Lock the flywheel and tighten the sprocket bolt to the specified torque **(see illustrations)**.

54 Refit the coolant pump, using a new seal. Insert but do not tighten its securing bolts.

55 Fit the drivebelt backplate, then fit and secure the idler pulley **(see illustration)**.

56 Refit the injection pump mounting bracket **(see illustration)** then refit the pump. Fit the Woodruff key and the pump sprockets. Tighten the sprocket centre nut.

57 Fit the camshaft sprocket and a new retaining bolt, but do not tighten the bolt yet **(see illustration)**.

29.49 Fitting the camshaft carrier

29.52b Tightening a thermostat housing bolt

29.53a Fitting the crankshaft sprocket

29.53b Tightening the crankshaft sprocket bolt

29.55 Securing the drivebelt idler pulley

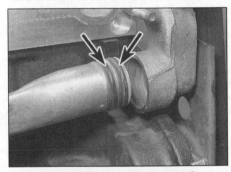

29.56 Fitting the fuel injection pump bracket

29.57 Camshaft sprocket loosely fitted

29.63 Refitting the dipstick tube

29.65 Use new seals (arrowed) on the large coolant pipe

29.67 Fitting the breather pipe between the dipstick tube and the cam carrier

58 Bring the crankshaft to TDC, No 1 firing. Similarly align the pump sprocket timing mark and bring the camshaft to approximately the correct position, ie. both lobes for No 1 cylinder inclined upwards and those for No 4 downwards. Proceed carefully to avoid piston/valve contact.
59 Fit the camshaft drivebelt around the sprockets and the idler pulley. Observe the running direction of the old belt if it is being reused.
60 Adjust the camshaft drivebelt tension.
61 Adjust the valve timing.
62 Adjust the injection pump timing if necessary. Refit and secure the injection pipes.
63 Refit the dipstick tube using a new gasket. Note that a cable bracket is secured by the same bolts **(see illustration)**.
64 Refit the vacuum pump, using new seals.

65 Refit the large coolant pipe, using new seals **(see illustration)**.
66 Refit the cam cover, using a new gasket.
67 Refit the breather pipe between the dipstick tube and the cam carrier **(see illustration)**.
68 Refit the camshaft drivebelt covers. Remember that one of the cover bolts also secures a fuel pipe clip.
69 Refit the clutch, when applicable.
70 Refit and secure the manifolds, using new gaskets.
71 The oil filter and crankshaft pulley are best left until after the engine has been refitted. However, it is recommended that the alternator be refitted (with its engine mounting bracket, when applicable) while the engine is still out and access is good.

30 Engine - reconnection to transmission

Manual gearbox

1 If the clutch has been disturbed, make sure that the driven plate is centralised.
2 Offer the gearbox to the engine, twisting it back and forth slightly so that the splines on the input shaft enter the clutch driven plate. Do not allow the weight of the gearbox to hang on the input shaft.
3 Engage the gearbox with the dowels on the engine. Fit and tighten the engine-to-gearbox bolts.
4 Refit the starter motor and its heat shield. Fit the motor with its leads attached, since there is no access with the heat shield fitted.
5 Refit the clutch/flywheel access plate.

Automatic transmission

6 Make sure that the torque converter is fully engaged with the transmission **(see illustration)**.
7 Offer the transmission to the engine so that the coloured spot on the torque converter is as close as possible to the white spot on the driveplate.
8 Engage the transmission with the dowels on the engine, then fit and tighten the engine-to-transmission bolts.
9 Secure the torque converter to the driveplate using new bolts. Turn the crankshaft to bring

3B

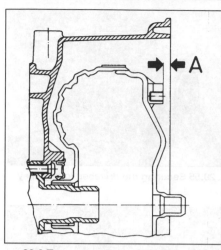

30.6 Torque converter fully engaged
A = 9 to 10 mm

the bolt holes into reach through the cover plate aperture.

10 Refit the starter motor and heat shield - see paragraph 4.

11 Refit the torque converter/driveplate access plate.

31 Engine/transmission - refitting

⚠️ *Warning: Do not attempt to fit the engine/transmission on your own, a minimum of two people will be required*

1 With the front of the vehicle raised and securely supported, position the engine/transmission under the engine bay. Connect the lifting tackle.

2 Carefully raise the unit into the engine bay. One person should operate the lifting tackle while another guides the unit into place and keeps watch for fouling.

3 Fit the mounting brackets to the engine/transmission and bodyframe. Some lifting and lowering of the unit will be necessary before all the bolts will go in. Do not tighten the bolts fully until all the mountings are fitted.

4 Remove the engine lifting tackle.

31.7 Crankshaft pulley-to-sprocket screws (arrowed)

31.6 Suspension bottom balljoint assembled - securing clip arrowed

5 Insert the driveshafts into the transmission, being careful not to damage the oil seals. Make sure that the retaining snap-rings engage inside the transmission.

6 Reconnect and secure the front suspension bottom balljoints. Do not forget the split pins or spring clips which secure the balljoint nuts **(see illustration)**.

7 Refit the crankshaft pulley if it was left off during engine refitting and tighten its screws **(see illustration)**.

8 Fit a new oil filter element.

9 Refit the alternator (if not already done) and tension its drivebelt.

10 Refit the power steering pump (when applicable) and tension its drivebelt.

11 Refit the throttle and cold start cables to the fuel injection pump.

12 Reconnect the fuel supply and return hoses to the fuel injection pump. Remember to secure the hoses to the camshaft drivebelt cover **(see illustration)**.

13 Refit the exhaust downpipe, using a new flange gasket and, if necessary, a new sealing ring at the flexible joint. Secure the pipe-to-transmission bracket, when fitted. In other versions the downpipe may be secured to an engine/transmission mounting.

14 Reconnect the gearshift linkage or cable. Refer to the appropriate Manual for petrol-engined vehicles for adjustment procedures.

15 Reconnect and adjust the clutch cable or kickdown cable.

16 Reconnect the speedometer cable. Secure it as far as possible away from the exhaust manifold and downpipe without straining the cable.

31.12 Fuel hose clip secured by drivebelt cover screw

17 If removed, refit the radiator and cooling fan.

18 Reconnect the cooling system hoses. Also reconnect the automatic transmission cooler lines, when applicable.

19 Refill the cooling system.

20 Reconnect the engine electrical services. Also reconnect the starter motor lead to the battery and the starter motor command lead.

21 Refit the air cleaner and its snorkel.

22 Refill the engine with oil.

23 Check the transmission oil level and top-up if necessary.

24 Reconnect the transmission earth strap.

25 Reconnect the battery earth lead.

26 Run the engine, referring first to the following Section, then refit the bonnet if it was removed.

27 Refit the front wheels, if not already done.

32 Engine - initial start-up after overhaul

1 If the final stages of head bolt tightening were deferred when the engine was on the bench, carry them out now (up to and including Stage 4).

2 Make sure there is sufficient clean fuel in the tank, that the battery is well charged and all lubricants and fluids have been replenished.

3 A good deal of cranking on the starter motor may be required to prime the fuel system (it is self-bleeding). Do not operate the starter for more than 10 seconds at a time, then pause for a similar period to allow the battery and starter motor to recover.

4 As soon as the engine is running, check that the oil pressure light has gone out. This will take a few seconds as the oil filter fills up. There may also be some noise from the valve gear until the hydraulic lifters are properly pressurised with oil.

5 Check for leaks of oil, coolant and fuel. Be prepared for some smoke and fumes as assembly lubricant burns off.

6 Allow the engine to reach operating temperature, then adjust the idle speed.

7 Stop the engine and check the tightness of the exhaust downpipe joints. Also check for oil or coolant leaks while stopped.

8 Carry out the Stage 5 tightening of the cylinder head bolts.

9 Check engine oil and coolant levels and top-up if necessary. Take precautions against scalding if the engine is still hot.

10 Road test the vehicle to check that the engine is performing acceptably.

11 If new bearings and/or pistons have been fitted, the engine should be run in at reduced speed and load for the first 600 miles (1000 km) or so. Change the engine oil and filter after this mileage.

12 Also after the first 600 miles (1000 km), the cylinder head bolts should be tightened through the angle specified for Stage 6. This should be done cold or warm (not hot).

Chapter 3 Part C:
Engine overhaul - 17D, 17DR & 17DTL engines

Contents

Degrees of difficulty

Easy, suitable for novice with little experience	**Fairly easy,** suitable for beginner with some experience	**Fairly difficult,** suitable for competent DIY mechanic	**Difficult,** suitable for experienced DIY mechanic	**Very difficult,** suitable for expert DIY or professional

Specifications

General

Engine type:

17D, 17DR . . . . Normally aspirated, 4-cylinder, four stroke, overhead camshaft, indirect injection, compression ignition.

17DTL . . . . Low boost turbocharged, 4-cylinder, four stroke, overhead camshaft, indirect injection, compression ignition.

Bore	82.5 mm
Stroke	79.50 mm
Displacement	1699 cc
Firing order	1-3-4-2 (No 1 at pulley end)
Compression ratio	22 : 1

Maximum power:

17D	57 bhp @ 4600 rpm
17DR	60 bhp @ 4600 rpm
17DTL	67 bhp @ 4500 rpm

Maximum torque:

17D, 17DR	105 Nm @ 2400 rpm
17DTL	132 Nm @ 2400 rpm

Camshaft drivebelt tension

17D (using gauge KM-510-A):

New belt, warm	7.5
New belt, cold	9.5
Run-in belt, warm	5.0
Run-in belt, cold	9.0
17DR, 17DTL	By automatic tensioner

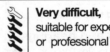

3C

Cylinder head

	Thickness	Identification
Gasket thickness and identification:		
Piston projection up to 0.80 mm	1.35 to 1.45 mm	None
Piston projection 0.80 to 0.90 mm	1.44 to 1.55 mm	One notch
Piston projection above 0.90 mm	1.54 to 1.65 mm	Two notches
Valve clearance adjustment	Automatic by hydraulic tappets	
Valve seat width in head:		
Inlet	1.3 to 2.0 mm	
Exhaust	1.3 to 2.6 mm	
Valve stem play in guide:		
Inlet	0.015 to 0.047 mm	
Exhaust	0.030 to 0.062 mm	
Recess of valve head when fitted	0.25 to 0.75 mm	
Swirl chamber projection	0.00 to 0.02 mm	
Sealing surface finish - peak-to-valley height	0.025 mm max	
Overall height of head:		
Maximum	106.10 mm	
Minimum	105.75 mm	
Deviation of sealing surface from true	0.05 mm max	

Valves

Length	123.25 mm
Head diameter:	
Inlet	36 mm
Exhaust	32 mm
Stem diameter (standard):	
Inlet	7.970 to 7.985 mm
Exhaust	7.955 to 7.970 mm
Valve guide bore (standard)	8.000 to 8.017 mm
Valve stem oversizes:	
Marked K1	+ 0.075 mm
Marked K2	+ 0.150 mm
Marked A	+ 0.250 mm
Valve sealing face angle	44°

Camshaft and bearings

Camshaft identification code letter	C
Camshaft run-out	0.04 mm
Camshaft endfloat	0.09 to 0.21 mm
Cam lift (inlet and exhaust)	5.80 mm

Cylinder bores

	Diameter (± 0.005 mm)	Identification
Production grade 1	82.45 mm	5
	82.46 mm	6
	82.47 mm	7
Production grade 2	82.48 mm	8
	82.49 mm	99
	82.50 mm	00
	82.51 mm	01
	82.52 mm	02
	82.53 mm	03
Production grade 3	82.54 mm	04
	82.55 mm	05
	82.56 mm	06
	82.57 mm	07
	82.58 mm	08
	82.59 mm	09
	82.60 mm	1
Oversize (0.5 mm)	82.97 mm	7 + 0.5
	82.98 mm	8 + 0.5
	82.99 mm	9 + 0.5
	83.00 mm	0 + 0.5
Oversize (1.0 mm)	83.47 mm	7 + 1.0
	83.48 mm	8 + 1.0
	83.49 mm	9 + 1 0
	83.50 mm	0 + 1.0

Pistons

Make	Mahle or Alcan
Marking (maker's identity):	
Mahle	m
Alcan	D
Diameter:	
Mahle	0.030 mm less than bore diameter
Alcan	0.020 mm less than bore diameter
Grade marking	As for cylinder bore
Projection at TDC (used to determine head gasket thickness)	0.80 to 0.90 mm
Clearance in bore:	
Mahle	0.020 to 0.040 mm
Alcan	0.015 to 0.035 mm

Piston rings

Thickness:	
Compression rings	1.978 to 1.990 mm
Oil scraper ring	2.975 to 2.990 mm
End gap (fitted):	
Compression rings	0.2 to 0.4 mm
Oil scraper ring	0.250 to 0.500 mm
Vertical clearance in groove	Not stated
Gap offset	180°

Gudgeon pins

Length	64.7 to 65.0 mm
Diameter	25.995 to 26.000 mm
Clearance in piston	0.007 to 0.011 mm
Clearance in connecting rod	0.014 to 0.025 mm

Connecting rods

Weight variation (in same engine)	8 g. max
Endfloat on crankshaft	0.070 to 0.242 mm
Bearing running clearance	0.019 to 0.063 mm

Identification - rod marking:	Bearing shell colour code	Bearing clearance
17D, 17DR:		
I	Blue	0.025 to 0.054 mm
II	Black	0.027 to 0.056 mm
III	Brown	0.029 to 0.058 mm
17DTL:		
I	None	0.025 to 0.054 mm
II	Blue	0.027 to 0.056 mm
III	White	0.029 to 0.058 mm

Note that upper bearing shells fitted to the 17DTL engine are reinforced and marked with an "S"

Crankshaft and bearings

Crankshaft run-out	0.03 mm max
Crankshaft endfloat	0.070 to 0.302 mm

Main bearing journal:	Diameter	Size marking
Standard	57.982 mm	Green
Standard	57.995 mm	Brown
0.25 undersize	57.732 mm	Green/Blue
0.25 undersize	57.745 mm	Brown/Blue
0.50 undersize	57.482 mm	Green/White
0.50 undersize	57.495 mm	Brown/White

Main bearing:	
Shell wall thickness	1.989 to 2.001 mm
Running clearance	0.015 to 0.041 mm
Out-of-round	0.005 mm max
Taper	0.004 mm max
Big-end bearing:	
Out-of-round	0.005 mm max
Taper	0.004 mm max

Flywheel

Run-out	0.5 mm max
Refacing limit (depth of material removed from clutch wear face)	0.3 mm max

3C

Lubrication system

System type	Wet sump, pressure feed, full flow filter
Lubricant type/specification/capacity	Refer to *"Lubricants, fluids and capacities"*
Oil pressure (at idle, engine warm)	1.5 bar (22 lbf/in2)
Oil filter type	
17D, 17DR	Champion G105
17DTL	Champion F208
Oil pump tolerances:	
Gear backlash:	
17D, 17DR	0.175 to 0.225 mm
17DTL	0.100 to 0.145 mm
Inner gear recess below housing:	
17D, 17DR	0.03 to 0.10 mm
17DTL	0.03 to 0.08 mm
Outer gear recess below housing:	
17D, 17DR	0.03 to 0.10 mm
17DTL	0.04 to 0.09 mm
Oil cooler thermostat - 17DTL only:	
Opening commences at	107°C
Fully open at	120°C

Coolant pump

Type	Impeller
Drive	From camshaft drivebelt

Thermostat

Opening commences at	92°C
Fully open at	107°C
Marking	92

Torque wrench settings

	Nm	lbf ft
Cylinder head		
Cylinder head bolts*:		
Stage 1	25	18
Stage 2	Angle-tighten a further 90°	
Stage 3	Angle-tighten a further 90°	
Stage 4	Angle-tighten a further 45°	
Warm-up engine, then:		
Stage 5	Angle-tighten a further 30°	
Stage 6	Angle-tighten a further 15°	
Camshaft		
Housing cover to housing	8	6
Thrustplate to housing	8	6
Sprocket to camshaft*:		
Stage 1	75	55
Stage 2	Angle-tighten a further 60°	
Stage 3	Angle-tighten a further 5°	
Drivebelt guide roller to cylinder block	40	30
Drivebelt tension roller to cylinder block	25	18
Crankshaft		
Pulley to sprocket	20	15
Sprocket to crankshaft*:		
Stage 1	145	107
Stage 2	Angle-tighten a further 30°	
Stage 3	Angle-tighten a further 10°	
Flywheel to crankshaft		
Stage 1	50	37
Stage 2	Angle-tighten a further 30°	
Stage 3	Angle-tighten a further 5°	
Main bearing caps*:		
Stage 1	50	37
Stage 2	Angle-tighten a further 45°	
Stage 3	Angle-tighten a further 15°	
Connecting rod caps*:		
Stage 1	35	26
Stage 2	Angle-tighten a further 45°	
Stage 3	Angle-tighten a further 15°	

Lubrication system

Pump to cylinder block	6	4
Cover to pump	6	4
Inlet pipe to pump	8	6
Pressure switch to pump	30	22
Safety valve to pump	30	22
Filter to pump	15	11
Pump inlet pipe bracket to cylinder block	6	4
Cooler thermostat to pump	40	30
Cooler adapter to pump	23	17
Pipelines to cooler	30	22
Pipelines to filter adapter	30	22
Feedline to cylinder block	30	22
Feedline to turbocharger	30	22
Pressure line to turbocharger	15	11
Return line to sump	45	33
Return line to turbocharger	20	15
Sump:		
Pan to cylinder block**	5	3.5
Drain plug	45	33

Cooling system

Pump to cylinder block	25	18
Pipe to cylinder block	20	15
Outlet port to thermostat housing	8	6
Temperature sensor to thermostat housing	11	8
Thermostat housing to cylinder head	15	11

Power steering system

Pump mounting bracket to cylinder block	40	30

Engine mountings

Left-hand:		
Mounting bracket to transmission	60	44
Flexible mounting to bracket	60	44
Flexible mounting to sidemember	65	47.5
Right-hand:		
Mounting bracket to cylinder block	60	44
Flexible mounting to bracket	35	26
Flexible mounting to sidemember	65	47.5
Rear:		
Mounting bracket to transmission	60	44
Flexible mounting to bracket	45	33
Flexible mounting to crossmember	40	30

Other components

Vacuum pump to camshaft housing	28	5
Alternator mounting bracket to cylinder block	40	30
Fuel injection pump mounting bracket to cylinder block	25	18
Turbocharger support to cylinder block	25	18
Starter motor mounting bracket to cylinder block	25	18
Starter motor to cylinder block:		
Engine side	45	33
Transmission side	75	55
Crankcase ventilation separator to cylinder block	15	11
Transmission to cylinder block	60	44

*Bolts must be renewed every time.
**Use thread-locking compound.

1 General information

17D engine

This engine closely resembles the 16DA unit from which it is derived and which it replaces. There are however a number of detail changes designed to improve flexibility and to reduce noise level and vibration.

The most significant change is the increase in cylinder bore size, which increases cylinder capacity and gives improved torque output, with a consequent improvement in mid-range acceleration. Internally, the unit is little changed from its predecessor, although the pistons have been lightened to reduce engine noise and vibration and the cylinder head has received detail modifications. These include thickening and reinforcement by means of internal ribbing of the lower section to reduce valve leakage at cranking speed and thus improve cold starting.

External changes include a revised inlet system which employs a new cast aluminium alloy manifold and resonator assembly linked by flexible trunking to a remote filter unit located to the rear of the right-hand headlight.

3C

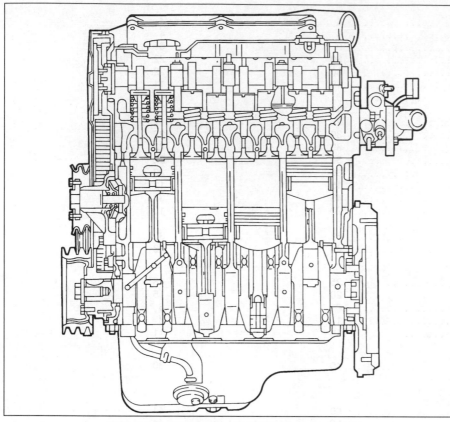

1.0 Longitudinal section of 17DTL diesel engine

The camshaft cover has also been modified, with the oil filler now located at the right-hand end, and changes have been made to the camshaft drivebelt covers of which two versions have been fitted since the introduction of this engine type.

In addition to the mechanical revisions to the engine, there have been a number of changes to the engine ancillaries. A new Lucas/CAV injection pump has been introduced, featuring an automatic cold start system in place of the previous manual arrangement. The new pump also includes an electronic speed governor and a solenoid-operated fuel shut-off valve which allows the engine to be stopped by turning the key to the off position. Detail changes have also been made to the existing Bosch injection pump which continues as an alternative standard fitment on these engines. An electrically-heated fuel filter is used, allowing the engine to operate at lower ambient temperatures without the risk of fuel waxing.

17DR engine

This engine is a further development of the 17D unit and features revisions to the swirl chambers, resulting in an increased power output. An exhaust gas recirculation (EGR) system is also employed, to ensure that the engine will meet existing and proposed diesel exhaust emission regulations.

The engine is also fitted with a spring-loaded automatic camshaft drivebelt tensioner to ensure correct belt tensioning on assembly and to eliminate the need for regular belt retensioning as part of routine maintenance.

17DTL engine

Introduced in August 1994, this engine is fitted to the Astra only **(see illustration)** and incorporates a low pressure turbocharger which enables the engine to produce appreciably greater power and torque than its predecessor, the 17DR unit.

Otherwise, this engine closely resembles the 17DR unit from which it is derived. There are however a number of changes incurred by the fitting of the turbocharger. These include:

The fitting of strengthened big-end bearing upper shells
The incorporation of an oil cooler and thermostat
The fitting of an oil cooler between the oil filter and pump
The incorporation of spray nozzles to aid piston cooling
The fitting of modified main bearing shells to facilitate the spray nozzles
The connection of turbocharger oil feed and return lines to the cylinder block and sump pan respectively
Reduction of the oil pump working tolerances

2 Major operations possible with the engine in the vehicle

Refer to Section 2, Chapter 3B.

3 Engine oil and oil filter - renewal

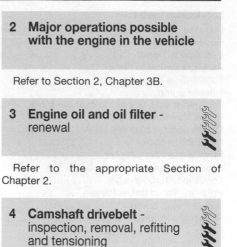

Refer to the appropriate Section of Chapter 2.

4 Camshaft drivebelt - inspection, removal, refitting and tensioning

Caution: A camshaft drivebelt which is damaged, oil-soaked or fuel soaked must be renewed or it will fail, resulting in serious engine damage.

17D engine

1 The camshaft drivebelt arrangement employed on this engine is largely unchanged from its predecessors and as such can be dealt with as described in Section 4 of Chapter 3B. Note, however, that revisions to the belt covers and air filter assembly dictate some changes of approach when working on the drivebelt components.

2 Both the Cavalier and the Astra/Belmont models have a new air filter system, with a remote filter housing attached to the inner wing area at the right-hand side of the engine bay. To gain access to the drivebelt covers, it will be necessary to remove the filter housing.

3 Two versions of the moulded plastic drivebelt covers have been used since the introduction of this engine, the later version being identified by the squared-off top surface of the outer belt cover. On the earlier version, a screwdriver blade can be used to release the outer cover retaining clips and the cover sections can then be removed as required to gain access to the drivebelt. On the later version, the method of retention is by bolts instead of clips. This arrangement is, in fact, the same as used on the 17DR engine.

17DR and 17DTL engines

General information

4 A spring-loaded automatic camshaft drivebelt tensioner is fitted to these engines. This tensioner automatically sets the drivebelt to the correct tension on assembly and maintains that tension for the life of the belt. The revised procedures for removal, inspection and refitting of the drivebelt, tensioner and related components are as follows:

Inspection

5 Disconnect the battery earth lead.

6 The cover is a two-piece assembly, it being necessary to remove the upper part prior to

4.7 Removing the camshaft drivebelt upper cover

4.9 The crankshaft pulley viewed through the front wheel arch

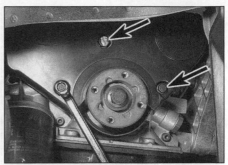

4.10 Removing the camshaft drivebelt lower cover retaining bolts

removal of the lower part. Remove the auxiliary drivebelt(s) and the air cleaner assembly for access to the drivebelt cover. The power steering drivebelt (where applicable) should be removed as described in the relevant petrol-engine Manual.

7 To remove the upper part of the cover, undo the five securing bolts and lift it off the engine **(see illustration)**.

8 With the drivebelt thus exposed, turn the engine and inspect the belt for damage or contamination. Pay particular attention to the roots of the teeth, where cracking may occur. Renew the belt if it is damaged or contaminated. If necessary, attend to the source of contamination.

9 From under the front wheel arch, undo the four crankshaft pulley retaining bolts and withdraw the pulley from the drivebelt sprocket **(see illustration)**.

10 Undo the remaining three bolts and remove the lower part of the cover from the engine **(see illustration)**.

11 Refitting the covers is a reversal of removal.

Removal, refitting and tensioning

12 The procedure for engines with an automatic drivebelt tensioner is essentially the same as described in Section 4 of Chapter 3B, except that it is not necessary to remove the engine mounting, nor to slacken the coolant pump mounting bolts and move the pump to adjust the belt tension. Instead, belt adjustment is catered for by means of the automatic tensioner, as follows.

4.13 Release the drivebelt tensioner securing bolt, then turn the tensioner arm with an Allen key until the belt is slack

13 To release the belt tension prior to removal, unscrew the drivebelt tensioner securing bolt slightly then, with a suitable Allen key inserted in the slot on the tensioner arm, turn the tensioner arm until the timing belt is slack **(see illustration)**. Tighten the securing bolt slightly to hold the tensioner in this position. The drivebelt can now be removed.

14 Prior to fitting the drivebelt, first ensure that the coolant pump is correctly positioned by checking that the lug on the pump flange is aligned with the corresponding lug on the cylinder block. If this is not the case, slacken the pump mounting bolts slightly and move the pump accordingly. Tighten the bolts to the specified torque on completion.

15 Initially refit the drivebelt as described in Section 4 of Chapter 3B, ensuring that No 1 piston is still at TDC, that the injection pump sprocket mark is still aligned and the camshaft position is still correct **(see illustration)**. On 17DTL engines, flywheel position for TDC must be determined by the

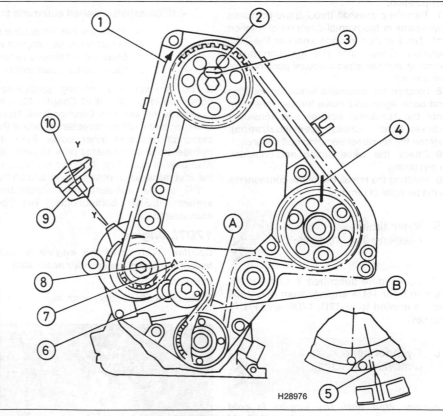

4.15a Camshaft drivebelt routing

A	To tension drivebelt	
B	To loosen drivebelt	
1	Direction of rotation	
2	Reference hole	
3	Flat valve lifter high point - cam 2	
4	Fuel injection pump marking - No.1 cylinder TDC	
5	Flywheel marking - No.1 cylinder TDC	
6	Tensioning roller	
7	Tensioning roller pointer	
8	Alignment mark - tensioning roller	
9	Alignment mark - coolant pump	
10	Alignment mark - cylinder block	

3C

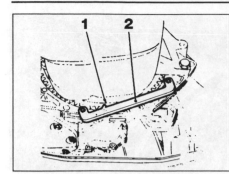

4.15b On 17DTL engines, flywheel position for TDC must be determined by the use of a setting tool (Adjuster KM-851)

1 Flywheel marking - No.1 cylinder TDC
2 Setting tool

use of a setting tool (Adjuster KM-851) fitted next to the flywheel as shown **(see illustration)**.

16 Tension the drivebelt by first slackening the automatic tensioner securing bolt and moving the tensioner arm anti-clockwise until the tensioner pointer is at its stop. Tighten the tensioner securing bolt to hold the tensioner in this position.

17 Turn the crankshaft through two complete revolutions in the normal direction of rotation until No 1 piston is once again at the TDC position. Check that the injection pump sprocket and camshaft sprocket positions are still correct.

18 Slacken the automatic tensioner securing bolt once again and move the tensioner arm until the tensioner pointer and tensioner bracket notch coincide **(see illustration)**. Tighten the tensioner securing bolt securely.

19 Check the valve timing and injection pump timing.

20 Refitting the remainder of the components is the reversal of removal.

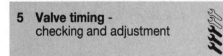

5 Valve timing - checking and adjustment

The procedure described in Chapter 3B, Section 5 for 16DA engines from May 1989 can be applied to all 17D, 17DR and 17DTL engines.

6 Cylinder head - removal and refitting

Caution: Wait until the engine is cold before removing the cylinder head bolts

17D and 17DR engines

1 As mentioned in Section 1, certain modifications have taken place to the camshaft drivebelt covers and ancillary components on these engines, which slightly alter the procedures for certain operations.

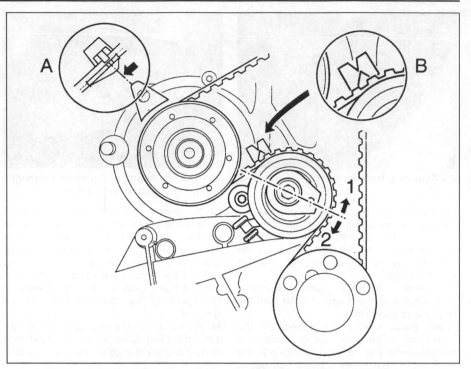

4.18 Camshaft drivebelt automatic tensioner details - 17DR and 17DTL engines

A Alignment lugs on coolant pump and cylinder block
B Tensioner pointer aligned with notch in tensioner bracket
1 Move the tensioner arm anti-clockwise to release the belt tension
2 Move the tensioner arm clockwise to tension the belt

2 The removal and refitting procedures contained in Section 6 of Chapter 3B, are essentially the same for these engines. Note, however, that it will be necessary to unbolt the camshaft drivebelt inner cover from its cylinder head attachments prior to removal. Also bear in mind that there are revisions to the inlet manifold on both engines, and on the 17DR engine, exhaust gas recirculation system (EGR) components will be encountered.

17DTL engine

Caution: Wait until the engine is cold before removing the cylinder head bolts

Removal

3 Disconnect the battery earth lead.

4 Drain the cooling system, recovering the coolant if it is fit for re-use.

5 Release the air filter housing inlet scoop from the vehicle front crossmember and manoeuvre it clear of the housing. Detach the air filter housing outlet tube retaining clamp and remove the housing after having released its base securing nuts **(see illustration)**.

6 Remove the alternator drivebelt and (when fitted) the power steering pump drivebelt.

7 Remove the brake servo vacuum line and the EGR system vacuum supply hose from the vacuum pump **(see illustration)**.

8 Unbolt the exhaust downpipe from the engine manifold. Release the pipe from its mounting bracket and move it slightly downwards. Recover the manifold flange gasket.

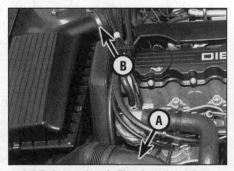

6.5 Release the air filter housing inlet scoop (A) and outlet tube retaining clamp (B)

6.7 Remove brake servo vacuum line (A) and vacuum hose (B) from vacuum pump

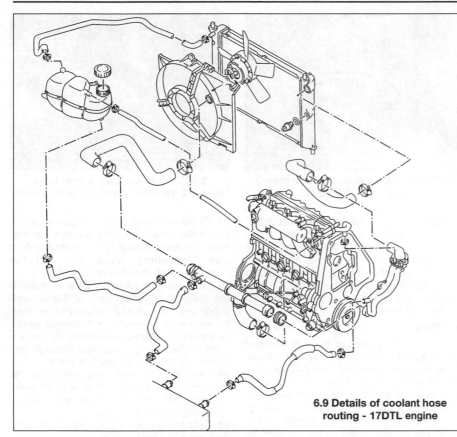

6.9 Details of coolant hose routing - 17DTL engine

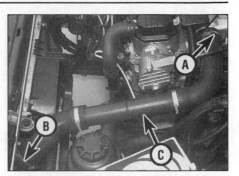

6.11 Disconnect the plenum chamber to charge air cooler hose

- A Hose to plenum chamber clamp
- B Hose to charge air cooler clamp
- C Pipe to cylinder head securing bolt

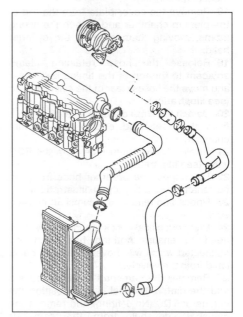

6.12 Charge air cooler to turbocharger and plenum chamber hose connections

9 Disconnect the radiator top hose, the two hoses from the thermostat housing and the hose from the coolant pump flange **(see illustration)**.

10 Detach the coolant pipe from the rear of the cylinder head by removing its two securing bolts and pulling it out of the thermostat housing. Recover the gasket from the thermostat housing.

11 Disconnect the plenum chamber to charge air cooler hose **(see illustration)**.

12 Disconnect the charge air cooler to turbocharger hose at the turbocharger, remove the charge air pipe to cylinder head securing bolts and move the pipe clear of the head **(see illustration)**.

13 Disconnect the glow plug feed wire from the bus bar **(see illustration)**.

14 Disconnect the throttle cable from the fuel injection pump and move it clear of the cylinder head.

15 Clean around the fuel injection pipe unions, then unscrew them from the injectors and from the injection pump. Be prepared for fuel spillage. Disconnect the fuel return line and move it to one side **(see illustration)**.

16 Unplug the two electrical cable connectors from the thermostat housing **(see illustration)**.

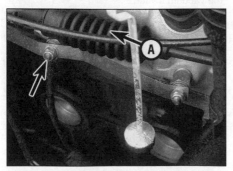

6.13 Disconnect the glow plug feed wire (arrowed) from the bus bar

A Throttle cable

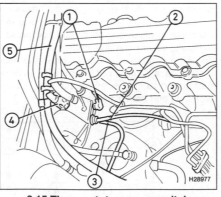

6.15 Thermostat, vacuum switch and fuel line connections

1 *Electrical connection - thermostat*
2 *Hose connection - vacuum switch*
3 *Hose connection - vacuum switch*
4 *Electrical connection - thermostat*
5 *Fuel return line*

6.16 Unplug the two electrical cable connectors (arrowed) from the thermostat housing

3C

6.19 Release the hose retaining clamp

6.21 Unplug the vacuum pipe (arrowed) from the EGR valve

6.22 Disconnect the breather hose (arrowed) from the camshaft housing cover

17 Disconnect the two hose connections from the vacuum switch located beneath the thermostat housing.

18 Remove the cover plate from the top of the plenum chamber and detach the wiring looms, moving them clear of the cylinder head.

19 Release the hose retaining clamp adjacent to the top of the timing belt cover and move the hoses clear of the cylinder head **(see illustration)**.

20 Detach the small diameter charge air hose from the right-hand end of the plenum chamber.

21 Unplug the vacuum pipe from the EGR valve **(see illustration)**.

22 Disconnect the breather hose from the camshaft housing cover **(see illustration)**.

23 Unbolt and remove the camshaft housing cover.

24 Carry out a final check around the cylinder head to ensure nothing has been left connected which will prevent the head being lifted from the vehicle.

25 Remove the camshaft drivebelt covers and the clutch/flywheel cover, position the engine at TDC (No 1 firing) and remove the camshaft drivebelt from the camshaft sprocket. Refer to Section 4 for details. If the valve timing has been satisfactory so far, make sure that the camshaft is locked or that marks are made so that the timing is not lost.

26 Detach the drivebelt rear cover from the cylinder head by first removing its two securing bolts and then easing it clear of the camshaft end.

27 Slacken the cylinder head bolts a quarter turn each, working in a spiral sequence from outside to inside. Follow the same sequence and slacken the bolts another half turn, then remove the bolts and washers. Obtain new bolts for reassembly.

28 Remove the camshaft carrier and the camshaft.

29 Recover the loose valve gear (cam followers, thrust pads and hydraulic lifters) from the top of the head - see illustrations, Section 6, Chapter 3B. Immerse the hydraulic lifters in a container of clean engine oil to avoid any possibility of draining. Keep all of the components in order if they are to be reused.

30 Lift off the cylinder head and manifolds, using the manifolds as handles to rock it free if necessary. Do not prise between the mating faces if the cylinder head sticks. A couple of lugs are provided at the ends of the block and head for prising. Recover the gasket.

31 Clean and examine the cylinder head and engine block mating faces.

Refitting

32 Commence refitting of the cylinder head by selecting the correct gasket. Three thicknesses of gasket are available and they are identified by the presence or absence of notches in the gasket edge - **see illustration 6.19, Chapter 3B**. It is essential if the pistons have been disturbed, to measure piston projection as described in the Section for complete reassembly and then select the correct gasket. See *Specifications* for piston projection and gasket thickness figures.

33 Fit the new head gasket to the cylinder block. Make sure the gasket is the right way up - it is marked OBEN/TOP. Do not use any jointing compound.

34 Place the head on the block, ensuring that the dowels engage in their recesses.

35 Refit the valve lifters, thrust pads and cam followers to their original locations (if applicable), lubricating them generously with clean engine oil. If new hydraulic lifters are being used, initially immerse each one in a container of clean engine oil and compress it (by hand) several times to charge it.

36 Wipe clean the camshaft carrier and head mating faces and coat them with jointing compound to GM spec 15 03 166. Fit the camshaft and carrier to the head.

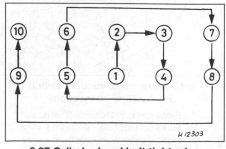

6.37 Cylinder head bolt tightening sequence

37 Fit the new head bolts with their washers. Nip up the bolts in a spiral sequence, working from the centre outwards in the order shown **(see illustration)**. Make sure that the camshaft carrier is pulled down evenly.

38 In the same sequence, tighten the bolts to the Stage 1 specified torque. Subsequent tightening is by angular rotation rather than torque. Use a protractor or a marked card if necessary to indicate the angles. Tighten the bolts in the same sequence through the angles specified for Stages 2, 3 and 4.

39 Refit the drivebelt rear cover to the cylinder head, ensuring that it is properly aligned over the camshaft end before tightening its securing bolts.

40 Refit and tension the camshaft drivebelt, then check the valve timing.

41 Refit the camshaft drivebelt covers and the clutch/flywheel cover.

42 Refit the camshaft housing cover with a new gasket and tighten its securing bolts to the specified torque loading.

43 Reconnect the breather hose to the camshaft housing cover.

44 Reconnect the vacuum pipe to the EGR valve.

45 Reconnect the small diameter charge air hose to the right-hand end of the plenum chamber.

46 Replace the hoses in their retaining clamp adjacent to the top of the timing belt cover.

47 Refit the wiring looms and cover plate to the top of the plenum chamber.

48 Reconnect the two hose connections to the vacuum switch.

49 Reconnect the two electrical cable connectors to the thermostat housing.

50 Reconnect the fuel return line and fuel injection pipe unions.

51 Reconnect the throttle cable to the fuel injection pump.

52 Reconnect the glow plug feed wire to the bus bar.

53 Refit the charge air pipe to the cylinder head and reconnect the charge air cooler hose to the turbocharger.

54 Reconnect the plenum chamber to charge air cooler hose.

55 Refit the coolant pipe to the rear of the cylinder head, pushing it into the thermostat housing whilst using a new gasket.

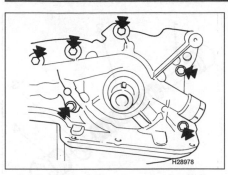

9.1 Position of oil pump securing bolts

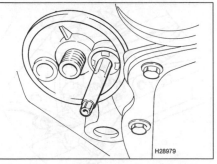

10.2 Using an M10 (third stage) threading tap to cut a thread in the oil bypass valve closure washer

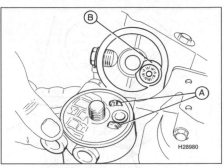

10.5 Ensure that the oil cooler adapter guide pins (A) engage around the oil bypass valve housing (B)

56 Reconnect the radiator top hose, the two hoses to the thermostat housing and the hose to the coolant pump flange.

57 Refit the exhaust downpipe to the engine manifold, using a new gasket, and then refit the pipe to its mounting bracket.

58 Reconnect the brake servo vacuum line and the vacuum hose to the vacuum pump.

59 Refit and tension the alternator drivebelt and (when fitted) the power steering pump drivebelt.

60 Refit the air filter housing and its inlet scoop

61 Replace all cut cable and hose ties. Check that no connections have been overlooked, then refill the cooling system.

62 Check, and if necessary replenish, the engine oil.

63 Reconnect the battery and start the engine.

64 Run the engine to operating temperature, then stop it and tighten the head bolts in the sequence shown through the angle specified for Stage 5.

65 After approximately 600 miles (1000 km) have been covered, tighten the bolts through the angle specified for Stage 6. This should be done with the engine cold or warm (not hot).

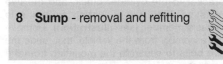

7 Camshaft - removal and refitting

Refer to Section 7, Chapter 3B, whilst noting the information given in the *Specifications* and Section 6 of this Chapter.

8 Sump - removal and refitting

1 Refer to Section 8, Chapter 3B, whilst noting the information given in the *Specifications* of this Chapter.

2 Where necessary, remove the flywheel cover plate from the bottom of the bellhousing for access to the sump end.

3 If working on the 17DTL engine, detach the turbocharger oil return line from the sump

before removing the sump retaining bolts. After fitting the sump, reconnect the oil line and tighten it to the specified torque setting. Check the connection for leaks after the engine is started.

9 Oil pump - removal and refitting

Refer to Section 9, Chapter 3B, whilst noting the information given in the *Specifications* of this Chapter **(see illustration)**.

If working on the 17DTL engine, note the information given in Section 12 with regard to the oil cooler adapter.

10 Oil bypass valve - renewal

Removal

1 Remove the oil filter and, on 17DTL engines, the oil cooler adapter.

2 Using an M10 (third stage) threading tap, cut a thread in the valve closure washer **(see illustration)**.

3 Screw an M10 sized bolt into the cut thread and remove the valve from its seat.

Fitting

4 Fit the new valve by driving it into its housing, using a drift of approximately 15 mm diameter.

5 When fitting the oil cooler adapter to 17DTL engines, ensure that the guide pins engage around the valve housing **(see illustration)**.

11 Oil cooler - removal and refitting (17DTL engine)

1 The oil cooler is located in front of the radiator, along its lower edge, and does not normally require any maintenance other than cleaning of its matrix. Should it however become damaged, renew it as follows.

Removal

2 Gaining access to the cooler will necessitate removal of the front body panelling - refer to the relevant petrol-engine Manual.

3 Unscrew the oil feed and return pipelines from the cooler, catching any escaping oil in a drip tray **(see illustration)**.

4 Remove the two cooler mounting bolts and ease the cooler forward to remove it from the vehicle.

Refitting

5 Refitting is the reverse of the removal procedure, noting the following points:

a) *Tighten all connectors to the specified torque settings*

b) *On completion, check the engine oil level and top-up as necessary*

c) *Check for signs of oil leakage around disturbed connections once the engine has been started and warmed-up to normal operating temperature*

12 Oil cooler adapter - removal and refitting (17DTL engine)

1 The oil cooler adapter is situated between the oil filter and pump.

Removal

2 After removal of the oil filter, remove the central banjo bolt securing the oil cooler

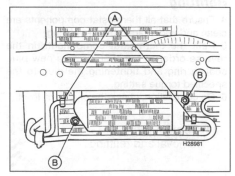

11.3 Unscrew the oil cooler feed and return pipelines (A) and mounting bolts (B)

3C

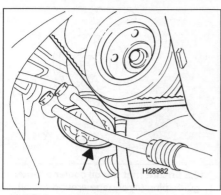

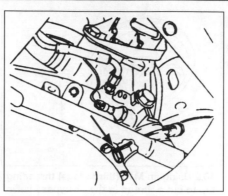

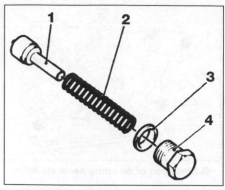

12.2 Remove the oil cooler adapter banjo bolt (arrowed)

13.1 The oil cooler thermostat (arrowed) is fitted within the oil cooler adapter

13.3 Oil cooler thermostat components

1	Expandable element	3	Sealing ring
2	Spring	4	Closure plug

adapter to the pump **(see illustration)**. Discard the sealing ring located beneath the adapter.

3 For the purpose of oil pump removal, position the adapter with its pipelines to one side, suspending the unit so as to avoid placing a strain on the lines.

4 To remove the adapter completely, disconnect the pipelines from it.

Refitting

5 When refitting the adapter, use a new sealing ring and coat the threads of its banjo bolt with locking compound to GM spec. 15 10 177.

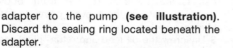

13 Oil cooler thermostat -
removal and refitting (17DTL engine)

1 The oil cooler thermostat is fitted within the oil cooler adapter **(see illustration)**.

Removal

2 Position a container beneath the thermostat retaining plug and remove the plug, catching any emerging oil. Note that the plug will be under spring pressure.

3 Discard the plug sealing ring and withdraw the spring and element **(see illustration)**.

Refitting

4 Ensure that all thermostat components are clean and undamaged before refitting.

5 Refit the thermostat components in the reverse order of removal, using a new plug sealing ring and tightening the plug to the specified torque setting.

6 On completion, check the engine oil level.

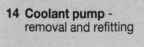

14 Coolant pump -
removal and refitting

1 The procedure for removal and refitting of the coolant pump on these engines is

essentially the same as described in Section 10 of Chapter 3B, but due to the modifications to the camshaft drivebelt covers and tensioner, bear in mind the following:

Removal

2 Remove the camshaft drivebelt as described in Section 4.

3 On the 17D engine, remove the additional bolt below the coolant pump which secures the camshaft drivebelt inner cover.

4 On the 17DR and 17DTL engines, remove the camshaft drivebelt automatic tensioner assembly after the drivebelt has been removed.

5 Note the corresponding positions of the pump flange and cylinder block alignment lugs.

Refitting

6 On the 17DR and 17DTL engines, when refitting the pump and prior to refitting the drivebelt, first ensure that the pump is correctly positioned by checking that the lug on the pump flange is aligned with the corresponding lug on the cylinder block.

7 Refit and tension the camshaft drivebelt.

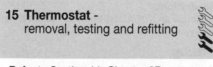

15 Thermostat -
removal, testing and refitting

Refer to Section 11, Chapter 3B.

16 Pistons and connecting rods -
removal and refitting

1 Refer to Section 12, Chapter 3B, whilst noting the information given in the *Specifications* of this Chapter.

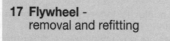

17 Flywheel -
removal and refitting

Refer to Section 13, Chapter 3B.

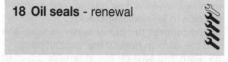

18 Oil seals - renewal

1 Refer to Section 14, Chapter 3B, whilst noting the information given in the *Specifications* of this Chapter.

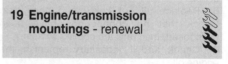

19 Engine/transmission mountings - renewal

Note: *Only remove and refit one engine mounting at a time*

1 The removal and refitting procedures for the engine mounting arrangement fitted to the engines covered in this Chapter are virtually identical for all types, and are as follows **(see illustration)**:

2 It is possible to remove and refit the front mountings from above but access is improved if the work is carried out from below. If so, raise and securely support the front of the vehicle on axle stands.

3 Take the weight of the engine/transmission on a hoist, or use a jack and a wooden block from below. Where necessary, remove the inner wheel arch liner if working on the right-hand mounting.

Right-hand front mounting

4 Undo the three bolts securing the mounting bracket to the cylinder block, and the two bolts securing the mounting to the side chassis member **(see illustration)**. Remove the assembly from the vehicle, then undo the two bolts to separate the mounting from the bracket.

5 Refitting is a reversal of removal. Tighten the bolts to the torque wrench settings given in the *Specifications* at the start of this Chapter.

Left-hand front mounting

6 Undo the two bolts securing the mounting to the transmission bracket and the two bolts

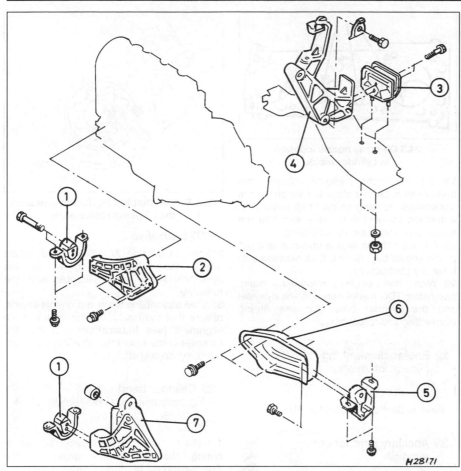

19.1 Engine mounting components

1 *Right-hand front mounting*
2 *Right-hand front mounting bracket*
3 *Rear mounting*
4 *Rear mounting bracket*
5 *Left-hand front mounting*
6 *Left-hand front mounting bracket*
7 *Right-hand front mounting bracket (vehicles with power steering)*

securing the mounting to the side chassis member **(see illustration)**. Note the transmission earth strap secured by one of the mounting bolts (where applicable). Remove the mounting from the vehicle.

7 Refitting is a reversal of removal. Tighten the bolts to the torque wrench settings in the *Specifications* at the start of this Chapter.

Rear mounting

8 Undo the two bolts securing the mounting to the transmission bracket and the two nuts securing the mounting to the crossmember **(see illustration)**. Remove the mounting.

9 Refitting is a reversal of removal. Tighten the bolts to the torque wrench settings in the *Specifications* at the start of this Chapter.

19.4 Right-hand front engine mounting-to-side chassis member securing bolts (arrowed)

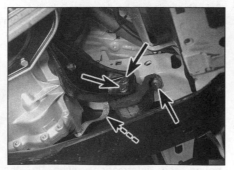

19.6 Left-hand front engine mounting and transmission bracket attachments (arrowed)

20 Engine/transmission - methods of removal

Refer to Section 16, Chapter 3B.

21 Engine - removal

Note illustrations: *When carrying out the procedures detailed in this Section for the 17DTL engine, refer to the illustrations shown in Section 6 for cylinder head removal.*

1 The recommended method of engine removal is from above, leaving the transmission in the vehicle. It will be necessary to raise and support the front of the vehicle for some of the following operations. Ensure adequate means of support are used when the vehicle is raised.
2 Remove the bonnet.
3 Disconnect and remove the battery.
4 Drain the cooling system, taking precautions against scalding if the coolant is hot.
5 Remove the radiator top and bottom hoses completely, together with the heater and expansion tank hoses.
6 On 17DTL engines, remove the plenum chamber to charge air cooler hose and the charge air cooler to turbocharger hose.
7 Remove the complete air cleaner housing assembly together with its inlet scoop (where fitted).
8 Disconnect all the electrical leads to the engine, making notes or attaching labels if there is any possibility of confusion later. The wiring to be disconnected is largely dependent on model type, but will include the following:
a) Oil pressure switch.
b) Alternator.
c) Coolant temperature sender.
d) Injection pump wiring.
e) Glow plug feed to bus bar.
f) Radiator fan and thermoswitch.
9 Removal of the radiator and cooling fan is recommended, both to improve access and to reduce the risk of damage. See Chapter 6.

3C

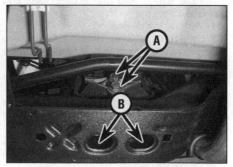

19.8 Rear engine mounting-to-transmission bracket bolts (A), and mounting-to-crossmember nuts accessible through holes (B) in the crossmember

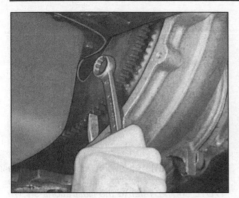

21.18 Unbolting the torque converter from the driveplate

10 Clean around the fuel inlet and return unions at the injection pump, then disconnect them. Be prepared for fuel spillage. Cap the open unions (eg. with polythene and rubber bands) to keep fuel in and dirt out. Detach the fuel hoses from their engine clip(s).
11 Disconnect the throttle cable from the fuel injection pump.
12 Remove the alternator drivebelt.
13 On vehicles equipped with power steering, remove the power steering pump from the engine and place it to one side without disconnecting any of the fluid hoses.
14 Disconnect the brake servo vacuum pump hose at the vacuum pump.
15 Undo the four bolts and remove the crankshaft pulley.
16 Unbolt and remove the starter motor and its heat shield.
17 Unbolt and remove the clutch or torque converter cover plate from the bottom of the bellhousing.
18 On automatic transmission models, unbolt the torque converter from the driveplate **(see illustration)**. Turn the crankshaft to gain access to the bolts through the cover plate aperture in the bellhousing. Obtain new bolts for reassembly.
19 On all models, bring the engine to TDC, No 1 firing. With the transmission removed there will be no TDC indicated.
20 Unbolt the exhaust downpipe from the manifold flange and the flexible joint and remove it from the vehicle.
21 Remove the oil filter.
22 On 17DTL engines, disconnect the feed and return lines from the oil cooler adapter and move them clear of the engine
23 Attach suitable lifting gear to the engine and just take the weight of the unit.
24 Support the transmission with a jack and undo all the bolts securing the engine to the transmission bellhousing.
25 Remove the right-hand engine mounting, together with the mounting bracket, from the cylinder block.
26 Make a final check to ensure that all connections to the engine have been removed and that there is nothing in the way that is likely to interfere when the engine is lifted out.

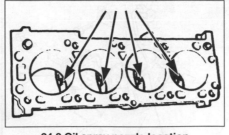

24.3 Oil spray nozzle location in cylinder block

27 Separate the engine from the transmission. Do not allow the weight of the transmission to hang on the input shaft. With automatic transmission, make sure that the torque converter stays in its housing.
28 Carefully lift the engine upwards and out of the engine bay, turning it as necessary to clear any obstructions.
29 With the engine removed, make alternative TDC marks between the flywheel and the cylinder block for use during dismantling and reassembly.

22 Engine dismantling - general information

Refer to Section 19, Chapter 3B.

23 Ancillary components - removal
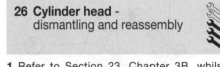

Refer to Section 20, Chapter 3B.

24 Engine - complete dismantling
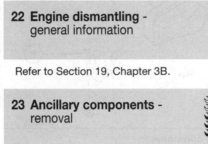

1 Refer to Section 21, Chapter 3B, whilst noting the following:

17DTL engine

2 This engine is equipped with oil spray nozzles to aid piston cooling. To remove these nozzles, first remove the crankshaft.
3 Each nozzle can be driven from its location in the cylinder block by careful use of a 6 mm diameter drift, working through the cylinder bore **(see illustration)**.

25 Oil pump - dismantling, overhaul and reassembly
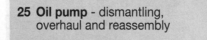

17D and 17DR engines

1 Refer to Section 22, Chapter 3B, whilst noting the information given in the *Specifications* of this Chapter.

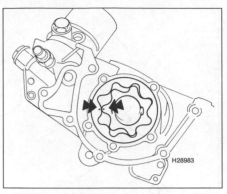

25.3 Ensure that the marks (arrowed) on the oil pump rotors align

17DTL engine

2 Refer to Section 22, Chapter 3B, whilst noting the information given in the *Specifications* of this Chapter and the following.
3 When assembling the pump on this engine, ensure that the marks on each rotor are in alignment **(see illustration)** and that the recesses in the inner rotor align correctly with the pump drive shaft.

26 Cylinder head - dismantling and reassembly
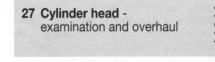

1 Refer to Section 23, Chapter 3B, whilst noting the information given in the *Specifications* of this Chapter and the following:
2 Note that on 17D and 17DR engines, the inlet valves are equipped with spring seat rings whereas the exhaust valves have rotation devices. On 17DTL engines, both the inlet and exhaust valves are equipped with rotation devices.
3 The non-ferrous drift used to drive out the swirl chambers should be of 6 mm diameter.

27 Cylinder head - examination and overhaul
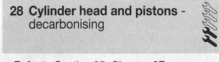

Refer to Section 24, Chapter 3B, whilst noting the information given in the *Specifications* of this Chapter.

28 Cylinder head and pistons - decarbonising

Refer to Section 25, Chapter 3B.

29 Examination and renovation - general information

Refer to Section 26, Chapter 3B.

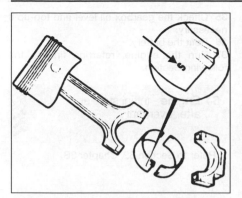

30.3 The upper half of the big-end bearing shells fitted to the 17DTL engine can be identified by the letter "S" (arrowed)

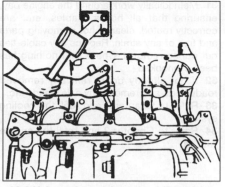

32.2 Using a 6 mm diameter drift to drive each new oil spray nozzle into position

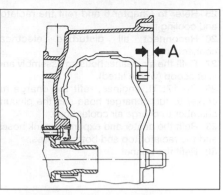

33.8 Torque converter fully engaged
A = 9 to 10 mm

30 Engine components - examination and renovation

1 Refer to Section 27, Chapter 3B, whilst noting the information given in the *Specifications* of this Chapter and the following:
2 The main bearing shells supplied for the 17DTL engine have additional holes for the spray nozzles of the piston cooling system. Under no circumstances fit the bearing shells supplied for the 17D and 17DR engines.
3 The upper half of the big-end bearing shells supplied for the 17DTL engine are reinforced and can be identified by the letter "S" stamped on their outer surface **(see illustration)**. Do not fit any other type of shell.

31 Engine reassembly - general information

Refer to Section 28, Chapter 3B.

32 Engine - complete reassembly

1 Refer to Section 29, Chapter 3B, whilst noting the information given in the *Specifications* of this Chapter and the following:

17DTL engine

2 To refit the oil spray nozzles to this engine, carefully drive each new spray nozzle into position using a 6 mm diameter drift as shown **(see illustration)**.

Crankshaft and main bearings

3 The main bearing shells supplied for this engine have additional holes for the spray nozzles of the piston cooling system. Under no circumstances fit the bearing shells supplied for the 17D and 17DR engines.

Pistons and connecting rods

4 The upper half of the big-end bearing shells supplied for this engine are reinforced and can be identified by the letter "S" stamped on their outer surface. Do not fit any other type of shell.

Oil pump and sump

5 Note the information given in Section 12 with regard to the oil cooler adapter.
6 After fitting the sump, reconnect the turbocharger oil return line to the sump and tighten it to the specified torque setting. Check the connection for leaks after the engine is started.

33 Engine - refitting

 Warning: Do not attempt to fit the engine/transmission on your own, a minimum of two people will be required

1 A minimum of two people will be required to carry out this operation. One person should operate the lifting tackle whilst the other guides the unit into place and keeps watch for fouling. It will be necessary to raise and support the front of the vehicle for some of the following operations. Ensure adequate means of support are used when the vehicle is raised.
2 Carefully lower the unit into the engine bay until it aligns with its right-hand mounting.
3 Reconnect the engine to the transmission as follows:

Engines with manual gearbox

4 If the clutch has been disturbed, make sure that the driven plate is centralised.
5 Offer the engine to the gearbox, twisting it back and forth slightly so that the splines on the input shaft enter the clutch driven plate. Do not allow the weight of the engine to hang on the input shaft.
6 Engage the gearbox with the dowels on the engine. Fit and tighten the engine-to-gearbox bolts to the specified torque loading.
7 Refit the clutch/flywheel access plate.

Engines with automatic transmission

8 Make sure that the torque converter is fully engaged with the transmission **(see illustration)**.
9 Offer the engine to the transmission so that the coloured spot on the torque converter is as close as possible to the white spot on the driveplate.
10 Engage the transmission with the dowels on the engine, then fit and tighten the engine-to-transmission bolts to the specified torque loading.
11 Secure the torque converter to the driveplate using new bolts. Turn the crankshaft to bring the bolt holes into reach through the cover plate aperture.
12 Refit the torque converter/driveplate access plate.

All engines

13 Align and reassemble the right-hand mounting, tightening all bolts to the specified torque loading.
14 Remove the engine lifting tackle and any support from beneath the transmission.
15 On 17DTL engines, reconnect the feed and return lines to the oil cooler adapter, ensuring both lines are correctly routed and secured.
16 Fit a new oil filter.
17 Reconnect the exhaust pipe to the manifold, using a new flange gasket.
18 Refit the starter motor and its heat shield.
19 Refit the crankshaft pulley and tighten its retaining bolts to the specified torque setting.
20 Reconnect the brake servo vacuum pump hose to the vacuum pump.
21 On vehicles with power steering, reattach the power steering pump assembly to the engine, taking care not to place any strain on its hoses, then fit and tension its drivebelt, referring to Chapter 2.
22 Refit and tension the alternator drivebelt, referring to Chapter 2.
23 Reconnect the throttle cable to the fuel injection pump.
24 Reconnect the fuel inlet and return unions to the fuel injection pump, having removed any blanking materials or plugs.

3C

25 Refer to Chapter 6 and refit the radiator and cooling fan.

26 Reconnect all disturbed electrical connections

27 Refit the air cleaner housing assembly and inlet scoop (where fitted).

28 On 17DTL engines, refit the charge air cooler to turbocharger hose and the plenum chamber to charge air cooler hose.

29 Refit the heater and expansion tank hoses and the radiator top and bottom hoses.

30 Refit the bonnet.

31 Methodically work around the engine bay, ensuring that all hoses, cables, etc. are correctly routed, clear of hot or moving parts and free of any strain. Replace any cable-ties cut during removal. Check that nothing has been overlooked

32 If not already done, refit any removed roadwheels and remove any axle stands etc.

33 Refer to Chapter 2 and refill the cooling system.

34 Refer to Chapter 2 and refill the engine with oil.

35 Check the gearbox oil level and top-up if necessary.

36 Refit the battery.

37 Run the engine, referring first to the following Section.

34 Engine - initial start-up after overhaul

Refer to Section 32, Chapter 3B.

Chapter 3 Part D:
Engine overhaul - 17DT engine

Contents

Degrees of difficulty

Easy, suitable for novice with little experience	**Fairly easy,** suitable for beginner with some experience	**Fairly difficult,** suitable for competent DIY mechanic	**Difficult,** suitable for experienced DIY mechanic	**Very difficult,** suitable for expert DIY or professional

3D

Specifications

General

Engine type	Turbocharged, 4-cylinder, 4-stroke, overhead camshaft, indirect injection, compression ignition.
Designation	TC 4 EE 1
Bore	79.00 mm
Stroke	86.00 mm
Displacement	1686 cc
Firing order	1-3-4-2 (No 1 at pulley end)
Compression ratio	22.0 : 1
Maximum power	82 bhp @ 4400 rpm
Maximum torque	124 lbf ft) @ 2400 rpm

Camshaft drivebelt

Tension	Automatically tensioned by tension roller

Cylinder head

	Thickness (fitted)	Identification
Gasket thickness and identification:		
Piston projection 0.58 to 0.64 mm	1.40 to 1.55 mm	No hole
Piston projection 0.65 to 0.71 mm	1.45 to 1.60 mm	One hole
Piston projection 0.72 to 0.78 mm	1.50 to 1.65 mm	Two holes
Valve clearance adjustment	By exchanging shims	

Valve seat width in head:
Inlet:
New seats .... 1.2 to 1.5 mm
Run-in seats .... 2.0 mm maximum
Exhaust:
New seats .... 1.2 to 1.5 mm
Run-in seats .... 2.0 mm maximum
Valve stem play in guide:
Inlet:
Normal .... 0.023 to 0.056 mm
Maximum permissible .... 0.080 mm
Exhaust:
Normal .... 0.030 to 0.063 mm
Maximum permissible .... 0.095 mm
Recess of valve head when fitted:
Inlet .... 0.5 to 1.0 mm
Exhaust .... 0.5 to 1.0 mm
Swirl chamber projection .... 0.001 to 0.030 mm
Sealing surface finish deviation:
Head to block .... 0.0 to 0.1 mm
Head to manifold .... 0.0 to 0.15 mm
Overall height of head:
Maximum .... 131.45 to 131.55 mm
Minimum .... 131.25 mm

Valves

Clearances:
Inlet .... 0.15 mm
Exhaust .... 0.25 mm
Length:
Inlet .... 104.05 mm
Exhaust .... 103.95 mm
Head diameter:
Inlet .... 34.6 mm
Exhaust .... 30.6 mm
Stem diameter (standard):
Inlet .... 6.959 to 6.977 mm
Exhaust .... 6.960 to 6.978 mm
Valve guide bore (standard) .... 7.000 to 7.015 mm
Valve sealing face angle .... 45°

Camshaft and bearings

Camshaft radial run-out .... 0.00 to 0.05 mm
Camshaft endfloat .... 0.05 to 0.20 mm
Cam lift:
Inlet .... 8.47 to 8.67 mm
Exhaust .... 8.57 to 8.77 mm
Permissible bearing play
Normal .... 0.040 to 0.082 mm
Maximum .... 0.11 mm

Cylinder bores

	Diameter	Identification
Production size:		
A	79.000 to 79.009 mm	Coefficient on crankcase
B	79.010 to 79.019 mm	Coefficient on crankcase
C	79.020 to 79.029 mm	Coefficient on crankcase
Rebore limit	79.2 mm	
Bore out-of-round and taper	0.015 mm max	

Pistons

	Diameter	Identification
Production size:		
A	78.975 to 78.984 mm	Coefficient on piston head
B	78.985 to 78.994 mm	Coefficient on piston head
C	78.995 to 79.004 mm	Coefficient on piston head
Clearance in bore	0.016 to 0.034 mm	
Projection at TDC (used to determine head gasket thickness)	0.58 to 0.78 mm	

Piston rings

Thickness:	
Compression	2.0 mm
Oil scraper	3.0 mm
End gap (fitted):	
Top compression	0.25 to 0.80 mm
Centre compression and oil scraper	0.20 to 0.80 mm
Vertical clearance in groove:	
Top compression	0.12 to 0.18 mm
Centre compression	0.05 to 0.15 mm
Oil scraper	0.025 to 0.150 mm
Gap offset	90°

Gudgeon pins

Length	63.8 to 64.0 mm
Diameter	26.995 mm
Clearance:	
In piston	0.002 to 0.012 mm
In connecting rod	0.008 to 0.050 mm

Connecting rods

Weight variation (in same engine)	4 g.
Torsion	0.05 mm
Parallelism	0.05 mm
Endfloat on crankshaft	0.20 to 0.40 mm
Bearing running clearance	0.025 to 0.100 mm

Identification - rod marking:	Bearing shell colour code	Bearing clearance
I	Blue	0.025 to 0.054 mm
II	Black	0.027 to 0.056 mm
III	Brown	0.029 to 0.058 mm

Crankshaft and bearings

Bearing journal out-of-round and taper	0.0025 mm
Shaft run-out (measured at centre main bearing journal)	0.00 to 0.06 mm
Shaft endfloat	0.06 to 0.30 mm
Main bearing running clearance	0.03 to 0.08 mm

Main bearing journal size marking:	Diameter
□□	51.918 to 51.928 mm
□	51.928 to 51.938 mm

Main bearing shell size marking:	Journal marking	Bearing play
Blue	□□	0.032 to 0.058 mm
Black	□	0.030 to 0.056 mm
Black	□□	0.032 to 0.058 mm
Brown	□	0.030 to 0.056 mm
Brown	□□	0.032 to 0.058 mm
Green	□	0.030 to 0.056 mm

Flywheel

Run-out	0.5 mm max
Refacing limit (depth of material removed from clutch wear face)	0.3 mm max

Lubrication system

System type	Wet sump, pressure feed, full flow filter
Lubricant type/specification/capacity	Refer to "Lubricants, fluids and capacities"
Filter type	Champion F208
Oil pressure (at idle, engine warm)	2.0 bar

Lubrication system (continued)

Oil pump tolerances:
    Pump shaft to cylinder block:

New shaft	0.040 to 0.125 mm
Run-in shaft	0.20 mm max

    Rotors to pump cover:

New rotors	0.035 to 0.100 mm
Run-in rotors	0.15 mm max

    Outer rotor to cylinder block:

New rotor	0.24 to 0.36 mm
Run-in rotor	0.40 mm max

Outer rotor to inner rotor mesh:

New rotors	0.13 to 0.15 mm
Run-in rotor	0.20 mm max

Oil cooler thermostat:

Opening commences at	80.5 to 83.5°C
Fully open at	95°C

Coolant pump

Type	Impeller
Drive	From crankshaft via V-belt

Coolant thermostat

Type	Twin valve

Identification:

Main valve	88
Auxiliary valve	85

Opening commences at:

Main valve	86 to 90°C
Auxiliary valve	83 to 87°C
Fully open at	100°C

Torque wrench settings

	Nm	lbf ft
Cylinder head		
Cylinder head bolts:		
Stage 1	40	30
Stage 2	Tighten a further 60 to 75°	
Stage 3	Tighten a further 60 to 75°	
Cover bolts	8	6
Camshaft		
Drivebelt sprocket bolts	10	7
Drivebelt cover to cylinder block	8	6
Drivebelt guide roller to cylinder block	76	55
Drivebelt tension roller to cylinder block	19	15
Bearing cap to cylinder head	19	15
Crankshaft		
Pulley-to-sprocket bolts	20	15
Drivebelt sprocket centre bolt	196	144
Flywheel to crankshaft:		
Stage 1	30	22
Stage 2	Tighten a further 45 to 60°	
Main bearing caps	88	66
Connecting rod caps:		
Stage 1	25	18
Stage 2	Tighten a further 100°	
Stage 3	Tighten a further 15°	
Rear seal bracket to cylinder block	10	7
Lubrication system		
Pump cover to cylinder block	10	7
Pump inlet pipe to cylinder block	19	15
Drivebelt pulley to pump	44	33
Pressure regulator valve	40	30
Pressure switch	20	15
Cooler to cylinder block central hollow screw	49	36
Cooler to cylinder block securing bolt	26	20
Cooler thermostat housing to cylinder head	19	15

Torque wrench settings	Nm	lbf ft
Lubrication system (continued)		
Cooler thermostat cover to cylinder head	30	22
Cooler banjo bolt to cylinder block	49	37
Filter to cylinder block	15	11
Return hose connection to turbocharger	10	7
Pressure line to turbocharger	15	11
Pressure line connection - turbocharger	41	30
Pressure line to cylinder block pipe connection (cap nut)	28	21
Pressure line to cylinder block pipe connection	20	15
Line to vacuum pump	25	18
Line to vacuum pump banjo bolt	22	16
Line to cylinder block	15	11
Sump:		
Upper part to cylinder block	10	7
Lower part to upper part	10	7
Drain plug	78	56
Baffle plate to cylinder block	19	15
Cooling system		
Pump to cylinder block	20	15
Drivebelt pulley to pump	10	7
Temperature sensor to thermostat housing	8	6
Thermostat housing to cylinder head	30	22
Thermostat housing cover to housing	30	22
Drain plug to cylinder block	39	30
Line to turbocharger	8	6
Pipe to cylinder block	95	70
Power steering system		
Pump mounting bracket to cylinder block	60	44
Mountings		
Right-hand mounting bracket:		
To cylinder block	40	30
To mounting	45	33
Engine rear damping block:		
To bracket	45	33
To crossmember	40	30
Engine right-hand damping block to bracket	35	26
Engine left-hand damping block to bracket	60	44
Engine left and right-hand damping blocks to sidemember	65	47
Other components		
Alternator mounting bracket to cylinder block	38	27
Vacuum pump to alternator	7	5
Starter motor to cylinder block	40	30
Turbocharger support to cylinder block	51	37
Transmission to cylinder block	60	44

3D

1 General information

Installed in the Astra and Cavalier, this engine is turbocharged and of four-cylinder overhead camshaft design **(see illustrations)**. The cylinder head is of light alloy construction and the block is of iron. The crankshaft runs in five main bearings.

The camshaft is belt-driven from the crankshaft sprocket. The same belt drives the oil pump and the fuel injection pump. Belt tension is automatically adjusted by means of a spring and pulley adjuster.

The coolant pump is driven by a V-belt which runs from the crankshaft pulley, as is the power steering pump and alternator (which has the vacuum pump attached).

Lubrication is by means of the crankshaft driven pump, oil being drawn from the sump and pumped through a full flow filter before entering the main oil galleries in the block and crankshaft. The oil is cooled by passing through a cooler unit located between the oil filter and cylinder block.

Valve clearance adjustment is by means of exchanging shims. Maintenance tasks are mostly straightforward but operations which involve disturbing or checking the valve timing should not be undertaken unless the necessary equipment is available.

2 Major operations possible with the engine in the vehicle

1 Since the cylinder head, sump and camshaft drivebelt covers can all be removed with the engine in the vehicle, most dismantling can be carried out without removing the engine. However, access to some areas is difficult and if much work is to be done, it may be quicker in the long run to remove the engine.

2 Removal of the oil pump and crankshaft front and rear oil seals entails removal of the sump, due to the sump end holding studs passing through the seal retaining plates.

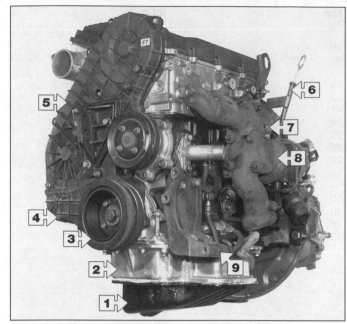

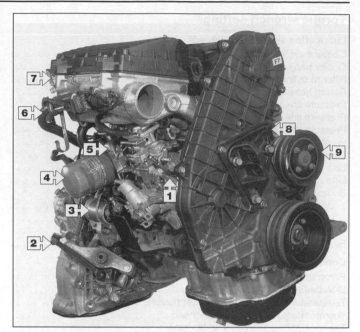

1.0a Front three-quarter view of 17DT diesel engine

1 Sump (lower section)
2 Sump (upper section)
3 Crankshaft pulley
4 Camshaft drivebelt lower cover
5 Camshaft drivebelt upper cover
6 Oil level dipstick
7 Exhaust manifold
8 Turbocharger
9 Alternator mounting bracket

1.0b Rear three-quarter view of 17DT diesel engine

1 Fuel injection pump
2 Gearchange linkage assembly
3 Starter motor solenoid
4 Oil filter
5 Oil cooler
6 Engine wiring loom
7 Intake manifold and air filter casing
8 Engine mounting plate
9 Coolant pump pulley

3 In theory, even the crankshaft and main bearings can be removed with the engine installed but this is not recommended unless there is some compelling reason for not removing the engine.

3 Engine oil and oil filter - renewal

Refer to Chapter 2.

4 Camshaft drivebelt - inspection, removal, refitting and tensioning

Caution: A camshaft drivebelt which is damaged, oil-soaked or fuel soaked must be renewed or it will fail, resulting in serious engine damage.

Note: The procedure described in this Section relates to one particular vehicle, therefore allowances must be made for individual model and year variations. Reference to the under-bonnet views contained in Chapter 2 will show detail differences of hose and cable routing etc.

1 The camshaft drivebelt (sometimes called the timing belt) also drives the oil pump and fuel injection pump **(see illustration)**.

Inspection

2 Refer to Chapter 2.

4.1 Camshaft drivebelt and associated components

1 Camshaft drivebelt
2 Tensioner pulley
3 Pulley bolt
4 Bolt
5 Tensioner bolt
6 Adjuster screw
7 Washer
8 Tensioner spring
9 Guide roller
10 Roller bolt
11 Camshaft sprocket
12 Sprocket bolt
13 Sprocket flange
14 Flange screw
15 Crankshaft sprocket
16 Locating pin
17 Flange disc
18 Fuel injection pump sprocket
19 Sprocket nut
20 Oil pump sprocket
21 Sprocket nut
22 Drivebelt upper front cover
23 Cover seal
24 Cover seal
25 Drivebelt lower front cover
26 Cover seal
27 Cover seal
28 Drivebelt rear cover
29 Cover bolt
30 Cover screw
31 Cover screw

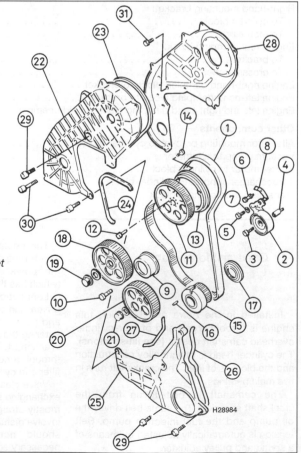

4.10 Align the timing mark on the crankshaft pulley with the reference pointer on the engine block to bring No 1 piston to TDC on the firing stroke

4.11a Insert the locking bolt (arrowed) through the camshaft sprocket . . .

4.11b . . . and insert the locking bolt through the injection pump sprocket

Removal

3 Disconnect the battery earth lead.

4 Remove the drivebelt upper cover as explained in drivebelt inspection.

5 Turn the steering wheel so that access to the side of the engine can be gained through the right-hand wheel arch, in front of the roadwheel.

6 Support the engine by positioning a jack beneath its sump and raising it slightly. Protect the sump by placing a piece of thick wood between it and the jack.

7 Remove the engine right-hand mounting by first removing its two centre bolts. Remove the two mounting to vehicle body retaining bolts and then the three mounting to engine bolts to allow the complete mounting assembly to be withdrawn.

8 Slacken the power steering pump upper and lower retaining bolts to allow the pump to be moved towards the engine, see Chapter 6. With the V-belt slackened, detach it from the crankshaft, coolant pump and power steering pump pulleys.

9 Slacken the alternator pivot and retaining bolts and move it towards the engine. With the V-belt slackened, detach it from the crankshaft, coolant pump and alternator pulleys.

10 Turn the crankshaft in the normal direction of rotation until the timing mark on its pulley aligns with the reference pointer on the engine block **(see illustration)**. In this position No 1 piston is at TDC on the firing stroke.

11 Now check that the locking bolt holes in the camshaft and fuel injection pump sprockets are aligned with their respective threaded holes in the engine casing before inserting the locking bolts (bolt sizes M6 x 1.00 for camshaft and M8 x 1.25 for injection pump) **(see illustrations)**.

12 Mark the fitted position of the crankshaft pulley. Remove the four pulley retaining bolts and detach the pulley, gently tapping its rim to free it if necessary.

13 Undo the three bolts and remove the lower part of the drivebelt cover from the engine.

14 Release the drivebelt tensioner by loosening the pulley centre bolt, the upper spring bracket securing bolt and the lower pivot securing nut. Push the tensioner spring towards the front of the engine to release belt tension and then nip tight the bracket securing bolt.

15 Mark the running direction of the drivebelt if it is to be reused. Also take care not to kink the belt, nor get oil, grease etc. on it.

16 Slip the belt off the injection pump sprocket first and then the remaining sprockets to remove it from the engine .

Refitting and tensioning

17 Commence refitting by first placing the drivebelt over the camshaft sprocket and then the injection pump sprocket etc. until it is correctly routed **(see illustration)**. The crankshaft must not be disturbed and the camshaft and fuel injection pump sprockets should still be locked in alignment.

18 Remove the camshaft and fuel injection pump sprocket alignment bolts.

19 Release the tensioner spring bracket securing bolt to allow the tensioner to act upon the drivebelt. Turn the crankshaft against the normal direction of rotation by approximately 60 degrees to automatically tension the drivebelt and then tighten the

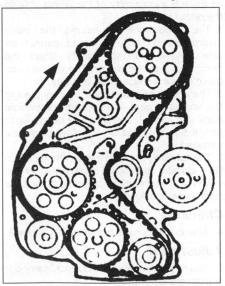

4.17 Ensure the camshaft drivebelt is correctly routed

Arrow denotes direction of belt travel

tensioner pulley centre bolt, the upper spring bracket securing bolt and the lower pivot securing nut to the specified torque settings (where given).

20 Refit the lower part of the drivebelt cover to the engine, renewing any damaged sealing strips and tightening the retaining bolts to the specified torque setting **(see illustration)**.

21 Refit the crankshaft pulley in its previously noted position, tightening the retaining bolts to the specified torque setting.

22 Refit and tension both auxiliary drivebelts, referring to the appropriate Section of Chapter 2.

23 Refit the engine right-hand mounting in the reverse sequence to removal, tightening all retaining bolts to the specified torque settings see Section 19.

24 Refit the upper part of the drivebelt cover, renewing any damaged sealing strips and tightening the retaining bolts to the specified torque setting.

25 Refit all other removed components.

26 Remove the jack from beneath the engine and reconnect the battery earth lead.

---

5 Valve timing - checking and adjustment

Note: *When carrying out the following procedure, refer to the illustrations referred to in the previous Section on camshaft drivebelt removal and refitting.*

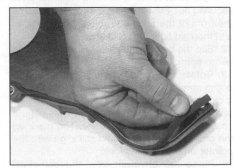

4.20 Checking the sealing strip in the lower front section of camshaft drivebelt cover

Checking

1 Disconnect the battery earth lead.

2 Gain access to the camshaft drivebelt upper cover by first removing the air inlet collector box from its mounting on the right-hand side of the engine bay - see previous Section.

3 Release the brake servo vacuum line retaining clamp and pull the line from the servo unit.

4 Remove the upper part of the cover by undoing its nine securing bolts (noting their respective lengths) and lifting it from position.

5 Turn the crankshaft in the normal direction of rotation until the timing mark on its pulley aligns with the reference pointer on the engine block. In this position No 1 piston is at TDC on the firing stroke.

6 Now check that the valve timing is correct by ensuring that the locking bolt holes in the camshaft and fuel injection pump sprockets are aligned with their respective threaded holes in the engine casing before inserting the locking bolts (bolt sizes M6 x 1.00 for camshaft and M8 x 1.25 for injection pump). The mark on the crankshaft pulley should align with the pointer on the engine block.

Adjustment

7 If the locking bolt holes in the camshaft and fuel injection pump sprockets are not in alignment with their respective threaded holes in the engine casing, then the valve timing must be adjusted as follows.

8 Turn the steering wheel so that access to the side of the engine can be gained through the right-hand wheel arch, in front of the roadwheel.

9 Support the engine by positioning a jack beneath its sump and raising it slightly. Protect the sump by placing a piece of thick wood between it and the jack.

10 Remove the engine right-hand mounting by first removing its two centre bolts. Remove the two mounting to vehicle body retaining bolts and then the three mounting to engine bolts to allow the complete mounting assembly to be withdrawn. This will expose the drivebelt tensioner assembly.

11 Release the drivebelt tensioner by loosening the pulley centre bolt, the upper spring bracket securing bolt and the lower pivot securing nut. Push the tensioner spring towards the front of the engine to release belt tension and then nip tight the bracket securing bolt.

12 Slip the belt off the camshaft and injection pump sprockets.

13 Rotate the camshaft and fuel injection pump sprockets by the least amount until the locking bolt holes are aligned with their respective threaded holes in the engine casing. Insert the locking bolts. The mark on the crankshaft pulley should still align with the pointer on the engine block.

14 Place the drivebelt over the camshaft sprocket and then the injection pump sprocket.

6.8 Use the flat of a large screwdriver to depress the valve lifter and then remove the shim

15 Remove the sprocket locking bolts.

16 Release the tensioner spring bracket securing bolt to allow the tensioner to act upon the drivebelt. Turn the crankshaft against the normal direction of rotation by approximately 60 degrees to automatically tension the drivebelt and then tighten the tensioner pulley centre bolt, the upper spring bracket securing bolt and the lower pivot securing nut to the specified torque settings (where given).

17 Confirm valve timing by turning the crankshaft in the normal direction of rotation two full turns and rechecking that all timing marks are in correct alignment.

18 With valve timing correct, reassemble all disturbed components whilst noting the specified torque settings.

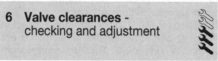

6 Valve clearances - checking and adjustment

Note: *Never attempt to carry out valve clearance adjustment with the pistons at TDC as there is a possibility of the valves striking the piston crown.*

1 The importance of having the valve clearances correctly adjusted cannot be overstressed, as they vitally affect the performance of the engine. The engine must be cold for the check to be accurate.

2 The engine can be turned over by placing the engine in gear and rocking the vehicle back and forth. The engine will be easier to turn if the fuel injectors or glow plugs are removed.

3 The following procedure is for the valves of No 1 cylinder and should be repeated for the valves of the other three cylinders. Check the clearances as follows:

Checking

4 Refer to the appropriate Section of Chapter 2.

Adjustment

5 Should a clearance be incorrect, carry out adjustment as follows.

6 Turn the crankshaft until the tip of the cam of the valve to be adjusted is pointing upwards.

6.9 Determine the thickness of each shim

7 Rotate the valve lifter so that its groove points towards the front of the engine.

8 Depress the lifter by using GM tool KM - 650 or alternatively, the flat of a large screwdriver placed carefully between the edge of the lifter and the camshaft. With the lifter depressed, use the flat of a small screwdriver to flip the shim out of the lifter (a magnetic pick-up tool is particularly useful for this task) **(see illustration)**.

9 Use the following formulae for determining the thickness of the replacement shim **(see illustration)**:

Thickness of original fitted shim	*3.25 mm*
Plus measured valve clearance of	*0.25 mm*
Equalling	*3.50 mm*
Minus specified valve clearance of	*0.15 mm*
Equals thickness of required shim	*3.35 mm*

10 Once selected, the replacement shim should be coated in clean engine oil and fitted in the depressed lifter with its size mark facing downwards.

11 With the valve clearances of all four cylinders checked and if necessary, adjusted, turn the engine over and recheck the adjusted clearances

12 On completion, refit the cylinder head cover with a new gasket.

7 Cylinder head - removal and refitting

Caution: Wait until the engine is cold before removing the cylinder head bolts

Note: *The procedure described in this Section relates to one particular vehicle, therefore allowances must be made for individual model and year variations. Reference to the under-bonnet views contained in Chapter 2 will show detail differences of hose and cable routing etc.*

Removal

1 Disconnect the battery earth lead.

2 Drain the cooling system, recovering the coolant if it is fit for re-use.

3 Remove the camshaft drivebelt as detailed in Section 4.

7.4 Removing the air filter housing with element

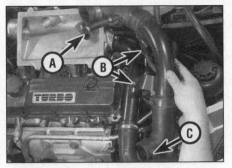

7.5 Removing the air filter to turbocharger feed hose

A *Feed hose to head cover breather pipe clip*
B *Centre section mounting brackets*
C *Feed hose to turbocharger clamp*

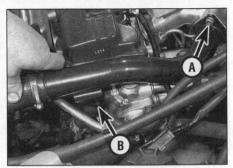

7.6 Removing the charge air cooler to inlet manifold hose

A *Two bolts at manifold*
B *Mounting bracket*
C *Charge air cooler hose clamp*

4 Unscrew the four air filter housing retaining bolts. Release the housing hose clamp and remove the housing with filter element **(see illustration)**.

5 Remove the air filter to turbocharger feed hose by disconnecting the following **(see illustration)**:

a) The feed hose to cylinder head cover breather pipe clip
b) The two mounting bracket bolts supporting the centre section of feed hose
c) The feed hose to turbocharger clamp

6 Remove the charge air cooler to inlet manifold hose by disconnecting the following **(see illustration)**:

a) The two bolts at the casing
b) The single mounting bolt on the side of the cylinder head
c) The hose clamp at the charge air cooler

7 To facilitate removal of the inlet manifold, proceed as follows:

a) Loosen the pipe union of No 1 fuel injector to allow movement of the pipe and access to the manifold securing bolt obscured by it **(see illustration)**
b) Release the cable-ties from the manifold **(see illustration)**
c) Disconnect the manifold heater multiplug
d) From beneath the manifold, disconnect the manifold to injection pump air hose

8 Remove the five bolts and two nuts which secure the inlet manifold to the cylinder head, working in a diagonal sequence. Withdraw the manifold and recover the gasket.

9 Remove the exhaust manifold heat shield. Note that the special insulating washers are

retained on each of the shield securing bolts by a retaining plate which should stay in place as long as the bolts are unscrewed only enough for them to disengage from the manifold **(see illustration)**.

10 From beneath the vehicle, disconnect the exhaust pipe from the turbocharger.

11 Remove the two nuts securing the coolant pipe to the front of the cylinder head.

12 Remove the three power steering pump mounting bracket bolts and move the pump assembly clear of the engine.

13 Remove the exhaust manifold securing bolts and studs, working in the reverse of the tightening sequence. Pull the manifold fowards to clear the cylinder head and recover the gasket. Note that the manifold will only move a little because of the turbocharger mounting still being attached. If the manifold securing studs cannot be removed then the turbocharger will have to be released from the engine block, see Chapter 4.

14 Remove the camshaft sprocket by removing its three retaining bolts and pulling it from position.

15 Detach the drivebelt rear cover from the cylinder head by first removing its two securing bolts and then easing it clear of the camshaft end **(see illustration)**.

16 Remove the two bolts retaining the thermostat housing to the cylinder head and move the housing clear of the head with the hoses still attached **(see illustration)**.

7.7a Loosening the pipe union of No 1 fuel injector to allow access to the inlet manifold securing bolt

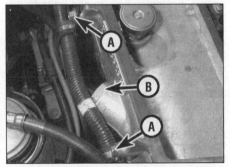

7.7b Release the cable ties (A) from the inlet manifold and disconnect the manifold heater multiplug (B)

7.9 Removing the exhaust manifold heat shield

7.15 Remove the camshaft drivebelt rear cover securing bolts (arrowed)
A *Camshaft sprocket locating pin*

7.16 Remove the thermostat housing retaining bolts (arrowed)

3D

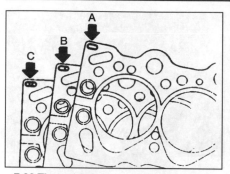

7.26 Three thicknesses of cylinder head gasket are available and are identified by holes in the position arrowed

A *No hole indicates fitted thickness of 1.40 to 1.55 mm*

B *1 hole indicates fitted thickness of 1.45 to 1.60 mm*

C *2 holes indicates fitted thickness of 1.50 to 1.65 mm*

17 Detach the coolant hose from the oil cooler thermostat housing, see Section 13.

18 Disconnect the electrical wire from the glow plug bus bar.

19 Disconnect the fuel return line from the No 3 injector. Be prepared for fuel spillage.

20 Clean around the injection pipe unions, then unscrew them from the injectors and from the injection pump. Unscrewing the unions from the pump is difficult and should be carried out in the following sequence:

a) *Unscrew No 1 union and ease the pipe away from the pump to expose No 2 union*

b) *Unscrew No 2 union and remove pipes 1 and 2 as an assembly*

c) *Repeat the above procedure with unions Nos 3 and 4*

21 Blank off all exposed pipe connections to prevent the ingress of dirt and moisture.

22 Remove the cylinder head cover (with attached baffle plate) to expose the cylinder head securing bolts. Discard the gasket.

23 Slacken the cylinder head bolts a little at a time, working in the reverse sequence to that used for tightening. Remove the bolts with washers and discard them. Obtain new bolts for reassembly.

24 Lift off the cylinder head. Do not prise between the mating faces if the cylinder

heads sticks, but if necessary, tap around the mating faces with a soft-faced mallet to break the gasket seal. Recover the gasket.

25 Clean and examine the cylinder head and engine block mating faces.

Refitting

26 Commence refitting by selecting the correct cylinder head gasket. Three thicknesses of gasket are available and they are identified by the presence or absence of holes in the position shown **(see illustration)**. It is essential if the pistons have been disturbed, to measure piston projection as described in the Section for complete reassembly and then select the correct gasket. See *Specifications* for piston projection and gasket thickness figures.

27 Fit the new cylinder head gasket to the block, positioning it over the locating dowels. It can only be fitted the right way up **(see illustration)**. Do not use jointing compound.

28 Bring the pistons to mid-stroke (90° BTDC) and place the head on the block, making sure that the dowels engage in their recesses.

29 Fit the new cylinder head retaining bolts with their washers. Nip up the bolts in a spiral sequence, working from the centre outwards in the order shown **(see illustration)** and in the tightening sequence specified. Use a protractor or a marked card to indicate the angular rotation of each bolt **(see illustration)**.

30 Refit the cylinder head cover with a new gasket, tightening its securing bolts to the specified torque setting **(see illustration)**.

31 Remove all blanking materials from the pipe connections.

32 Reconnect the injection pipe unions to the injectors and pump, working in the reverse sequence to removal.

33 Reconnect the fuel return line to the No 3 injector.

34 Reconnect the electrical wire to the glow plug bus bar.

35 Reattach the coolant hose to the oil cooler thermostat housing.

36 Refit the thermostat housing to the cylinder head, using a new gasket and tightening its securing bolts to the specified torque setting.

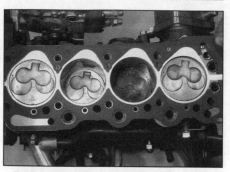

7.27 Fitting a new cylinder head gasket

37 Refit the drivebelt rear cover to the cylinder head, ensuring it is correctly aligned over the camshaft end before tightening its two securing bolts to the specified torque.

38 Refit the camshaft sprocket over its alignment pin on the camshaft end. Refit its three retaining bolts and tighten them to the specified torque setting.

39 Refer to Chapter 4 and refit the exhaust manifold with turbocharger (if necessary).

40 From beneath the vehicle, reconnect the exhaust pipe to the turbocharger. Tighten its securing bolts to the specified torque setting.

41 Refit the exhaust manifold heat shield, taking care not to displace the special insulating washers.

42 Reattach the power steering pump mounting bracket to the engine, tightening its securing bolts to the specified torque setting.

43 Reattach the coolant pipe to the cylinder head.

44 Refer to Chapter 4 and refit the inlet manifold to the cylinder head.

45 Ensure that the following components associated with the inlet manifold are reconnected:

a) *The manifold to injection pump air hose*

b) *The manifold heater multiplug*

c) *All cable-ties*

d) *The pipe union of No 1 fuel injector*

46 Refit the charge air cooler to inlet manifold hose by connecting the following:

a) *The hose securing clamp at the charge air cooler*

b) *The single mounting bolt on the side of the cylinder head*

c) *The two bolts at the casing*

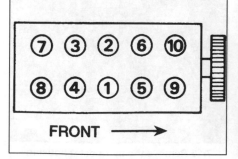

7.29a Cylinder head bolt tightening sequence

7.29b Measuring the angular rotation of each cylinder head bolt

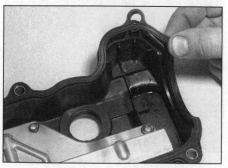

7.30 Fitting a new gasket to the cylinder head cover

47 Refit the air filter to turbocharger feed hose by connecting the following:
a) *The feed hose to turbocharger securing clamp*
b) *The two mounting bracket bolts supporting the centre section of feed hose*
c) *The feed hose to cylinder head cover breather pipe clip*

48 Refer to Chapter 2 and refit the air filter element and its housing, reconnecting the housing hose connections.

49 Refit the camshaft drivebelt as detailed in Section 4.

50 Refill the cooling system.

51 Check that nothing has been overlooked, then reconnect the battery and start the engine.

8 Camshaft - removal and refitting

Removal

1 Remove the camshaft drivebelt as detailed in Section 4.

2 Remove the camshaft sprocket by removing its three retaining bolts and pulling it from position **(see illustration)**.

3 Detach the drivebelt rear cover from the cylinder head by first removing its two securing bolts and then easing it clear of the camshaft end.

4 Remove the cylinder head cover (with attached baffle plate) to expose the camshaft. Discard the gasket.

5 Slacken the nuts securing the camshaft bearing caps one turn at a time, working from end to end in a diagonal sequence so that the camshaft is released gradually.

6 Before removing the bearing caps, note their fitted positions. Each cap is embossed with an arrow which points to the engine timing side and which incorporates the cap number **(see illustration)**.

7 Remove the bearing caps.

8 Lift out the camshaft with its end oil seal. Remove and discard the seal. Note also the sealing plug at the opposite end of the shaft housing.

9 Refer to the Section for general examination and renovation when examining the camshaft and associated components.

Refitting

10 Commence refitting by lubricating the lower half bearing surfaces with clean engine oil **(see illustration)**.

11 With the valve clearance shims in place, refit the camshaft, positioning it with the dowel pin at its sprocket end facing upwards.

12 Lubricate the cam bearing surfaces with clean engine oil.

13 Coat the mating surfaces of No. 1 cap with sealant (to GM spec. 15 03 294) in the areas shown **(see illustration)**, taking great care to keep sealant off all moving surfaces.

14 Fit the bearing caps, making sure that they are the right way round and in the correct order. Tighten the cap retaining nuts, a little at a time and in the sequence shown, until the caps are seated and the specified torque setting obtained **(see illustration)**.

15 Fit a new oil seal to the camshaft end as described in Section 18. There is a temptation to fit this seal to the camshaft before it is installed, but to do so risks pinching or cocking the seal as the bearing cap is tightened.

16 Lubricate the cam lobes liberally with clean engine oil, or with special cam lube if supplied with a new camshaft.

17 Reattach the drivebelt rear cover to the cylinder head.

18 Refit the camshaft sprocket, tightening its retaining bolts to the specified torque setting.

19 Refit and tension the camshaft drivebelt as detailed in Section 4.

20 With the valve clearances checked and adjusted, refit the housing end sealing plug **(see illustration)** and then the cylinder head cover with a new gasket.

21 Observe any running-in instructions which may be supplied with a new camshaft.

8.2 Removing the camshaft sprocket

8.6 Remove each camshaft bearing cap. Each cap is embossed with an arrow which incorporates the cap number (arrowed)

8.10 Lubricate the camshaft lower half bearing surfaces with clean engine oil

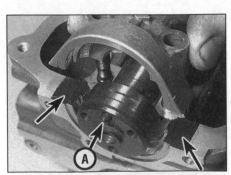

8.13 Coat the mating surfaces (arrowed) of No. 1 camshaft bearing cap with sealant
A   Camshaft sprocket locating pin

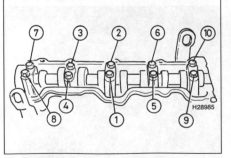

8.14 Camshaft bearing cap tightening sequence

8.20 Refitting the camshaft housing end sealing plug

3D

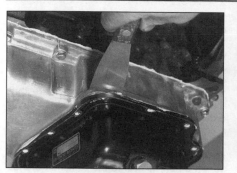

9.3 Use a thin, wide blade to separate the sump mating faces

9 Sump - removal and refitting

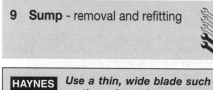

HAYNES HINT *Use a thin, wide blade such as that of a paint stripping tool to break the sealant on the sump mating faces*

Removal

Lower section

1 Raise and securely support the front of the vehicle, or place it over a pit.

2 Remove the sump drain plug and drain the engine oil into a suitable container. Refit the plug when draining is complete, tightening it to the specified torque setting.

3 Remove the steel lower section of the sump by first unscrewing its securing bolts. The sump mating face is sealed with a liquid sealant and will be stuck fast. To separate the sump mating faces, use a thin, wide blade such as that of a paint stripper to break the seal and ease the faces apart **(see illustration)**.

Upper section

4 Removing the front section of exhaust pipe will give greater clearance when removing the alloy upper section of the sump. With the lower section of sump removed, unscrew the bolts and nuts securing the upper section to the cylinder block, if necessary, removing the cover plate from the bottom of the bellhousing to facilitate access to the two left-hand nuts. Two of these bolts are inside the sump.

5 Again, the mating face is sealed with a liquid sealant and will be stuck fast. To separate the sump from the block, gently tap downwards on the upwards facing surfaces of the sump using a soft-faced mallet. Ease the sump away from the block, taking care to avoid damaging the studs at either end.

Refitting

6 Before refitting, clean the inside of both sections of the sump. Remove all traces of sealant from the sump and block faces.

7 Commence refitting by applying RTV sealant (to GM spec 15 03 294) to the appropriate mating face **(see illustration)**.

9.7 Apply RTV sealant to the sump mating face before fitting

8 Secure each section, tightening the bolts in an even sequence to the specified torque.

9 Refit the cover plate to the bottom of the bellhousing and reconnect any disturbed exhaust system connections.

10 With the drain plug fitted and tightened, refill the engine with oil.

10 Oil pump - removal and refitting

Removal

1 Raise and support the front of the vehicle and remove the front right-hand roadwheel.

2 Remove the camshaft drivebelt and the sump as described in the previous Sections.

3 Lock the crankshaft sprocket by refitting the V-belt pulley to it and making a pulley holding tool from an old V-belt and a clamping tool.

10.5 Lock the oil pump sprocket in position and remove the sprocket securing nut

10.8b . . . followed by the pump outer rotor

4 Remove the crankshaft sprocket centre bolt with its washer, remove the pulley and use a puller to draw the sprocket off the crankshaft end. Retain the disc located behind the sprocket and the key in the crankshaft end.

5 Lock the oil pump sprocket in position by placing a socket through one of its holes and over one of the pump securing bolts. The sprocket centre securing nut can now be removed and the sprocket withdrawn from the pump shaft **(see illustration)**. Note the flat on the shaft for reference when refitting.

6 Remove the pump cover bolts, noting that one of the bolts is longer than the other eight.

7 To separate the pump cover from the cylinder block, use a thin, wide blade such as that of a paint stripping tool to break the seal and ease the faces apart.

8 Withdraw the pump inner and outer rotors from their housing **(see illustrations)**.

Refitting

9 Commence refitting by lubricating the lips of the pump and crankshaft oil seals contained in the pump cover with clean engine oil. The crankshaft end and oil pump shaft must both be clean, free from burrs and also lubricated.

10 Refit the oil pump rotors in their housing, lubricating them with clean engine oil and checking for free movement.

11 Degrease the pump cover to cylinder block mating faces. Fit a new O-ring in the cover groove surrounding the pump rotors, coating it with RTV sealant (to GM spec 15 03 294). Apply the same type of sealant to the mating face of the pump cover **(see illustration)**.

10.8a Withdraw the oil pump inner rotor . . .

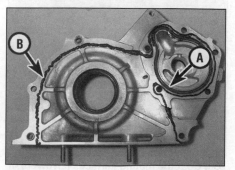

10.11 Pump cover O-ring (A) and sealant (B) on the mating face of the cover

12 Carefully place the pump cover in position over the crankshaft end and oil pump shaft and secure it with the retaining bolts. Each bolt must be coated with sealant and tightened to the specified torque given at the start of this Chapter.

13 Refit the oil pump sprocket and tighten its retaining nut to the specified torque.

14 Refit the disc, crankshaft key, crankshaft sprocket and retaining bolt with its washer, tightening the bolt to the specified torque.

15 Refit the camshaft drivebelt and the sump. Refit the roadwheel and lower the vehicle to the ground.

11.1 Removing the oil pressure regulating valve

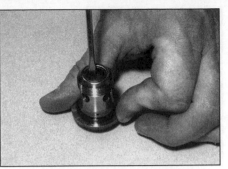

11.4 Testing the oil pressure regulating valve

c) Refill the cooling system
d) Check the engine oil level and top-up as necessary
e) Check for signs of oil or coolant leaks once the engine has been started and warmed-up to normal operating temperature

11 Oil pressure regulating valve - removal, testing and refitting

Removal

1 This valve can be removed by unscrewing it from its location in the bottom of the cylinder block, on the right-hand side **(see illustration)**. Be prepared for a certain amount of oil spillage.

2 Discard the valve sealing ring.

Testing

3 Inspect the top of the valve piston for adhering particles and wipe clean if necessary.

4 Test for free movement of the valve piston by carefully pushing it down with the flat of a small screwdriver, as shown **(see illustration)**.

5 If the piston is stuck, stiff to move or in any way damaged, then the valve must be renewed.

Refitting

6 Check that the valve is clean and fit a new sealing ring.

7 Screw the valve into its housing and tighten it to the specified torque setting.

8 Replenish the engine oil.

12 Oil cooler - removal and refitting

1 The oil cooler is located between the oil filter and cylinder block. It does not normally require any maintenance. Should it however become damaged, renew it as follows.

Removal

2 With the engine in the vehicle, access to the cooler is very difficult and will necessitate removal of the starter motor from underneath the vehicle to give access. Disconnect the battery earth lead before removing the motor.

3 Drain the cooling system and disconnect the hoses from the cooler.

4 Unscrew the oil filter, catching any escaping oil in a drip tray.

5 Unscrew the filter adapter from the centre of the cooler and remove the cooler to cylinder block securing bolt **(see illustration)**.

6 Withdraw the cooler, catching any escaping oil, and discard its sealing ring.

7 Check the oil filter bypass valve is clean and free to move **(see illustration)**.

Refitting

8 Refitting is the reverse of the removal procedure, noting the following points:

a) Renew the cooler sealing ring **(see illustration)**
b) Tighten all connectors to the specified torque settings

13 Oil cooler thermostat - removal, testing and refitting

Removal

1 Drain the cooling system, saving the coolant if it is fit for re-use.

2 Disconnect the coolant hose from the thermostat housing cover.

3 Unbolt the cover from the thermostat housing. Remove the cover and lift out the thermostat, using the flat of a screwdriver **(see illustrations)**.

4 Remove and discard the thermostat sealing ring and discard the cover gasket.

Testing

5 Test the thermostat by suspending it in a saucepan of cold water and bringing the water to the boil. The thermostat should not contact the saucepan. The thermostat should be closed until the water is nearly boiling, when it should start to open. The precise opening temperature is given in the *Specifications*.

3D

12.5 Unscrewing the filter adapter from the centre of the oil cooler

A Oil cooler to cylinder block securing bolt

12.7 Check the oil filter bypass valve (arrowed) is clean and free to move

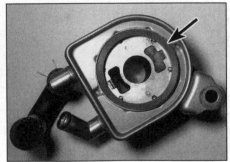

12.8 Renew the oil cooler sealing ring (arrowed)

13.3a Unbolt the oil cooler thermostat cover from the cylinder head . . .

13.3b . . . to allow inspection of the oil cooler thermostat

6 Renew the thermostat if it does not open and close as described, or if it is obviously damaged.

Refitting

7 Insert a new sealing ring into the housing cover and relocate the thermostat, using a length of tube of the appropriate diameter to carefully drive it into position against its stop.
8 Refit the cover, using a new gasket and tighten its retaining bolts to the specified torque setting.
9 Reconnect the coolant hose to the cover and refill the cooling system.

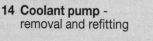

14 Coolant pump - removal and refitting

Removal

1 Drain the cooling system, saving the coolant if it is fit for re-use.
2 Slacken the power steering pump upper and lower bolts to allow the pump to be moved towards the engine. With the V-belt slackened, detach it from the crankshaft, coolant pump and power steering pump pulleys.
3 Slacken the alternator pivot and retaining bolts and move it towards the engine. With the V-belt slackened, detach it from the crankshaft, coolant pump and alternator pulleys.
4 Remove the four nuts which secure the

coolant pump pulley and remove the pulley from the pump.
5 Remove the five bolts which retain the coolant pump **(see illustration)**. Gently tap the pump with a soft-faced mallet to break its seal with the cylinder block and remove the pump. Be prepared for a good quantity of coolant to be released.
6 Pump overhaul is not a DIY job, consult a GM dealer or engineering shop.

Refitting

7 Use a new gasket when refitting the pump and ensure that both mating surfaces are clean **(see illustration)**.
8 Refit the five pump retaining bolts and tighten them to the specified torque setting.
9 Refit the pump pulley and its four retaining nuts, tightening them to the specified torque setting.
10 Refit the two V-belts and tension them as detailed in Chapter 6B.
11 Refill the cooling system.

15 Cooling system thermostat - removal, testing and refitting

Removal

1 Drain the cooling system, saving the coolant if it is fit for re-use.
2 Disconnect the coolant hose from the thermostat housing cover.

3 Unbolt the cover from the thermostat housing. Remove the cover and lift out the thermostat.
4 Discard the cover gasket.

Testing

5 Test the thermostat by suspending it in a saucepan of cold water and bringing the water to the boil. The thermostat should not contact the saucepan. The thermostat should be closed until the water is nearly boiling, when it should start to open. The precise opening temperature is given in the *Specifications*. It is not so easy to check the fully open temperature, since this is above the boiling point of water in an open pan.
6 Renew the thermostat if it does not open and close as described, or if it is obviously damaged.

Refitting

7 Relocate the thermostat in its housing with its bore hole uppermost **(see illustration)**.
8 Refit the cover to the thermostat housing, using a new gasket, and tighten the retaining bolts to the specified torque setting.
9 Reconnect the coolant hose to the cover and refill the cooling system.

16 Pistons and connecting rods - removal and refitting

Note: *It is necessary to obtain new connecting rod cap retaining nuts and gudgeon pin retaining rings before commencing this operation.*

Removal

1 Remove the cylinder head to expose the top of the pistons.
2 Remove the sump assembly.
3 Remove the oil inlet pipe with sealing ring by releasing its one securing bolt and pulling it from the cylinder block **(see illustration)**.
4 Unbolt the oil baffle plate to expose the crankshaft.
5 Examine the connecting rods and caps for identification and match marks. Normally, the

14.5 The engine coolant pump

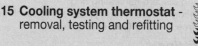

14.7 Position a new gasket before refitting the coolant pump

15.7 Fit the thermostat in its housing with its bore hole uppermost and fit a new gasket before refitting the cover

16.3 Removing the oil inlet pipe

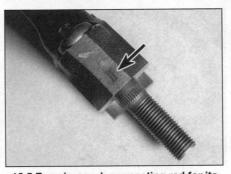

16.5 Examine each connecting rod for its bearing shell allocation markings (arrowed)

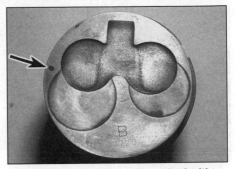

16.9 Each piston crown is marked with a dot (arrowed) which should face the timing side of the engine

connecting rods and caps are marked on one side with the cylinder number and on the other side with the bearing shell allocation **(see illustration)**. If no markings are present, make paint or punch marks to identify the rods and caps and to make sure that the caps are refitted the right way round.

6 Bring two of the pistons to BDC. Remove the connecting rod cap nuts and discard them. Take off the caps and push the pistons up through the top of the block. Recover the bearing shells, keeping them with their original rods if they are to be reused. If purchasing new bearing shells, note that either standard or oversize outside diameter shells may have been fitted in production. Shell sizes are identified by a blue, black or brown marking, see *Specifications*.

7 If there is a pronounced wear ridge at the top of the bore, the piston or its rings may be damaged during removal. This can be avoided by removing the ridge with a tool known as a ridge reamer. Such a degree of bore wear would probably mean that a rebore was necessary, which would also entail the fitting of new pistons in any case.

8 Bring the other two pistons to BDC and remove them.

9 If it is proposed to separate the pistons from the connecting rods, make identifying marks on the piston crowns first so that they can be refitted to their original rods and the right way round. The pistons are normally marked with a dot which should face the timing side of the engine **(see illustration)**.

10 Remove the retaining ring from the gudgeon pin bore on one side of the piston by levering it from position with the flat of a screwdriver **(see illustration)**. From the other side, press out the gudgeon pin by hand. No great force should be required. Never refit used retaining rings

Refitting

11 When refitting the pistons to the connecting rods, oil the gudgeon pins liberally with clean engine oil first. Push the pins home and secure them with the new retaining rings. Some patience may be needed when fitting these rings as they are liable to spring out.

12 If new pistons or rings are to be fitted to old bores, it is essential to deglaze the bores to allow the new rings to bed in. Do this using medium grit emery paper, or a flap wheel in an electric drill, with a circular up-and-down action. The aim is to produce a criss-cross pattern on the bores. Protect the bearing journals on the crankshaft by covering them with masking tape during this operation. Clean the bores thoroughly with a paraffin-soaked rag and dry them with a clean cloth. Then remove the masking tape from the journals and clean them.

13 Begin refitting by laying out the pistons, connecting rods, caps and shells in order. If the piston rings have been removed, refit them and stagger the gaps (see Section 33).

14 Make sure that the seats for the bearing shells are absolutely clean, then press the shells into their seats in the rods and

caps, aligning the locating tangs correctly **(see illustration)**.

15 Lubricate the bores and the piston rings with clean engine oil. Fit a piston ring compressor to the first piston to be fitted. Turn the crankshaft to bring the journal for that piston to BDC.

16 Insert the rod and piston into the block so that the base of the ring compressor rests on the block. Make sure that the piston is the right way round (dot on crown pointing towards timing side) and that the connecting rod is also the right way round - refer to the marks made when dismantling.

17 Drive the piston into the bore by tapping the piston crown with, for example, the wooden handle of a hammer. If the piston does not want to go in, do not use more force but release the compressor and see if a ring has jammed. Remove the compressor as the piston enters the bore.

18 Lubricate the crankpin with clean engine oil and guide the connecting rod onto it, pushing the piston down the bore. Take care that the protruding studs do not scratch the crankpin and check that the bearing shell is not displaced.

19 Fit the connecting rod cap, again making sure that the shell is not displaced. Fit the new nuts and tighten them to the specified torque **(see illustration)**.

20 Repeat the operations on the other pistons and rods.

21 Refit the oil baffle plate, tightening its retaining bolts finger-tight.

3D

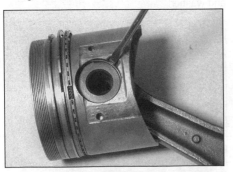

16.10 Using a screwdriver to remove a gudgeon pin retaining ring

16.14 Press each bearing shell into its connecting rod, aligning the locating tang (arrowed)

16.19 Measuring the angular rotation of each connecting rod cap nut

16.22 Push a new sealing ring into the block before refitting the oil inlet pipe

17.1 Mark each component for alignment before removing the flywheel

17.3 Fabricate a tool with which to lock the flywheel ring gear in position

22 Push a new sealing ring into the cylinder block **(see illustration)**, lightly lubricate the ring and refit the oil inlet pipe into it. Retain the pipe with its securing bolt, tightening it finger-tight.

23 Tighten the oil baffle plate retaining bolts in a diagonal sequence to the specified torque setting.

24 Refit the sump assembly.

25 Refit the cylinder head.

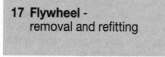

17 Flywheel -
removal and refitting

Removal

1 Before commencing this operation, ensure that each component is marked for alignment with its corresponding part **(see illustration)**.

2 Remove the clutch assembly as described in the appropriate Manual for petrol-engined vehicles.

3 Lock the flywheel ring gear in position using the tool shown **(see illustration)** and loosen its retaining bolts.

4 The flywheel is very heavy and must be supported as the retaining bolts are removed. With the bolts and ring washer removed, lift away the flywheel, noting the fitted position of the plastic spacer in the crankshaft end **(see illustration)**.

5 Obtain new bolts for reassembly.

Refitting

6 When refitting the flywheel, align all components as marked during removal.

7 Apply thread locking compound (to GM spec. 15 10 177) to the threads of the new bolts. Fit the bolts and tighten them to the specified torque settings. Use a protractor or a marked card to indicate the angular rotation of each bolt **(see illustration)**.

8 Refit the clutch assembly.

18 Oil seals - renewal

Note: *Lubricate the lips of each new oil seal before fitting*

17.4 Remove the flywheel bolts and ring washer. Note fitted position of the plastic spacer in the crankshaft end (arrowed)

Camshaft front seal

1 Refer to Section 4 and remove the camshaft drivebelt.

2 With the camshaft sprocket locking bolt in position, loosen the sprocket retaining bolts. Remove the locking bolt, the sprocket retaining bolts and the sprocket.

3 Detach the camshaft drivebelt rear cover from the cylinder head by first removing its two securing bolts and then easing it clear of the camshaft end.

4 Holding the drivebelt rear cover clear of the camshaft end, use the flat of a screwdriver to carefully lever the camshaft seal from position, taking care not to damage the surface of the seal housing.

5 Fill the lips of the new seal with clean engine oil. Clean the seal seat then press the seal into position, lips inwards. Take care not

18.5a Position the camshaft front seal in its housing . . .

17.7 Measuring the angular rotation of each flywheel retaining bolt

to damage the seal lips. Use a piece of tube or a socket to seat the seal **(see illustrations)**.

6 Refit the camshaft drivebelt rear cover to the cylinder head, tightening its retaining bolts to the specified torque setting.

7 Refit the camshaft sprocket over its alignment pin. Refit the sprocket retaining bolts finger-tight only. Refit the sprocket locking bolt and fully tighten the sprocket retaining bolts to the specified torque setting.

8 Refit and tension the camshaft drivebelt then check the valve timing, referring to the appropriate Sections of this Chapter.

Crankshaft front seal

9 Remove the camshaft drivebelt (Section 4).

10 Lock the flywheel ring gear in position, using the tool shown for flywheel removal, and remove the crankshaft sprocket retaining bolt and washer.

18.5b . . . and use a socket to seat the seal

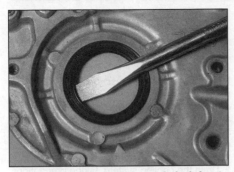

18.13 Carefully lever the crankshaft front seal from its housing with the flat of a screwdriver

18.15 Using a socket to seat the crankshaft front seal

18.18 Carefully lever the oil pump driveshaft seal from its housing with the flat of a screwdriver

11 Using a puller if necessary, remove the crankshaft sprocket followed by the backing ring and Woodruff key. Remove the seal as follows:

12 If the engine is assembled, carefully drill or punch a hole in the oil seal face. Screw in a self-tapping screw and use this to pull out the seal using pincers.

13 With the engine dismantled and the seal retaining plate removed from the engine, the seal can be carefully levered from position with the flat of a screwdriver (see illustration). Removal of the plate will necessitate removal of the sump and oil pump drive sprocket.

14 To fit the new seal, first fill its lips with clean engine oil and clean out the seal seat in the retaining plate. Cover the step on the crankshaft end with adhesive tape to protect the seal lip.

15 Press the seal into position, lips inwards, and use a piece of tube or a socket to seat the seal (see illustration). Remove the adhesive tape.

16 Refit the Woodruff key, backing ring, crankshaft sprocket, washer and retaining bolt. With the flywheel ring gear locked in position, tighten the retaining bolt to the specified torque.

17 Refit and tension the camshaft drivebelt then check the valve timing, referring to the appropriate Sections of this Chapter.

Oil pump seal

18 The oil pump driveshaft seal is contained in the same retaining plate as the crankshaft front seal. If the plate is removed from the engine then the seal can be renewed by using the method described for the crankshaft seal (see illustration).

19 To gain access to the seal with the engine assembled, first refer to Section 4 and remove the camshaft drivebelt.

20 Mark the fitted position of the pump drive sprocket in relation to the crankshaft sprocket. Lock the sprocket in position by passing a socket and bar through it and placing the socket over one of the plate retaining bolt heads, as shown for oil pump removal.

21 Remove the pump sprocket nut and pull the sprocket from position to expose the seal.

22 Carefully drill or punch a hole in the oil seal face. Screw in a self-tapping screw and use this to pull out the seal using pincers.

23 Cover the step on the pump shaft end with adhesive tape to protect the seal lip and clean out the seal seat in the retaining plate.

24 Fill the lips of the new seal with clean engine oil and press it into position, lips inwards. Use a piece of tube or a socket to seat the seal then remove the adhesive tape from the shaft end.

25 Refit the pump sprocket over its shaft alignment flat. With the sprocket locked in position, tighten its retaining nut to the specified torque.

26 Refit and tension the camshaft drivebelt then check the valve timing, referring to the appropriate Sections of this Chapter.

Crankshaft rear seal

27 The engine must be separated from the gearbox for this operation.

28 Remove the clutch and flywheel.

29 With the engine dismantled and the seal retaining plate removed from the engine, the seal can be carefully driven from position by using a hammer and parallel punch (see illustration). Removal of the retaining plate will necessitate removal of the sump. Fitting the new seal can be achieved using two flat pieces of wood and a vice to press it into positon.

30 If the engine is assembled, carefully drill or punch a hole in the oil seal face. Screw in a self-tapping screw and use this to pull out the seal using pincers. Fit the new seal as follws.

18.29 The crankshaft rear seal can be driven from its housing using a hammer and parallel punch

31 Cover the crankshaft end with adhesive tape to protect the seal lip and clean out the seal seat in the retaining plate.

32 Fill the lips of the new seal with clean engine oil and press it into position, lips inwards. Use a piece of large diameter tube to seat the seal then remove the adhesive tape from the shaft end.

33 Refit the flywheel and clutch and reconnect the engine to the gearbox.

Valve stem seals

34 Refer to the Section for cylinder head dismantling and reassembly.

19 Engine/transmission mountings - renewal

Note: Only remove and refit one engine mounting at a time

1 The flexible mountings can be renewed if they have deteriorated. To facilitate removal, take the weight of the engine/transmission on a hoist, or use a jack with a protective wooden block from below. Only remove and refit one mounting at a time.

2 Unbolt the mounting brackets from the engine/transmission and from the bodyframe (see illustrations). Separate the flexible component from the brackets.

3D

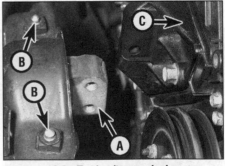

19.2a Engine/transmission right-hand mounting assembly

A Flexible mounting to engine bracket bolt location
B Flexible mounting to vehicle body bolts
C Engine bracket

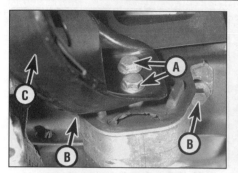

19.2b Engine/transmission left-hand mounting assembly
A Flexible mounting to engine bracket bolts
B Flexible mounting to vehicle body bolts
C Engine bracket

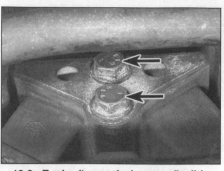

19.2c Engine/transmission rear flexible mounting to engine bracket bolts

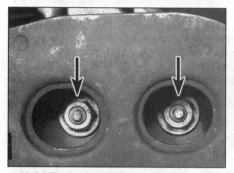

19.2d Engine/transmission rear flexible mounting to vehicle body nuts

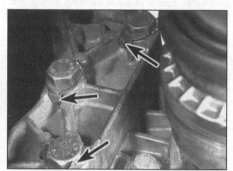

**19.2e Engine/transmission rear mounting engine bracket bolts.
Note locking washer tabs (arrowed)**

3 Fit the new flexible component and refit the mounting. Only nip up the retaining bolts at first, then tighten them to the specified torque.
4 Lower the hoist or jack and check that the mounting is not under strain. Slacken and retighten the bolts as necessary.

20 Engine/transmission - methods of removal

1 During this project, the engine/transmission was removed from the vehicle as a complete assembly by the conventional method of lifting it out of the engine bay.
2 Engine lifting gear of adequate capacity will be required. To provide clearance to remove the engine/transmission from the vehicle, the bonnet should be raised as far as possible without causing damage to the windscreen and then tied in position.
3 The procedures described in the next Section and in the Section for refitting relate to one particular vehicle, therefore allowances must be made for individual model and year variations. Reference to the under-bonnet views contained in Chapter 2 will show detail differences of hose and cable routing etc.

21 Engine/transmission - removal

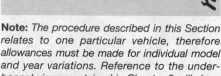

Note: *The procedure described in this Section relates to one particular vehicle, therefore allowances must be made for individual model and year variations. Reference to the under-bonnet views contained in Chapter 2 will show detail differences of hose and cable routing etc.*
1 Disconnect the battery earth lead.
2 Drain the cooling system, taking precautions against scalding if the coolant is hot.
3 Remove the air inlet collector box from its mounting on the right-hand side of the engine bay - see Section 4.
4 Protect the exposed section of radiator matrix with a piece of wood or similar to prevent the risk of it being damaged during engine removal **(see illustration).**
5 Release the filter housing to turbocharger feed hose by disconnecting the following:
   a) *The feed hose to cylinder head cover breather pipe clip* **(see illustration)**
   b) *The two mounting bracket bolts supporting the centre section of feed hose*
   c) *The feed hose to turbocharger clamp*
6 Remove the coolant hose from the base of the coolant reservoir then from the cylinder block and radiator, allowing the complete hose assembly to be removed from the vehicle once the two nuts securing the coolant pipe to the front of the cylinder head are removed **(see illustration).** Detach the top left-hand hose of the reservoir and secure it to one side.
7 Unscrew the four air filter housing bolts.
8 Remove the housing and hose assembly from the vehicle. Blank off the open turbocharger connection.
9 Remove the charge air cooler to inlet manifold hose by disconnecting the following:
   a) *The two bolts at the filter casing*
   b) *The single mounting bolt on the side of the cylinder head*
   c) *The hose securing clamp at the charge air cooler*
10 Release the cable-ties from the rear of the inlet manifold.

21.4 Protect the exposed section of radiator matrix

21.5 Releasing the cylinder head cover breather pipe clip
A Hose to filter housing clamp
B Hose to turbocharger clamp

21.6 Detach the coolant hose assembly from the base of the coolant reservoir, the front of the cylinder head, the cylinder block and the radiator

21.12 Detach the power steering pump mounting bracket from the engine

21.13a Disconnect the engine loom multiplug . . .

21.13b . . . the oil pressure switch cable plug . . .

21.13c . . . the main loom multiplug . . .

21.13d . . . the alternator plugs . . .

21.13e . . . and the glow plug connection

21.16 Disconnecting the two coolant hoses (arrowed) from the thermostat housing

21.17 Disconnecting the coolant reservoir hose from the thermostat housing

21.18 Removing coolant hose connecting the thermostat housing to the radiator

11 Remove the brake servo to vacuum pump line by pulling the line from the servo unit, unscrewing it from the pump and then releasing the line retaining clamps to allow the line to be removed from the vehicle.

12 Release tension on the power steering pump drivebelt. Detach the pump mounting bracket from the engine by removing its three securing bolts then move the pump assembly clear of the engine, taking care not to place any strain on the hoses **(see illustration)**.

13 Disconnect the following electrical connections, making notes or attaching labels to avoid confusion later. These appertain to the Cavalier, those for the Astra being similar:

a) *Engine loom multiplug (next to the brake servo unit)* **(see illustration)**

b) *Oil pressure switch cable plug (next to the battery)* **(see illustration)**

c) *Main loom multiplug (next to the battery - pull arrow back and twist plug to release)* **(see illustration)**

d) *Alternator plugs (at front of engine)* **(see illustration)**

e) *Glow plug feed to bus bar* **(see illustration)**

14 Clean around the fuel inlet and return unions at the injection pump then disconnect them, see Chapter 4. Be prepared for fuel spillage. Cap the open unions with polythene and rubber bands to keep fuel in and dirt out.

15 Disconnect the throttle cable from the fuel injection pump by unclipping its inner from the pump lever and then releasing its outer from the retaining bracket, see Chapter 4.

16 Disconnect the two coolant hoses from the injection pump cold start accelerator and the two hoses from the thermostat housing, tucking them back against the bulkhead of the engine bay **(see illustration)**.

17 Disconnect the coolant reservoir to thermostat housing hose from the housing and tuck it to one side **(see illustration)**.

18 Remove the coolant hose connecting the thermostat housing to the radiator, cutting the cable clips **(see illustration)**.

19 Disconnect the speedometer cable from the gearbox by unscrewing the knurled cap **(see illustration)**.

3D

21.19 Disconnecting the speedometer cable from the gearbox

21.20 Disconnecting the clutch cable inner from the operating lever

21.25 Disconnect the pipe from the charge air cooler and turbocharger

21.27 Release the gearchange linkage securing clamp (arrowed)

20 Disconnect the clutch cable outer from the gearbox casing bracket and its inner from the operating lever **(see illustration)**.

21 Raise and support the front of the vehicle and remove the front wheels.

22 It is advisable to remove the crankshaft pulley to provide clearance during engine removal. With both auxiliary drivebelts slackened, detach them from the crankshaft pulley.

23 Mark the fitted position of the crankshaft pulley. Remove the four pulley retaining bolts and detach the pulley, gently tapping its rim to free it if necessary.

24 Disconnect the exhaust pipe from the turbocharger and recover the flange gasket, see Chapter 4.

25 Disconnect the pipe routed from the bottom of the charge air cooler to the turbocharger **(see illustration)**.

26 Remove the alternator and mounting bracket assembly.

27 Disconnect the gearchange linkage by releasing the securing clamp and separating the linkage from the shaft **(see illustration)**. Push the linkage in towards the engine and secure it in position.

28 Separate the front suspension bottom balljoints.

29 Release both driveshafts from the gearbox, referring to the appropriate Manual for petrol-engined vehicles. Be prepared for oil spillage. Secure the driveshafts out of the way, taking care not to strain them.

30 Disconnect the earth strap from the left-hand side of the engine/transmission **(see illustration)**.

31 Refer to the appropriate Section of this Chapter and loosen the engine mounting bolts but do not attempt to remove them.

32 Take the weight of the engine/ transmission with the lifting gear, using the lifting eyes provided. The engine/transmission has to be lifted out at a slight angle with the timing side uppermost so it is advisable to have the lifting slings at differing lengths to achieve this.

33 Remove the engine mounting bolts, detaching completely the rear mounting flexible component.

34 Side-to-side clearance for raising the engine/transmission is very limited and an assitant will be required to hold components such as the power steering pump and driveshafts clear as the unit is raised. Removing the coolant and power steering reservoirs will improve matters slightly.

35 Check that no attachments have been overlooked, then raise the engine/ transmission clear of the vehicle.

22 Engine/transmission - separation

1 Clean the outside of the engine/ transmission.

2 Unbolt and remove the starter motor, see Chapter 5.

3 Unbolt and remove the lower cover plate from the bottom of the bellhousing **(see illustration)**.

4 Support the gearbox and remove its securing bolts. These bolts are of differing

lengths so note their fitted positions. Note also the positioning of cable clamps etc. beneath the bolt heads.

5 Separate the gearbox from the engine. Do not allow the weight of the gearbox to hang on the input shaft.

23 Engine dismantling - general information

Refer to Section 19, Chapter 3B.

24 Ancillary components - removal

1 If the engine is to be completely dismantled, then remove the following ancillary components (if not already done) whilst referring to the appropriate Chapter:

a) Alternator with vacuum pump
b) Inlet manifold
c) Exhaust manifold and turbocharger
d) Auxiliary drivebelts
e) Camshaft drivebelt and front covers
f) Oil pump
g) Coolant pump and thermostat
h) Fuel injection pump and bracket
i) Fuel injectors
j) Oil cooler and thermostat
k) Oil filter
l) Glow plugs
m) Clutch assembly
n) Wiring loom (Cavalier)

25 Engine - complete dismantling

1 Pull the dipstick tube from its location in the cylinder block and discard its sealing ring **(see illustration)**.

2 Remove the coolant pipe routed from the thermostat housing to the turbocharger.

3 Remove the bracket securing bolt situated adjacent to the coolant pipe at the opposite end of the turbocharger.

4 Disconnect the turbocharger oil feed pipe at the cylinder block.

21.30 Disconnecting the engine/transmission unit earth strap

22.3 Unbolting the lower cover plate from the bottom of the bellhousing

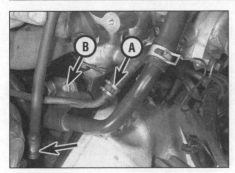

25.1 Pull the dipstick tube from its location in the cylinder block and discard its sealing ring (arrowed)

A *Coolant hose to pipe clamp*
B *Coolant pipe bracket*

5 Remove the coolant pipe from the cylinder block by releasing the two bolts at the pipe to block connection and then the securing clamps **(see illustration)**. Discard the pipe sealing ring and gasket.

6 Remove the camshaft drivebelt guide roller.

7 Remove the camshaft drivebelt tensioner.

8 Remove the camshaft drivebelt rear cover.

9 Remove the following items as described in the appropriate Sections, disregarding those instructions which have already been carried out in removing the engine:

a) *Cylinder head*
b) *Sump - upper and lower sections, without inverting the engine, so that sludge does not enter the crankcase*
c) *Pistons and connecting rods*
d) *Flywheel or driveplate*
e) *Crankshaft rear seal with retaining plate*

10 Invert the engine so that it is standing on the top face of the block.

11 Check that the main bearing caps are numbered 1 to 5 from the sprocket end. They should also be arrowed, the arrows facing the sprocket. Make identification marks if no numbers are present.

12 Remove the bolts which secure the main bearing caps in the sequence shown **(see illustration)**.

13 Lift off the main bearing caps, tapping them lightly to free them if they are stuck. Keep the bearing shells with their caps if they are to be reused. Clean all traces of sealant from No 1 cap.

26.2a Checking the oil pump outer rotor to inner rotor mesh . . .

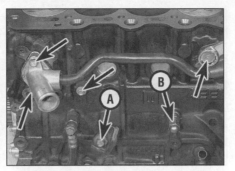

25.5 Remove the coolant pipe retaining bolts (arrowed)

A *Bracket securing bolt*
B *Turbocharger oil feed pipe connection*

14 Lift out the crankshaft, and put it somewhere safe and clean. Do not drop it, it is heavy.

15 Extract the upper half main bearing shells. Keep them in order if they are to be reused.

16 With the exception of semi-permanent items such as core plugs, dismantling of the engine is complete.

26 Oil pump - dismantling, overhaul and reassembly

Dismantling

1 The pump rotors are removed as part of the sequence given for pump removal in Section 10.

Overhaul

2 Clean the pump rotors and their housing before checking the shaft and rotor clearances given in *Specifications* **(see illustrations)**.

3 If any of these clearances are outside the specified tolerance, renew the components as necessary.

4 The oil pressure regulator valve should now be serviced as described in Section 11.

Reassembly

5 Fitting of the pump rotors and cover is included in the sequence given for pump refitting in Section 10.

26.2b . . . and checking the outer rotor to housing clearance

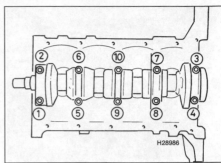

25.12 Main bearing cap bolt loosening sequence

27 Cylinder head - dismantling and reassembly

Dismantling

1 If not already done, remove the fuel injectors with their rail and the glow plugs with their connector bar.

2 Remove the two bolts retaining the cooling system thermostat housing to the cylinder head and discard the gasket.

3 Remove both engine lifting brackets.

4 Remove the two bolts retaining the oil cooler thermostat housing to the cylinder head and discard the gasket.

5 Remove the camshaft (Section 8) to expose the adjustment shims and valve lifters.

6 Remove each shim and lifter, carefully noting their fitted positions before transferring them to a segmented box **(see illustrations)**.

27.6a Remove each valve shim . . .

3D

27.6b . . . followed by its lifter

27.7 Depress the valve spring and extract the split collets

27.8a Remove the valve spring cap . . .

27.8b . . . followed by the valve spring

27.9a Pull the valve stem oil seal off the top of the valve guide . . .

27.9b . . . and withdraw the spring baseplate

7 A valve spring compressor will be needed to remove each valve and spring assembly. Fit the compressor foot to the head of a valve with the forked end over the valve spring cap. Operate the compressor so that the cap is depressed a little way and extract the split collets **(see illustration)**. If the cap seems to be stuck, remove the compressor and strike the cap smartly with a mallet, then try again.

8 With the collets removed, release the compressor and remove the spring cap and spring **(see illustrations)**. Withdraw the valve from the other side of the head.

9 Pull the valve stem oil seal from the top of the valve guide. New seals will be needed for reassembly. Withdraw the spring baseplate **(see illustrations)**.

10 Repeat these operations to remove the remaining valve assemblies. Keep each valve and its associated components separate, in a segmented box.

11 The swirl chambers can be driven out if necessary by using a drift fabricated to the dimensions shown **(see illustrations)**. This drift should be passed through the appropriate glow plug bore hole whilst taking care not to damage the cylinder head.

12 Each injector insulating sleeve can be driven out from the combustion chamber side by using a non-ferrous drift of 8 mm diameter.

13 Thoroughly clean the cylinder head and examine it and its components as described in the Section relating to head examination and overhaul.

Reassembly

14 Insert new injector insulating sleeves into the cylinder head, if necessary using a non-ferrous drift of the appropriate diameter to seat each one in position.

15 To fit a new swirl chamber, first align its dowel pin with the groove in the cylinder head then press the chamber with its metal washer into position. It is important not to exceed a pressure of 28 000 N. Once fitted, remove any projecting chamber material. The chamber must be free of any high spots and be seated without indentation, see *Specifications* for limits of projection. Check for projection as described in the Section relating to cylinder head examination and overhaul.

16 Lubricate a valve stem with clean engine oil and fit the valve into its guide **(see illustration)**.

17 From the other side of the head, fit the spring baseplate.

18 Lubricate the valve seal then press it into position over the valve stem. Use a length of tube or a small box spanner if necessary to push the seal onto its seat **(see illustration)**.

19 Fit the valve spring and the spring cap.

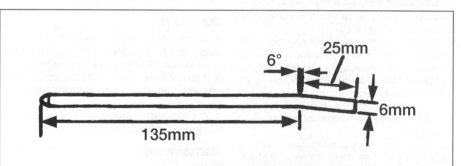

27.11a Each swirl chamber can be driven out by using a drift fabricated to the dimensions shown

27.11b To drive out a swirl chamber, pass the drift through the glow plug bore hole

27.16 Lubricate each valve stem before fitting

27.18 Use a length of tube to press each valve seal into position

20 Fit the valve spring compressor and depress the spring cap far enough to allow the collets to be fitted. A smear of grease on the valve stem will keep them in position. Carefully release the compressor, making sure that the collets are not displaced. Tap the spring cap with a mallet to settle the components.
21 Refit the other valve assemblies in a similar fashion.
22 Refit the valve shims and lifters in their previously noted positions, lubricating them with clean engine oil.
23 Refer to Section 8 and refit the camshaft.
24 Refer to Chapter 2 and check the valve clearances.
25 Refit the oil cooler thermostat housing with a new gasket, tightening the retaining bolts to the specified torque setting.
26 Refit the cooling system thermostat housing with a new gasket, tightening the retaining bolts to the specified torque setting.
27 Refit the fuel injectors with their rail and the glow plugs with their connector bar.
28 Refit both engine lifting brackets.

28 Cylinder head - examination and overhaul

Refer to the information given in Section 24, Chapter 3B, whilst noting the *Specifications* of this Chapter and disregarding any references to hydraulic valve lifters.

29 Cylinder head and pistons - decarbonising

Refer to Section 25, Chapter 3B.

30 Examination and renovation - general information

1 With the engine stripped and all parts thoroughly cleaned, every component should be examined for wear. The items listed in the following Sections should receive particular attention and where necessary be renewed or renovated.
2 So many measurements of engine components require great accuracy. It is advisable therefore to check your micrometer against a standard gauge occasionally to ensure that the instrument zero is set correctly.
3 If in doubt as to whether or not a particular component must be renewed, take into account not only the cost of the component but the time and effort which will be required to renew it if it subsequently fails at an early date.

31 Engine components - examination and renovation

1 Refer to the information given in Section 27, Chapter 3B, whilst noting the *Specifications* of this Chapter and the following differences:

Big-end and main bearing shells

2 Main and big-end bearing shells can be identified as to size by the markings shown in *Specifications*.

Connecting rods

3 The weight of each connecting rod is indicated by a number or colour mark on the rod cap - see *Specifications*.

Pistons and piston rings

4 Each top ring has a top marking (T) on its upper face. The second ring has a top marking (2T) which must also be uppermost.
5 A limit is specified for the vertical clearance of each piston ring in its groove.

Flywheel

6 Check the specified flywheel runout with a dial gauge and note the specified resurfacing limits.

Crankshaft spigot bearing

7 No spigot bearing is fitted.

Camshaft and carrier

8 Check the camshaft endfloat as shown **(see illustration)** and disregard all references to the following items:
 a) Camshaft carrier
 b) Camshaft thrust plate
 c) Camshaft cover filter

Valve lifters, cam followers and thrust pads

9 Disregard all references to the cam followers and thrust pads and note that the

31.8 Measuring camshaft endfloat

valve lifters are not hydraulic and need only be inspected for abnormal wear and damage.

32 Engine reassembly - general information

Refer to the information given in Section 28, Chapter 3B, whilst noting that no dial test indicator or any special tools other than the locking bolts mentioned in Section 5 will be needed to set valve timing.

33 Engine - complete reassembly

Note illustrations: *Where necessary, refer to the appropriate Sections of this Chapter for illustrations relating to component assembly.*

Crankshaft and main bearings

1 Blow out the oilways in the crankcase and crankshaft with an air line, if available, then inject clean engine oil into them.
2 Clean the main bearing shell seats in the crankcase and the shells themselves. New shells may have a protective coating which should be carefully removed.
3 Fit the upper half main bearing shells to their seats. Make sure that the oil holes and the locating tangs are correctly positioned **(see illustration)**.
4 Fit the thrust flanges to their location either side of No 2 bearing. Note that the oilways

33.3 Ensure that the oil hole and locating tang of each upper half main bearing shell align

3D

33.4 Fit the thrust flanges either side of No 2 main bearing, ensuring that the oilways (arrowed) face outboard

33.5 Lowering the crankshaft into position

33.7 Fit the main bearing caps . . .

33.9 . . . and tighten all bearing cap bolts progressively to the specified torque

33.11 Measuring crankshaft endfloat

must face outboard towards the crankshaft **(see illustration)**.

5 Apply clean engine oil to the bearing shells and thrust flanges, then lower the crankshaft into position **(see illustration)**, turning it once or twice to make sure it is seated.

6 Clean the shell seats in the main bearing caps and fit the shells to the caps, again making sure that they are the right way round.

7 Oil the shells and fit all the main bearing caps except No 1 **(see illustration)**. Observe the identification numbers and arrows on the caps to ensure correct positioning. It may be necessary to strike the caps with a mallet to seat them but take care not to displace the shells if doing so. Oil the threads of the new cap retaining bolts and tighten them finger-tight only.

8 Coat the mating faces of No 1 bearing cap with sealing compound to GM spec 15 03 294 and fit the cap and shell, taking care not to let oil contaminate the sealant. Tighten the cap bolts finger-tight only.

9 Tighten all bearing cap bolts progressively to the specified torque in the reverse sequence to that used for releasing **(see illustration)**.

10 Make sure that the crankshaft is still free to turn. Some stiffness is to be expected with new shells but obvious tight spots or binding should be investigated. See Section 21 for measurement of bearing clearances.

11 Measure the crankshaft endfloat, either with a dial test indicator on the crankshaft end or by using feeler blades at No 2 bearing thrust flange **(see illustration)**. Strike the shaft with a mallet at one end or the other to take up the

endfloat. Out-of-limit endfloat must be due to wear, or to incorrect regrinding.

Piston rings

12 Refer to the information given in Section 29, Chapter 3B, whilst noting the *Specifications* of this Chapter and the fitted position of the piston ring gaps **(see illustration)**.

Pistons and connecting rods

13 Refer to the information in Section 29, Chapter 3B, whilst noting the following:

a) *The dot on the piston crown must point towards the timing side*
b) *New cap retaining nuts must be fitted*
c) *The torque and angle settings specified at the beginning of this Chapter*

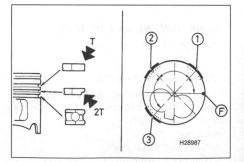

33.12 Fitted position of piston ring gaps
1   *Top compression ring (marked T)*
2   *Second compression ring (marked 2T)*
3   *Oil scraper ring*
F   *Dot on piston crown indicating timing side (fitted position)*

Oil pump and crankshaft front oil seal

14 Using clean engine oil, lubricate the lips of the oil pump and crankshaft oil seals contained in the pump cover. The crankshaft end and oil pump shaft must both be clean, free from burrs and also lubricated.

15 Refit the oil pump rotors in their housing, lubricating them with clean engine oil and checking for free movement.

16 Degrease the pump cover to cylinder block mating faces. Fit a new O-ring in the cover groove surrounding the pump rotors, coating it with RTV sealant (to GM spec 15 03 294). Apply the same type of sealant to the mating face of the pump cover.

17 Carefully place the pump cover in position over the crankshaft end and oil pump shaft and secure it with the retaining bolts. Each bolt must be coated with sealant and tightened to the specified torque.

Crankshaft rear oil seal and flywheel

18 With the crankshaft rear seal fitted in its retaining plate as described in the Section relating to seal renewal, proceed as follows.

19 Cover the crankshaft end with adhesive tape to protect the seal lip.

20 Degrease the retaining plate to cylinder block mating faces. Apply RTV sealant (to GM spec 15 03 294) to the mating face of the retaining plate as shown, ensuring the locating dowels are in position **(see illustration)**.

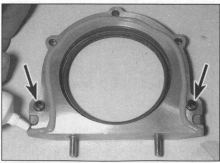

33.20 Applying sealant to the crankshaft rear oil seal retaining plate. Note the locating dowels (arrowed)

33.22 Fitting the crankshaft rear oil seal retaining plate

33.42 Fitting the camshaft drivebelt guide roller

33.43 Fitting the camshaft drivebelt tensioner assembly

21 Fill the lips of the seal with clean engine oil and press it into position over the crankshaft end. Once in position, remove any tape from the shaft end.

22 With the seal and retaining plate in position over the crankshaft end, fit and tighten the plate retaining bolts to the specified torque **(see illustration)**.

23 Position the flywheel, aligning all components as marked during removal.

24 Apply thread locking compound (to GM spec. 15 10 177) to the threads of the new bolts. Fit the bolts and tighten them to the specified torque settings. Use a protractor or a marked card to indicate the angular rotation of each bolt.

Sump and oil inlet pipe

25 Refit the oil baffle plate over the crankshaft assembly, tightening its retaining bolts finger-tight.

26 Push a new sealing ring into the cylinder block, lightly lubricate the ring and refit the oil inlet pipe into it. Retain the pipe with its securing bolt, tightening it finger-tight.

27 Tighten the oil baffle plate retaining bolts in a diagonal sequence to the specified torque setting.

28 Clean the inside of both the upper and lower sections of the sump, removing all traces of sealant from the sump and cylinder block faces.

29 Apply RTV sealant (to GM spec 15 03 294) to the appropriate mating face.

30 Secure each section of the sump, tightening the bolts in an even sequence to the specified torque.

Head gasket selection

31 Refer to the information given in Section 29, Chapter 3B, whilst noting the *Specifications* of this Chapter.

Cylinder head

32 Ensure that the cylinder block and head mating surfaces are clean.

33 Fit the new cylinder head gasket to the block, positioning it over the locating dowels. It can only be fitted the right way up. Do not use jointing compound.

34 Bring the pistons to mid-stroke (90° BTDC) and place the head on the block,

making sure that the dowels engage in their recesses.

35 Fit the new cylinder head retaining bolts with their washers. Nip up the bolts in a spiral sequence, working from the centre outwards in the order shown in Section 7, and in the tightening sequence specified. Use a protractor or a marked card to indicate the angular rotation of each bolt.

36 With the valve clearances checked for correct adjustment and the bearing surfaces lubricated with clean engine oil, refit the cylinder head cover with a new gasket, tightening its securing bolts to the specified torque setting.

Camshaft drivebelt and associated components

37 Refit the camshaft drivebelt rear cover, ensuring that it is correctly aligned over the camshaft end before tightening its securing bolts to the specified torque setting.

38 Refit the camshaft sprocket over its alignment pin on the camshaft end. Refit its retaining bolts and tighten them to the specified torque setting.

39 With the fuel injection pump fitted, refit the pump sprocket over the Woodruff key and pump shaft. Using a locking tool similar to that shown (see Chapter 4), tighten the sprocket centre nut to the specified torque setting.

40 Refit the oil pump sprocket, noting the flat on the pump shaft. Lock the sprocket in position by placing a socket through one of its holes and over one of the pump securing bolts or by using a locking tool similar to that used for the injection pump sprocket. The sprocket securing nut must now be tightened to the specified torque setting.

41 Refit the crankshaft sprocket with its Woodruff key, backing ring, washer and retaining bolt. With the flywheel ring gear locked in position, tighten the retaining bolt to the specified torque setting.

42 Refit the camshaft drivebelt guide roller, tightening its securing bolt to the specified torque setting **(see illustration)**.

43 Refit the camshaft drivebelt tensioner assembly. The tensioner pulley centre bolt, the upper spring bracket securing bolt and the

lower pivot securing nut must all be fully tightened on completion of tensioning the drivebelt **(see illustration)**.

44 Push the tensioner spring towards the front of the engine so that it is in its fully released position and then nip tight the bracket securing bolt to hold it in position.

45 Set all sprockets so that valve timing is correct when the camshaft drivebelt is fitted. Proceed as follows:

46 Refit the crankshaft pulley over its alignment pin on the sprocket, then turn the crankshaft in the normal direction of rotation until the timing mark on its pulley aligns with the reference pointer on the engine block. In this position No 1 piston is at TDC on the firing stroke. Remove the pulley.

47 Check that the locking bolt holes in the camshaft and fuel injection pump sprockets are aligned with their respective threaded holes in the engine casing before inserting the locking bolts (bolt sizes M6 x 1.00 for camshaft and M8 x 1.25 for injection pump).

48 Place the drivebelt over the camshaft sprocket and then the injection pump sprocket, etc. until it is correctly routed. Observe the running direction of the old belt if it is being reused. The crankshaft must not be disturbed during this procedure.

49 With the drivebelt fitted, remove the camshaft and fuel injection pump sprocket alignment bolts.

50 Release the tensioner spring bracket securing bolt to allow the tensioner to act upon the drivebelt. Turn the crankshaft against the normal direction of rotation by approximately 60 degrees to automatically tension the drivebelt and then tighten the tensioner pulley centre bolt, the upper spring bracket securing bolt and the lower pivot securing nut to the specified torque settings (where given).

51 Confirm valve timing by turning the crankshaft in the normal direction of rotation two full turns and rechecking that all timing marks are in correct alignment.

52 With valve timing correct, refit the lower part of the drivebelt cover to the engine, renewing any damaged sealing strips and tightening the retaining bolts to the specified torque setting.

3D

33.53 Fitting the engine right-hand mounting plate

33.55a Fitting a new coolant pipe union gasket . . .

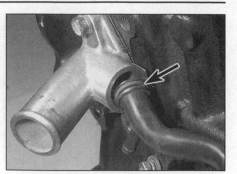

33.55b . . . and a new coolant pipe sealing ring (arrowed)

53 Refit the right-hand mounting plate to the engine, tightening its retaining bolts to the specified torque setting **(see illustration)**.
54 Refit the upper part of the drivebelt cover, renewing any damaged sealing strips and tightening the retaining bolts to the specified torque setting.

All other removed components

55 Refit the coolant pipe to the front of the cylinder block, renewing the pipe sealing ring and gasket **(see illustrations)**.
56 Reconnect the turbocharger oil feed pipe to the cylinder block.
57 Refit the bracket securing bolt situated adjacent to the coolant pipe at the opposite end of the turbocharger.
58 Refit the coolant pipe routed from the thermostat housing to the turbocharger.
59 Refit the dipstick tube into its location in the cylinder block, having renewed its sealing ring.
60 Adjust the injection pump timing if necessary then refit the following ancillary components (if not already done) whilst referring to the appropriate Chapter:

a) *Clutch assembly*
b) *Coolant pump and thermostat*
c) *Oil cooler and thermostat*
d) *Oil filter*
e) *Exhaust manifold and turbocharger*
f) *Inlet manifold*
g) *Fuel injectors*
h) *Glow plugs*
i) *Wiring loom (Cavalier)*
j) *Auxiliary drivebelts*

61 The crankshaft pulley and alternator are best left detached until after the engine has been refitted.

34 Engine/transmission - reconnection

1 If the clutch has been disturbed, make sure that the driven plate is centralised **(see illustration)**.
2 Offer the gearbox to the engine, twisting it back and forth slightly so that the splines on the input shaft enter the clutch driven plate. Do

not allow the weight of the gearbox to hang on the input shaft.
3 Engage the gearbox with the dowels on the engine. Fit and tighten the engine-to-gearbox bolts, remembering that they are of differing lengths and must be refitted in their previously noted positions. Remember also to position the cable clamps, etc. beneath the bolt heads.
4 Refit the cover plate to the bottom of the bellhousing.
5 Refit the starter motor.

35 Engine/transmission - refitting

> ⚠ **Warning: Do not attempt to fit the engine/transmission on your own, a minimum of two people will be required**

Note: *The procedure described in this Section relates to one particular vehicle, therefore allowances must be made for individual model and year variations. Reference to the under-bonnet views contained in Chapter 2 will show detail differences of hose and cable routing etc.*
Note illustrations: *When carrying out the procedures detailed in this Section, refer to the illustrations shown for removal of the engine/transmission.*
1 A minimum of two people will be required to carry out this operation. One person should operate the lifting tackle whilst the other guides the unit into place and keeps watch for

fouling. Raise and support the front of the vehicle and remove the front wheels.
2 The engine/transmission must be lowered into the engine bay at an angle of approximately 30° with the timing side uppermost, so it is advisable to have the lifting slings at differing lengths to achieve this **(see illustration)**.
3 Carefully lower the unit into the engine bay until it connects with its right-hand mounting. At this point, insert the right-hand driveshaft into the transmission whilst ensuring that the other is clear. Make sure that the shaft retaining ring is correctly fitted and engages inside the transmission.
4 Reassemble the right-hand mounting to locate the engine/transmission, tightening all bolts finger-tight only, then reposition the unit so that it is level.
5 Refit the remaining mounting assemblies to the engine/transmission and bodyframe. Some lifting and lowering of the unit will be necessary before all the bolts will go in. Do not tighten the bolts fully until all the mountings are fitted and then tighten to the specified torque settings.
6 Remove the engine lifting tackle.
7 Insert the left-hand driveshaft into the transmission, the wheel hub with shaft will have to be pulled away from the engine/transmission to achieve this. Make sure that the shaft retaining ring is correctly fitted and engages inside the transmission.
8 Reconnect and secure the front suspension bottom balljoints. Do not forget the split pins or spring clips which secure the balljoint nuts.

34.1 Using a socket and extension to centralise the clutch driven plate

35.2 Lower the engine/transmission unit into the engine bay at an angle

9 Reconnect the earth strap to the left-hand side of the engine/transmission.

10 Reconnect and adjust the gearchange linkage. Refer to the appropriate Manual for petrol-engined vehicles for adjustment procedures and tighten the linkage securing clamp on completion.

11 Refit the crankshaft pulley and tighten its retaining bolts to the specified torque setting.

12 Refit the alternator and mounting bracket assembly.

13 Refit and tension the alternator drivebelt, referring to Chapter 2.

14 Reconnect the pipe to the bottom of the charge air cooler and turbocharger.

15 Reconnect the exhaust pipe to the turbocharger, using a new flange gasket.

16 Refit both roadwheels and lower the vehicle.

17 Reconnect the clutch cable outer to the gearbox casing bracket and its inner to the operating lever.

18 Reconnect the speedometer cable to the gearbox and tighten the knurled retaining cap.

19 If removed, refit the coolant and power steering reservoirs.

20 Reconnect the coolant hoses at the following components:

a) *Thermostat housing to radiator*
b) *Coolant reservoir to thermostat housing*
c) *Fuel injection pump cold start accelerator (2 hoses)*
d) *Thermostat housing (2 hoses)*

21 Reconnect the throttle cable to the fuel injection pump by connecting its outer to the retaining bracket and clipping its inner to the pump lever.

22 Reconnect the fuel inlet and return unions to the fuel injection pump, having removed any blanking materials.

23 Reconnect the following electrical connections. These appertain to the Cavalier, those for the Astra being similar:

a) *Glow plug feed to bus bar*
b) *Alternator plugs (at front of engine)*
c) *Main loom multiplug (next to the battery)*
d) *Oil pressure switch cable plug (next to the battery)*
e) *Engine loom multiplug (next to the brake servo unit)*

24 Reattach the power steering pump assembly to the engine, taking care not to place any strain on the hoses, then fit and tension its drivebelt, referring to Chapter 2.

25 Reconnect the brake servo to vacuum pump line at the servo unit and pump. Refit the line retaining clamps.

26 Refit the cable-ties to the rear of the inlet manifold.

27 Refit the charge air cooler to inlet manifold hose by connecting the following:

a) *The hose securing clamp at the charge air cooler*
b) *The single mounting bolt on the side of the cylinder head*
c) *The two bolts at the filter casing*

28 Refit the air filter element into its housing and place the housing and hose assembly on the manifold, retaining it with the four bolts.

29 Refit the filter housing to turbocharger feed hose by connecting the following:

a) *The two mounting bracket bolts supporting the centre section of feed hose*
b) *The feed hose to turbocharger securing clamp*
c) *The feed hose to cylinder head cover breather pipe clip*

30 Refit the air inlet collector box to its mounting on the right-hand side of the engine bay.

31 Reconnect the coolant hose assembly to the base of the coolant reservoir then to the cylinder block and radiator. Secure the assembly to the front of the cylinder head with the two nuts.

32 Reattach the top left-hand hose to the coolant reservoir.

33 Remove any protection placed over the exposed section of radiator matrix.

34 Methodically work around the engine bay, ensuring that all hoses, cables, etc. are correctly routed, clear of hot or moving parts and free of any strain. Replace any cable-ties cut during removal. Check that nothing has been overlooked

35 Refer to Chapter 2 and refill the cooling system.

36 Refer to Chapter 2 and refill the engine with oil.

37 Check the gearbox oil level and top-up if necessary.

38 Reconnect the battery earth lead.

39 Run the engine, referring first to the following Section.

36 Engine - initial start-up after overhaul

1 Make sure that there is sufficient clean fuel in the tank, that the battery is well charged and that all lubricants and fluids have been replenished.

2 A good deal of cranking on the starter motor may be required to prime the fuel system (it is self-bleeding). Do not operate the starter for more than 10 seconds at a time, then pause for a similar period to allow the battery and starter motor to recover.

3 As soon as the engine is running, check that the oil pressure light has gone out. This will take a few seconds.

4 Check for leaks of oil, coolant and fuel. Be prepared for some smoke and fumes as assembly lubricant burns off.

5 Allow the engine to reach operating temperature, then adjust the idle speed.

6 Stop the engine and check for leaks.

7 Check engine oil and coolant levels and top-up if necessary. Take precautions against scalding if the engine is still hot.

8 Road test the vehicle to check that the engine is performing acceptably.

9 If new bearings and/or pistons have been fitted, the engine should be run in at reduced speed and load for the first 600 miles (1000 km) or so. Change the engine oil and filter after this mileage.

3D

Notes

Chapter 4 Part A:
Fuel/exhaust systems - 15D & 15DT engines

Contents

Degrees of difficulty

Easy, suitable for novice with little experience	**Fairly easy,** suitable for beginner with some experience	**Fairly difficult,** suitable for competent DIY mechanic	**Difficult,** suitable for experienced DIY mechanic	**Very difficult,** suitable for expert DIY or professional

Specifications

General

System type	Rear-mounted fuel tank, combined lift and injection pump, self-pumping system
Firing order	1-3-4-2 (No 1 at pulley end)
Air filter type	Champion U641
Fuel filter type	Champion L111

Fuel

Fuel type	Commercial diesel fuel (DERV)
Tank capacity	46 litres (10.1 gallons)

Injection pump

Manufacturer identification:	
Bosch no:	
15D engine	8 970 786 380 VE R 284
15DT engine	8 970 786 390 VE R 305
Drive	From camshaft drivebelt

Injectors

Type	2 jet - Pintaux
Identification	NP - DN OPD N 108
Opening pressure	142 to 162 bar

Adjustment data

Idle speed	830 to 930 rpm
Maximum speed:	
15D engine	5800 rpm
15DT engine	5600 rpm
Pump timing setting:	
15D engine	0.85 to 0.95 mm
15DT engine	0.63 to 0.73 mm

4A

Torque wrench settings

	Nm	lbf ft
Fuel injection pump		
Fuel lines to pump	25	18
Pump to cylinder block/flange	25	18
Pump to bracket	40	30
Sprocket to pump	64	47
Central vent bolt	20	15
Fuel injectors		
Injector holder to cylinder head	50	38
Injector nozzle union nut to nozzle	50	38
Injector nozzle to holder	45	33
Fuel line to nozzle	25	18
Return line to injector nozzle holder	30	22
Manifolds - 15D engine		
Inlet manifold to cylinder head	25	18
Exhaust manifold to cylinder head	30	22
Exhaust manifold to pipe	25	18
Manifolds - 15DT engine		
Inlet manifold to cylinder head	25	18
Charge air safety valve to inlet manifold	50	38
Charge air pipe to inlet manifold	20	15
Exhaust manifold to cylinder head	30	22
Heat shield to exhaust manifold	10	7
Turbocharger - 15DT engine		
Turbocharger to exhaust manifold	30	22
Turbocharger to exhaust pipe	65	47
Heat shield to turbocharger	10	7

1 General information and precautions

General information

The fuel and exhaust systems fitted to the 15D and 15DT engines follow normal practice for modern passenger diesel vehicles. A combined lift and injection pump, driven from the camshaft drivebelt, draws fuel from the tank and distributes it to each cylinder in turn. The injectors deliver a high pressure spray of fuel into the swirl chambers, where combustion starts. On the 15DT engine, this fuel spray is accompanied by pressurised air supplied by a turbocharger. Excess fuel from the pump and the injectors is returned to the tank. A filter, which also acts as a water trap, protects the pump from contaminated fuel.

Cold starting is assisted by pre-heating the combustion chambers electrically. This system is automatically controlled. A thermostatically-controlled cold start accelerator device attached to the side of the injection pump and interconnected to the engine cooling system, causes the pump to deliver extra fuel and alters the injection timing slightly to improve cold start performance.

Manual bleeding or venting of the fuel system is not necessary, even if the fuel tank is run dry. Provided that the battery is in good condition, simply cranking the engine on the starter motor will eventually bleed the system.

Note that the starter motor should not be operated for more than ten seconds at a time whilst allowing five seconds between periods of operation.

The fuel injection system is inherently robust and reliable. If the specified maintenance is carried out conscientiously it should give little trouble. Some components can only be overhauled or repaired by specialists and the home mechanic is warned against attempting operations beyond those described in this Chapter, unless qualified to do so.

Turbocharger - 15DT engine

The turbocharger, fitted as standard to the 15DT engine, enables the engine to produce appreciably greater power and torque than the normally-aspirated 15D unit.

Mounted between the exhaust manifold and front exhaust pipe, and driven by the exhaust gases, the turbocharger takes its air supply from the filter housing, through a plenum chamber and passes air under pressure to the inlet manifold.

Lubrication for the turbocharger is provided by a dedicated oil supply. The turbocharger has an integral wastegate valve and vacuum actuator diaphragm, which is used to control the boost pressure applied to the inlet manifold.

Catalytic converter - function

Refer to the information in Chapter 4D.

Precautions

Refer to the information in Chapter 4D.

2 Fuel system - contamination

Refer to Section 2, Chapter 4B.

3 Air filter - element renewal

Refer to the appropriate Section of Chapter 2.

4 Air cleaner housing - removal and refitting

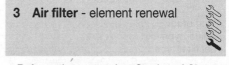

Removal

1 The air cleaner housing is mounted on the right-hand side of the engine bay.

2 To remove the housing, first detach the outlet tube retaining clamp at the engine manifold **(see illustration)**.

3 Release the housing inlet scoop from the vehicle front crossmember and manoeuvre it clear of the housing

4 Disconnect the front retainer at the housing base and pull the housing forward to release it from its rear retainer.

Refitting

5 Refitting is a reversal of removal.

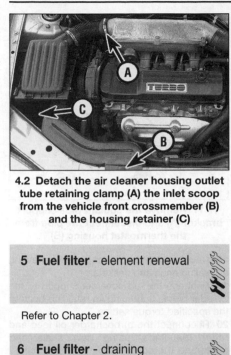

4.2 Detach the air cleaner housing outlet tube retaining clamp (A) the inlet scoop from the vehicle front crossmember (B) and the housing retainer (C)

5 Fuel filter - element renewal

Refer to Chapter 2.

6 Fuel filter - draining

Refer to Chapter 2.

7 Fuel filter heating element - location and renewal

Refer to Section 7, Chapter 4D.

8 Idle speed - checking and adjustment

Refer to Chapter 2.

9 Maximum speed - checking and adjustment

Refer to Section 9, Chapter 4D and the *Specifications* of this Chapter.

10 Cold start acceleration - checking and adjustment

Refer to Section 10, Chapter 4D.

11 Fuel injection pump timing - checking and adjustment

Refer to Section 11, Chapter 4D and the *Specifications* of this Chapter.

12 Fuel injection pump - removal, overhaul and refitting

1 Refer to Section 12, Chapter 4D and the *Specifications* of this Chapter.
2 Where the injection pump has an EGR system vacuum regulator valve, the valve setting must be checked and, if necessary, adjusted whenever the pump is disturbed. The same applies if a new valve is fitted.
3 Checking and adjustment of the vacuum regulator valve is only possible if a hand-operated vacuum pump/gauge is available. At the time of writing, no information was available for valve adjustment. Before carrying out any work on the fuel injection pump, seek advice from a Vauxhall/Opel dealer.

13 Idle stop solenoid - removal and refitting

Refer to Section 13, Chapter 4D.

14 Fuel injectors - removal, overhaul and refitting

Refer to Section 14, Chapter 4D and the *Specifications* of this Chapter.

15 Throttle cable - removal and refitting

This procedure is similar to that given in Section 13, Chapter 4B. Ignore any references to a throttle damper.

16 Fuel tank - removal and refitting

Refer to Section 16, Chapter 4D.

17 Turbocharger - removal and refitting (15DT engine)

Caution: Never run the engine with the turbocharger air inlet hose disconnected. Depression at the inlet can build up very suddenly if the engine speed is raised, increasing the risk of foreign objects being sucked in and ejected at very high speed.

Note: *Before removing the turbocharger, prevent the ingress of dirt by cleaning the area around all unions before disconnection. Store dismantled components in a sealed container to prevent contamination. Cover the turbocharger air inlet ducts to prevent debris entering and clean with lint-free cloth only.*

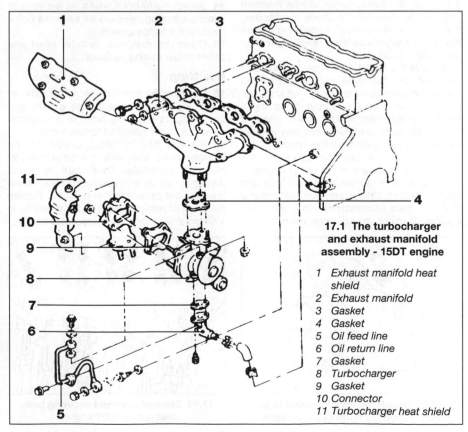

17.1 The turbocharger and exhaust manifold assembly - 15DT engine

1 *Exhaust manifold heat shield*
2 *Exhaust manifold*
3 *Gasket*
4 *Gasket*
5 *Oil feed line*
6 *Oil return line*
7 *Gasket*
8 *Turbocharger*
9 *Gasket*
10 *Connector*
11 *Turbocharger heat shield*

4A

17.5 Remove the plenum chamber to turbocharger feed hose (A) and the turbocharger to inlet manifold hose (B)

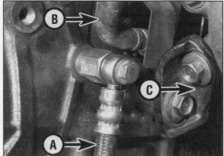

17.9 The turbocharger oil feed pipe (A) oil return pipe (B) and support bracket (C)

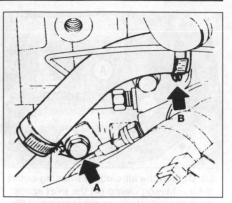

17.11 Remove the coolant pipe support bracket (A) and disconnect the pipe from the thermostat housing (B)

Note: *If the wastegate vacuum unit is damaged, then the complete turbocharger unit must be replaced.*

Removal

1 With the engine in the vehicle, it is recommended that the turbocharger and exhaust manifold are removed as one assembly **(see illustration)**.

2 Disconnect the battery earth lead.

3 Remove the air cleaner housing inlet pipe.

4 Refer to Chapter 6 and remove the cooling fan assembly.

5 Remove the plenum chamber to turbocharger feed hose by disconnecting it from the cylinder head cover, the centre section support, the plenum chamber and the turbocharger **(see illustration)**.

6 Remove the turbocharger to inlet manifold hose located beneath the above by unbolting it from the inlet manifold, unclipping it from the turbocharger and then releasing it from the cylinder head.

7 Remove the heat shields from the exhaust manifold and turbocharger. Note that the special insulating washers are retained on each of the shield securing bolts by a retaining plate which should stay in place as long as the bolts are unscrewed only enough for them to disengage from the manifold.

8 Disconnect the exhaust downpipe from the turbocharger and recover the flange gasket.

9 Disconnect the turbocharger oil feed and return pipelines, catching any escaping oil in a drip tray **(see illustration)**. Note the fitted position of any seals and renew them.

10 Unbolt the turbocharger support from the cylinder block.

11 Remove the coolant pipe support bracket from the cylinder head and disconnect the pipe from the thermostat housing, catching any escaping coolant in a drip tray **(see illustration)**.

12 Unbolt the lower coolant hose connection from the cylinder block and detach it from the pipe end, catching any escaping coolant **(see illustration)**.

13 Remove the exhaust manifold securing bolts and nuts, loosening them a little at a time at first whilst working in a diagonal sequence **(see illustration)**. Pull the manifold forwards to clear the cylinder head and lift the turbocharger/manifold assembly out of the engine bay. Recover the manifold gasket.

14 Detach the turbocharger from the exhaust manifold, having released its securing bolts. Recover the flange gasket.

15 Clean the manifold, cylinder head and turbocharger mating surfaces.

Refitting

16 Reattach the turbocharger to the exhaust manifold, fitting a new flange gasket and tightening its securing bolts in a diagonal sequence to the specified torque setting.

17 Place a new manifold gasket on the cylinder head and refit the turbocharger/ manifold assembly. Take care to avoid damaging any oil and coolant pipelines when lowering the assembly into position. Tighten the manifold retaining bolts and nuts evenly, in a diagonal sequence, to the specified torque.

18 Reconnect the coolant hoses, renewing all sealing rings and gaskets.

19 Reattach the turbocharger support to the cylinder block, tightening its retaining bolts to the specified torque setting.

20 Reconnect the turbocharger oil feed and return pipelines, using new seals and tightening the connections to the specified torque settings.

21 Refit the exhaust downpipe to the turbocharger, fitting a new flange gasket and tightening its securing bolts to the specified torque setting.

22 Refit both heat shields, tightening their securing bolts to the specified torque setting.

23 Refit the turbocharger to inlet manifold hose and the plenum chamber to turbocharger hose.

24 Refer to Chapter 6 and refit the cooling fan assembly.

25 Refit the air cleaner housing inlet pipe.

26 Replenish the engine oil and coolant.

27 Reconnect the battery and start the engine.

28 Check all disturbed connections for leaks.

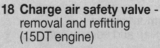

18 Charge air safety valve - removal and refitting (15DT engine)

1 The charge air safety valve is located in the front of the inlet manifold **(see illustration)**.

17.12 Unbolt the lower coolant hose connection from the cylinder block

17.13 Exhaust manifold securing bolts and nuts - 15DT engine

18.1 The charge air safety valve (arrowed)

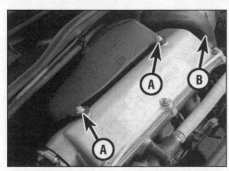

19.2 The air resonator box securing bolts (A) and lower hose clamp (B)

2 To remove the valve, unscrew it from the manifold casing.
3 When fitting the valve, coat its threads with locking compound to GM spec 15 10 177 and tighten it to the specified torque setting.

19 Manifolds - removal and refitting

Inlet manifold

15D engine

1 Disconnect the battery earth lead.
2 Detach the air resonator box from the plenum chamber by removing the lower hose clamp and the box securing bolts **(see illustration)**.
3 Where an EGR system is fitted, remove the valve and pipe assembly from the inlet and exhaust manifolds by removing the pipe flange to exhaust manifold bolts, the pipe to cylinder head support, the vacuum pipe from the valve and the valve to inlet manifold bolts **(see illustrations)**.
4 Detach the air cleaner housing outlet tube from the manifold by releasing its retaining clamp.
5 Detach the cylinder head cover to manifold vent hose **(see illustration)**.
6 Release all cable-ties from the manifold.
7 If fitted, disconnect the manifold heater.
8 Disconnect all remaining hoses from beneath the manifold.
9 Remove the manifold to cylinder head securing bolts and nuts, working in a diagonal sequence **(see illustration)**. Withdraw the manifold and recover the gasket.
10 Clean the manifold and cylinder head mating surfaces.
11 Refitting of the manifold is a reversal of removal.
12 Place a new gasket on the cylinder head and refit the manifold. Tighten the manifold retaining bolts evenly, in a diagonal sequence, to the specified torque setting.
13 Reconnect all disturbed hoses, cable-ties and electrical connections.
14 Reconnect the battery.

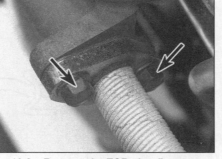

19.3a Remove the EGR pipe flange to exhaust manifold bolts (arrowed) . . .

19.5 Detach the cylinder head cover to manifold vent hose (arrowed)

15DT engine

15 Disconnect the battery earth lead.
16 Remove the hose from between the air cleaner housing and plenum chamber **(see illustration)**.
17 Remove the section of plenum chamber to turbocharger feed hose nearest to the manifold by disconnecting the hose to cylinder head cover breather pipe, the hose to plenum chamber securing clamp and the hose to pipe securing clamp.
18 Unbolt the turbocharger to inlet manifold pipe (located beneath the turbo) from the inlet manifold. Detach the pipe from the side of the cylinder head and ease it clear of the manifold.
19 Release all cable-ties from the manifold.

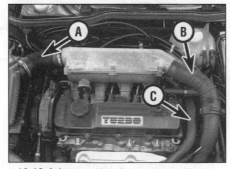

19.16 Inlet manifold hose connections - 15DT engine

A *Air cleaner housing to plenum chamber hose*
B *Plenum chamber to turbocharger feed hose*
C *Turbocharger to inlet manifold pipe*

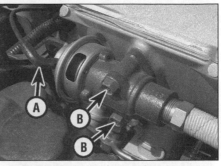

19.3b . . . the EGR valve vacuum pipe (A) and the valve to inlet manifold bolts (B)

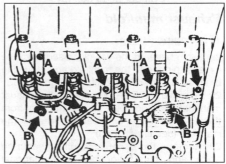

19.9 Remove the inlet manifold securing bolts (A) followed by the outer nuts (B)

20 Disconnect the manifold to fuel injection pump air hose **(see illustration)**.
21 If fitted, disconnect the manifold heater.
22 Remove the manifold to cylinder head securing bolts and nuts (see illustration for 15D engine), working in a diagonal sequence. Withdraw the manifold and recover the gasket.
23 Clean the manifold and cylinder head mating surfaces.
24 Refitting of the manifold is a reversal of removal.
25 Place a new gasket on the cylinder head and refit the manifold. Tighten the manifold retaining bolts evenly, in a diagonal sequence, to the specified torque setting.
26 Reconnect all disturbed hoses, cable-ties and electrical connections, renewing all seals and gaskets.
27 Reconnect the battery.

4A

19.20 Disconnecting the inlet manifold to fuel injection pump hose

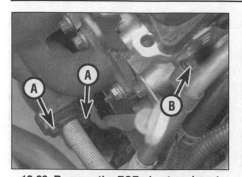

19.29 Remove the EGR pipe to exhaust manifold retaining bolts (A) and pipe to cylinder head bolt (B)

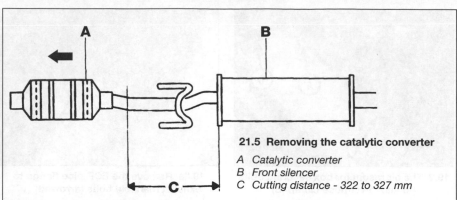

21.5 Removing the catalytic converter

A *Catalytic converter*
B *Front silencer*
C *Cutting distance - 322 to 327 mm*

Exhaust manifold

15D engine

28 From beneath the vehicle, disconnect the exhaust pipe from the manifold and mounting bracket. Recover the manifold flange gasket.
29 Remove the EGR pipe flange to exhaust manifold retaining bolts. Detach the pipe from the cylinder head and ease it free of the manifold **(see illustration)**.
30 Remove the exhaust manifold securing bolts and nuts, working in a diagonal sequence. Pull the manifold forwards to detach it from the cylinder head and lift it clear of the engine. Recover the gasket.
31 Clean the manifold and cylinder head mating surfaces.
32 Refitting is a reversal of removal.
33 Place a new gasket on the cylinder head and refit the manifold. Tighten the manifold retaining nuts and bolts evenly, a little at a time, in a diagonal sequence, to the specified torque setting.
34 Refit the EGR pipe assembly to the manifold and cylinder head, with a new flange gasket. Tighten its bolts to the specified torque.
35 Reconnect the exhaust pipe to the manifold, using a new gasket and tightening its bolts to the specified torque. Reconnect the exhaust pipe to its mounting bracket.

15DT engine

36 With the engine in the vehicle, it is recommended that the exhaust manifold and turbocharger are removed as one assembly. Refer to Section 17 of this Chapter.

20 Exhaust system - inspection

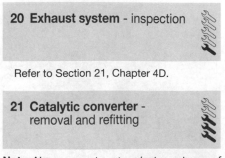

Refer to Section 21, Chapter 4D.

21 Catalytic converter - removal and refitting

Note: *Never use exhaust sealants upstream of a catalytic converter. Where applicable, ensure that the arrow on the converter's body*

points to the rear, in line with the exhaust gas flow. In most cases, a converter will fit correctly only one way, as the front and rear flanges will be either of different sizes or have offset studs to prevent incorrect installation.
Note: *If renewing rubber mountings, ensure the mounting nearest the catalytic converter is of the correct type. Due to the converter's high operating temperatures, this mounting must be of high-temperature resistant material.*

1 Fitted to later 15D engines and all 15DT engines, the catalytic converter is an integral part of the exhaust system and located forward of the front silencer. Individual components of this system can only be removed by cutting the exhaust pipe and then using suitable clamps and sleeves to join the new component to the remainder of the system. Individual component parts of the exhaust system are available from Vauxhall/Opel dealers.
2 It is recommended that renewal of the catalytic converter is entrusted to a Vauxhall/Opel dealer, or exhaust specialist. If you decide to attempt the job, proceed as follows.

3 Ensure the correct replacement parts are obtainable before cutting the system. Service information implies that the converter and front downpipe are supplied as a complete assembly.

Removal

4 To remove the converter with downpipe, first refer to the appropriate Manual for petrol-engined vehicles and remove the complete exhaust system from the vehicle.
5 Position the system on a flat surface and cut the pipe at a point 322 to 327 mm in front of the front silencer, as shown **(see illustration)**. Note the distance between the converter and front silencer.

Refitting

6 To connect the new and existing sections of exhaust system, it is necessary to fabricate a bush from tube which will fit closely inside the exhaust pipe. This bush should be 162 mm long and of 45 mm outside diameter **(see illustration)**.

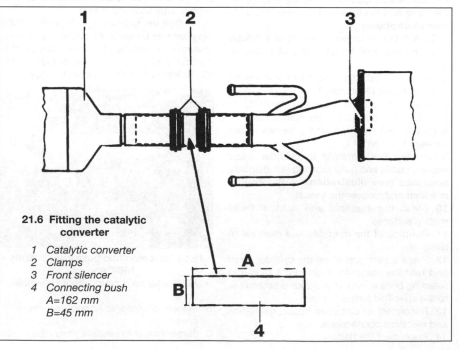

21.6 Fitting the catalytic converter

1 *Catalytic converter*
2 *Clamps*
3 *Front silencer*
4 *Connecting bush*
　 A=162 mm
　 B=45 mm

22.1a The EGR valve

22.1b The thermal-operated vacuum switch (arrowed)

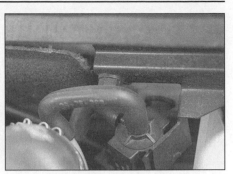

22.1c The vacuum delay valve

7 Clean the mating surfaces of the exhaust system and bush and then assemble the system securing the two ends of pipe to the bush with clamps. The distance between the converter and front silencer should be equal to that noted before the system was cut.

8 Before refitting the exhaust system, inspect all heat shields for damage, cracking and security and renew if necessary.

9 Refer to the appropriate Manual for petrol-engined vehicles and refit the exhaust system to the vehicle.

22 Exhaust gas recirculation (EGR) system - maintenance (15D engine)

Note: *At the time of writing, no service information was available for the EGR system fitted to certain 15D engines. The information contained in this Section is intended only as a guide to component location and inspection. Further information on EGR systems may be gleaned from Part C of this Chapter.*

1 The EGR system comprises the following components:

a) *The EGR valve - mounted on the inlet manifold and connected by a supply pipe to the exhaust manifold* **(see illustration)**.

b) *The Thermal-Operated Vacuum Switch - fitted to the thermostat housing* **(see illustration)**.

c) *The Vacuum Regulator Valve - mounted on the top of the fuel injection pump.*

d) *The Vacuum Delay Valve - fitted in the vacuum line* **(see illustration)**.

2 The system is virtually maintenance-free, the only routine operations necessary are checks for condition and security of the component parts.

3 Whenever the fuel injection pump is removed the vacuum regulator valve setting must be checked and, if necessary, adjusted. Checking and adjustment of the valve is only possible if a hand-operated vacuum pump/gauge is available. At the time of writing, no information was available for valve adjustment. It is therefore recommended that

before carrying out any work on the fuel injection pump, advice is sought from a Vauxhall/Opel dealer.

4 To check the system operation, warm the engine up to normal operating temperature and allow it to idle. Disconnect and reconnect several times the vacuum pipe from the top of the EGR valve. The valve should be heard to operate each time.

5 If the EGR valve does not operate and vacuum can be felt at the pipe end, first check the setting of the vacuum regulator valve.

6 If the vacuum regulator valve is functioning correctly, the fault must be in the EGR valve, which must then be renewed. If the valve is to be renewed, it is always worth first trying the effect of cleaning any carbon build-up from its passages to check whether this is the reason for the failure. If the valve diaphragm has failed, on the other hand, there is no alternative to the renewal of the complete valve unit.

7 If no vacuum can be felt, check back through the system until the leak or blockage is found and rectified.

4A

Chapter 4 Part B:
Fuel/exhaust systems - 16D & 16DA engines

Contents

Degrees of difficulty

Easy, suitable for novice with little experience	Fairly easy, suitable for beginner with some experience	Fairly difficult, suitable for competent DIY mechanic	Difficult, suitable for experienced DIY mechanic	Very difficult, suitable for expert DIY or professional

Specifications

General

System type	Rear-mounted fuel tank, combined lift and injection pump, self-pumping system
Firing order	1-3-4-2 (No 1 at pulley end)
Fuel filter type	Champion L113
Air filter element type	Champion U503

Fuel

Fuel type	Commercial diesel fuel (DERV)
Fuel tank capacity	42 to 61 litres (9.2 to 13.4 gallons) according to model

Injection pump

Manufacturer identification:	
16D engine (early models)	VE 2300 R 82
16D engine (later models)	VE 4/9 F 2400 RTV 8253
16DA engine	VE 4/9 F 2300 R 215
Drive	From camshaft drivebelt
Identification of No 1 cylinder union	D

Injectors

Manufacturer identification:	
16D engine (early models)	DN 05D 193
16D engine (later models)	DN 5D 193
16DA engine	Flat pintle type
Opening pressure:	
16D engine (new)	140 to 148 bar (2030 to 2146 lbf/in2)
16D engine (used)	135 bar (1958 lbf/in2)
16DA engine	135 bar (1958 lbf/in2)

Adjustment data

Idle speed	825 to 875 rpm
Maximum speed	5600 rpm
Injection commencement at idle	3 to 5° BTDC
Pump timing setting:	
16D engine	1.0 ± 0.05 mm
16DA engine	0.9 ± 0.05 mm

4B

Torque wrench settings

	Nm	lbf ft
Injection pump and brackets:		
Main bracket to block	25	18
Subsidiary brackets - M6 bolts	14	10
Subsidiary brackets - M8 bolts	25	18
Pump sprockets bolts	25	18
Injectors to head	70	52
Manifolds to head	22	16

1 General information and precautions

General information

The fuel supply and injection system fitted to the 16D and 16DA engines follows normal practice for modern passenger and light commercial diesel vehicles. A combined lift and injection pump, driven from the camshaft drivebelt, draws fuel from the tank and distributes it to each cylinder in turn. The injectors deliver a high pressure spray of fuel into the swirl chambers, where combustion starts. Excess fuel from the pump and the injectors is returned to the tank. A filter, which also acts as a water trap, protects the pump from contaminated fuel.

Cold starting is assisted by pre-heating the combustion chambers electrically. This system is automatically controlled. A driver-operated cold start control, similar to a manual choke control on petrol engines, causes the pump to deliver extra fuel and alters the injection timing slightly to improve cold start performance.

Unlike some older systems, manual bleeding or venting is not necessary even if the fuel tank is run dry. Provided that the battery is in good condition, simply cranking the engine on the starter motor will eventually bleed the system. Note that the starter motor should not be operated for more than ten seconds at a time whilst allowing five seconds between periods of operation.

The fuel injection system is inherently robust and reliable. If the specified maintenance is carried out conscientiously it should give little trouble. Some components can only be overhauled or repaired by specialists and the home mechanic is warned against attempting operations beyond those described in this Chapter, unless qualified to do so.

Precautions

Fuel - Warning

Many of the procedures given in this Chapter involve the disconnection of fuel pipes and system components which may result in some fuel spillage. Before carrying out any operation on the fuel system, refer to the precautions given in the "Safety first" Section at the beginning of this Manual and follow them implicitly.

Tamperproof adjustment screws - caution

Certain adjustment points in the fuel system are protected by "tamperproof" caps, plugs or seals. The purpose of such tamperproofing is to discourage adjustment by unqualified operators.

In some EEC countries (though not yet in the UK) it is an offence to drive a vehicle with missing or broken tamperproof seals. Before disturbing a tamperproof seal, satisfy yourself that you will not be breaking local or national anti-pollution regulations by doing so. Fit a new seal when adjustment is complete when this is required by law.

Do not break tamperproof seals on a vehicle which is still under warranty.

Working procedures

When working on fuel system components, scrupulous cleanliness must be observed, and care must be taken not to introduce any foreign matter into fuel lines or components. Care should be taken not to disturb any components unnecessarily. Before attempting work, ensure that the relevant spares are available. If persistent problems are encountered, it is recommended that the advice of a Vauxhall/Opel dealer or a specialist is sought.

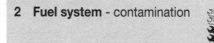

2 Fuel system - contamination

1 If, at any time, sudden fuel filter blockage, poor starting or otherwise unsatisfactory engine performance should be traced to the appearance of black sludge or slime within the fuel system, this may be due to corrosion caused by the presence of various micro-organisms in the fuel. These can live in the fuel tank if water is allowed to remain there in significant quantities, their waste products causing corrosion of steel and other metallic components of the fuel system.

2 If the fuel system is thought to be contaminated in this way, immediately seek the advice of a Vauxhall/Opel dealer or diesel specialist. Thorough treatment is required to cure the problem and to prevent it from occurring again.

3 If you are considering treating the vehicle on a DIY basis proceed as follows. Do not re-use contaminated fuel.

4 First drain and remove the fuel tank, flush it thoroughly with clean diesel fuel and use a torch to examine as much as possible of its interior. If the contamination is severe, the tank must be steam-cleaned internally and then flushed again with clean diesel fuel.

5 Disconnect the fuel feed and return hoses from the injection pump, remove the fuel filter element and flush through the system's feed and return lines with clean diesel fuel.

6 Renew the filter element, refit the fuel tank and reconnect the fuel lines, then fill the tank with clean diesel fuel and bleed the system as described above. Watch carefully for signs of the problem occurring again.

7 While it is unlikely that such contamination will be found beyond the fuel filter, if it is thought to have reached the injection pump, the pump may require cleaning. This is a task only for the Manufacturers agent. Do not attempt to disturb any part of the pump (other than the few adjustments detailed in this Manual) or to clean it yourself.

8 The most common cause of excessive quantities of water being in the fuel is condensation from the water vapour in the air. Diesel tanks (whether underground storage tanks or that in the vehicle) are more susceptible to this problem than petrol tanks because of petrol's higher vapour pressure. Water formation in the vehicle's tank can be minimised by keeping the tank as full as possible at all times and by using the vehicle regularly.

9 Note that proprietary additives are available to inhibit the growth of micro-organisms in vehicle fuel tanks or storage tanks.

10 If you buy all your fuel from the same source and suspect that to be the source of the contamination, the owner or operator should be advised. Otherwise, the risk of taking on contaminated fuel can be minimised by using only reputable filling stations which have a good turnover.

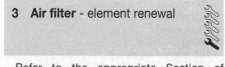

3 Air filter - element renewal

Refer to the appropriate Section of Chapter 2.

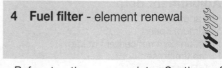

4 Fuel filter - element renewal

Refer to the appropriate Section of Chapter 2.

6.1 Heated fuel filter showing fuel temperature sensor (A) and heater unit (B)

5 Fuel filter - draining

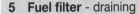

Refer to the appropriate Section of Chapter 2.

6 Heated fuel filter - location and servicing

On some later engines, an electric heating element is fitted between the filter housing and bowl. A sensor monitors the fuel temperature passing through the filter and if this falls to a point where fuel waxing is likely to occur, the heater is switched on to warm the fuel **(see illustration)**.

For most purposes, the filter can be dealt with as described in the appropriate Section of Chapter 2.

7 Idle speed - checking and adjustment

Refer to the appropriate Section of Chapter 2.

8 Maximum speed - checking and adjustment

 Warning: Keep clear of the cooling fan when making adjustments.

16D and early 16DA engines

Checking

1 There should not normally be any need to adjust the maximum speed, except after major component renewal.
2 Refer to Section 7 for ways of measuring engine speed. It is unwise to use the speedometer method, since there is a grave risk of injury or damage should anything go wrong.

3 Start the engine and gradually increase its speed, observing the tachometer or its equivalent until the governed maximum speed is reached. Do not accelerate the engine much beyond the specified maximum, should maladjustment make this possible.

Adjustment

4 If adjustment is necessary, remove the air cleaner snorkel to improve access. Slacken the locknut and turn the maximum speed adjuster screw until the desired result is obtained, then tighten the locknut without moving the screw **(see illustration)**. Refit the snorkel.

Later 16DA engines

Bosch VE fuel injection pump

5 The procedure for adjustment of the maximum speed is the same as described above. Note, however, that these later injection pumps have their maximum speed adjustment screws locked with a lead seal which must be removed for adjustment. As the screw should ideally be resealed after adjustment, it may be beneficial to leave this operation to a Bosch injection specialist **(see illustration)**.

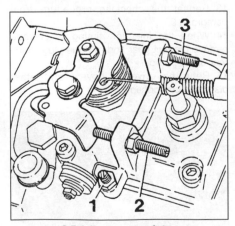

8.5 Adjustment points - Bosch VE injection pump
1 Idle speed adjustment screw
2 Engine speed control lever stop screw - **do not disturb**
3 Maximum speed adjustment screw

8.4 Adjusting the maximum speed

Lucas/CAV fuel injection pump

6 Maximum (cut-off) speed is set in production, using the cut-off speed stop screw **(see illustration)**. The screw is sealed with lead after adjustment has been made. As with all injection pumps it is not normally necessary to disturb the cut-off speed setting in normal circumstances, but if adjustment is necessary, it is recommended that this be carried out by a Lucas/CAV injection specialist.

9 Fuel injection pump timing - checking and adjustment

Checking

1 Timing of the injection pump should only be necessary in the following circumstances:

  a) When fitting a new or overhauled pump
  b) If the timing is suspected of being wrong
  c) If the timing belt has been re-tensioned or renewed

A dial test indicator with a long probe and a suitable support, will be needed.
2 The procedure as shown here was carried out during engine rebuilding. With the engine in the vehicle, it will be necessary to remove the drivebelt covers, the air cleaner snorkel and the clutch/flywheel cover.
3 Check the valve timing.
4 Bring the engine to TDC, No 1 firing. The timing mark on the pump sprocket must be aligned with the pip on the pump bracket **(see illustration)**.
5 Turn the engine against the normal direction of rotation so that the flywheel TDC mark is approximately 5.0 cm away from the TDC pointer.

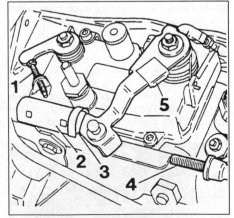

8.6 Adjustment points - Lucas/CAV injection pump
1 Idle speed stop screw
2 Plastic anti-tamper cap
3 Engine speed control lever stop screw - **do not disturb**
4 Cut-off speed stop screw
5 Timing value for individual pump (marked on plate)

4B

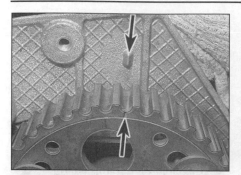

9.4 Injection pump sprocket timing mark aligned with mark on pump bracket

9.6 Removing the plug from the rear of the injection pump

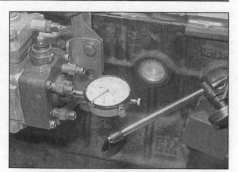

9.7 Dial test indicator mounted with its probe in the plug hole

9.10a Slacken the injection pump sprocket clamping bolts . . .

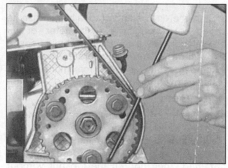

9.10b . . . and use a rod and mallet to move the inner part of the sprocket

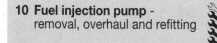

10 Fuel injection pump - removal, overhaul and refitting

6 Remove the central plug from the rear of the injection pump **(see illustration)**.

7 Mount the dial test indicator with its probe entering the central plug hole. Zero the indicator **(see illustration)**.

8 Be prepared for fuel spillage during subsequent operations. The manufacturers specify the use of a probe which screws into, and presumably seals, the plug hole.

9 Bring the engine back to TDC, No 1 firing. When the timing marks are aligned, the dial test indicator should show a lift corresponding to the desired timing setting - see *Specifications*.

Adjustment

10 If adjustment is necessary, slacken the three bolts which clamp together the two halves of the pump sprocket **(see illustration)**. Turn the inner part of the sprocket anti-clockwise (against the normal

direction of rotation) as far as the slots will allow. The fit between the two parts of the sprocket is tight and a rod or soft metal drift may be needed to encourage the inner part to move **(see illustration)**.

11 With the sprocket positioned as just described and the engine still at TDC, No 1 firing, the dial test indicator should again read zero. Reset it if necessary.

12 Turn the inner part of the sprocket clockwise until the dial test indicator shows the desired lift, then tighten the sprocket clamp bolts.

13 Repeat the checking procedure from paragraph 5.

14 When the injection timing is correct, remove the test gear and refit the plug to the rear of the pump.

15 Refit the drivebelt covers and other disturbed components.

Removal

1 Slacken the camshaft drivebelt and slip it off the pump sprocket.

2 If not already done, remove the air cleaner snorkel.

3 Disconnect the fuel feed and return hoses from the pump. Also disconnect the fuel return hose from the T-piece **(see illustrations)**. Be prepared for fuel spillage. Plug or cap the open unions (eg. with polythene and rubber bands) to keep fuel in and dirt out.

4 Clean around the unions, then remove the injection pipes. Do not separate the pipes from their brackets. Again, plug the open unions.

5 Disconnect the lead from the idle stop solenoid.

6 Disconnect the throttle and cold start cables from the pump.

7 Restrain the pump sprocket from turning and remove the central securing nut **(see illustration)**.

8 Remove the sprocket from the pump shaft. The use of a puller is recommended **(see illustration)**. If a "face" puller is used, it will have to be secured with the bolts which clamp the two parts of the sprocket together. If these bolts have been disturbed, the pump timing will have to be reset after refitting. Make

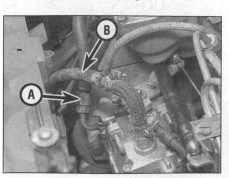

10.3a Fuel pump feed hose (A) and return hose (B) connections

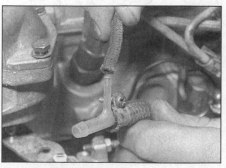

10.3b Disconnecting the injector fuel return hose

10.7 Remove the injection pump sprocket nut . . .

10.8 . . . and use a puller to remove the sprocket . . .

10.9 . . . taking care to retain the Woodruff key (arrowed)

10.10 Removing an injection pump securing bolt

10.12a Injection pump shaft oil seal (arrowed)

10.12b Top view of injection pump showing throttle lever and spring

10.12c Rear view of injection pump. Union D supplies No 1 cylinder. Arrow shows operating sequence

alignment marks between the parts of the sprocket if wished.

9 Recover the Woodruff key from the shaft if it is loose **(see illustration)**.

10 Remove the two bolts which secure the sprocket end of the pump to the bracket. Access to the bolt on the engine side is achieved with a socket and a long extension **(see illustration)**.

11 Remove the two bolts which secure the spring/damper bracket to the fuel pump bracket. Remove the pump complete with subsidiary brackets.

Overhaul

12 Overhaul of the pump by the home mechanic is limited to the renewal of peripheral seals, springs etc **(see illustrations)**. Consult a Vauxhall/Opel dealer first to find out what parts may be available. Many tamperproof seals and "Torx" screws will be observed around the pump, which are intended to discourage or detect unauthorised investigation. Do not break any seals if the pump is under warranty, or if it is hoped to obtain an exchange unit.

13 If a new pump is being fitted, transfer the brackets and other necessary components to it. Do not tighten the bracket bolts yet.

Refitting

14 Refit in the reverse order of removal, noting the following points:

a) *Slacken the subsidiary bracket bolts, then tighten them in the sequence shown (see illustration)*

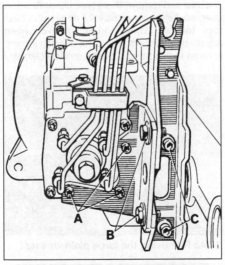

10.14 Injection pump bracket bolts - tighten in sequence A - B - C

b) *Tighten all fastenings to the specified torque, when known*

c) *Check the valve timing*

d) *Check the injection timing if the sprocket was separated, or if a new pump has been fitted*

15 A good deal of cranking on the starter motor will be required to prime the pump before the engine will run. Do not operate the starter for more than 10 seconds at a time, then pause for a 5 second period to allow the battery and starter motor to recover.

16 Check all fuel unions for leaks when the engine is running, and again when it has been stopped.

11 Idle stop solenoid - removal and refitting

1 The idle stop solenoid is energised all the time the engine is running. When the "ignition" is switched off, the solenoid cuts off the fuel supply at the pump and the engine stops.

Removal

2 To remove the solenoid, first disconnect the battery earth lead.

3 Disconnect the electrical lead from the screw terminal on top of the solenoid **(see illustration)**.

4B

11.3 Idle stop solenoid terminal (arrowed)

11.5 Idle stop solenoid, O-ring, spring and plunger

4 Clean around the solenoid, then unscrew it from the pump.

5 Recover the O-ring, spring and plunger **(see illustration)**. Cover the pump orifice to keep dirt out.

Refitting

6 Commence refitting by inserting the plunger and spring into the orifice **(see illustration)**.

7 Fit and tighten the solenoid, using a new O-ring. Do not overtighten.

8 Reconnect the solenoid and the battery.

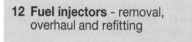

12 Fuel injectors - removal, overhaul and refitting

Warning: Exercise extreme caution when working on the fuel injectors. Never expose the hands or any part of the body to

12.3 Removing a fuel injector

12.4b . . . and the small corrugated washer

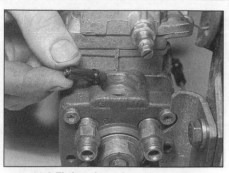

11.6 Fitting the solenoid plunger and spring

injector spray, as working pressure can cause the fuel to penetrate the skin with possibly fatal results. You are strongly advised to have any work which involves testing the injectors under pressure carried out by a Vauxhall/Opel dealer or fuel injection specialist.

Removal

1 Where necessary, remove the air cleaner snorkel.

2 Clean around the unions, then remove the injection pipes from the injectors and fuel pump. Plug or cap the open unions on the pump. Also remove the fuel return hoses from the injectors. Be prepared for fuel spillage.

3 Clean around the bases of the injectors, then unscrew and remove them **(see illustration)**. A deep socket spanner, size 27 mm, is the best tool to use. Open-ended, ring or even adjustable spanners may do at a pinch if there is room to use them. On later models (January

12.4a Removing the large plain washer . . .

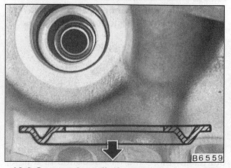

12.6 Correct installation of injector small washer - arrow points to cylinder head

---

1987 on), due to the alteration of the location of the crankcase vent hose connection, access to No 2 cylinder fuel injector is restricted. If a socket wrench is used, its diameter may require reducing by grinding.

4 Recover the injector washers. There are two per injector - the large one seals the injector carrier-to-head joint, the small one seals the injector tip **(see illustrations)**. Obtain new washers for reassembly.

Overhaul

5 Injectors can be overhauled, but this is not a DIY job. Consult a Vauxhall/Opel dealer or other reputable specialist.

Refitting

6 Commence refitting by inserting the small washers. Note that they must be fitted the right way up, as shown **(see illustration)**.

7 Fit the large washers, either way up, then screw in the injectors. Tighten the injectors to the specified torque.

8 Refit the return hoses and the injection pipes.

9 Run the engine and check that there are no leaks at the pipe unions. Check again with the engine stopped.

---

13 Throttle cable - removal and refitting

Removal

1 Prise the cable inner ball end fitting off its stud on the pump throttle lever **(see illustration)**. Access is tight and will be improved by removing the throttle damper which is secured by similar ball and socket fittings.

2 Free the cable outer grommet from the bracket on the pump **(see illustration)**.

3 Inside the vehicle, compress the spring and release the cable from the keyhole fitting on the pedal arm **(see illustration)**.

4 Free the cable from any clips or ties and remove it from under the bonnet.

13.1 Throttle cable ball end fitting (arrowed) next to throttle damper

13.2 Throttle cable outer grommet (arrowed) next to the other end of the throttle damper

13.3 Throttle cable fitting at pedal end

14.1a Cold start cable - spring clip arrowed

Refitting

5 Refit in the reverse order of removal. Adjust the position of the clip on the pump end of the cable outer so with the pedal released, there is a small amount of slack in the cable inner.

6 Remember to refit the throttle damper if it was removed.

14 Cold start cable -
removal and refitting

14.1b Close-up showing detail of spring clip

15.2a Fuel tank vent hoses

Removal

1 Free the cable inner at the pump end by releasing the spring clip which links it to the operating rod. Access is poor, but it is possible to release the clip by feel **(see illustrations)**.

2 Remove the clip which secures the cable outer grommet in its bracket.

3 Inside the vehicle, remove the cold start control knob by pressing out its roll pin. Undo the nut which secures the cable outer to the facia panel.

4 Withdraw the cable into the vehicle, removing additional interior trim if necessary. Refer to the appropriate Manual for petrol-engined models.

Refitting

5 Refit in the reverse order of removal. There is no provision for cable adjustment.

15 Fuel tank -
removal and refitting

1 This procedure is essentially the same as given in the Manual for petrol-engined vehicles, with the bonus that it is much less dangerous. The following points are also to be noted.

2 Inspect the vent hoses closely **(see illustration)** and renew them if they have become porous or are in any way suspect. It is possible for water to enter the tank through deteriorated vent hoses. It is important that the vent hose which carries the water deflector is correctly fitted. The hose should

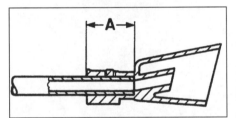

15.2b Vent hose correctly fitted into water deflector
A = at least 22.0 mm

be inserted into the water deflector as shown **(see illustration)**. Failure to do this could cause collapse of the fuel tank under certain conditions.

3 Do not confuse the fuel flow (suction) and return connections. From 1984 model year, the flow connection on the tank is marked with a blue sleeve and the flow pipe is coloured blue. In case of doubt, note that the flow connection is nearest the centre-line of the vehicle, while the return connection is nearer the right-hand side **(see illustration)**.

16 Manifolds -
removal and refitting

Inlet manifold

1 Disconnect the battery earth lead.
2 Remove the air cleaner.
3 Disconnect the breather hose from the

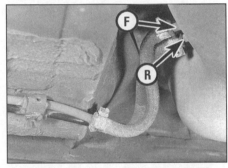

15.3 Fuel tank flow (F) and return (R) connections

camshaft cover. Note that the other end of this hose is attached to a distribution tube inside the manifold.

4 Remove the bolts which secure the inlet-to-exhaust manifold link. Recover the link and the clutch cable bracket **(see illustration)**.

4B

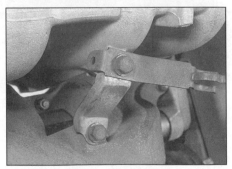

16.4 Manifold link and clutch cable bracket

16.5 Inlet manifold removal leaving gasket

16.9 Removing the exhaust manifold

16.10 New gasket fitted to exhaust downpipe flange

5 Remove the five nuts which secure the manifold to the head. Withdraw the manifold and recover the gasket **(see illustration)**.

6 Refit in the reverse order of removal. Use a new gasket and tighten the nuts evenly to the specified torque. Do not forget the clutch cable bracket.

Exhaust manifold

7 Remove the inlet manifold.

8 Remove the exhaust downpipe and recover the flange gasket.

9 Remove the seven nuts which secure the manifold to the head. Withdraw the manifold and recover the gasket **(see illustration)**.

10 Use new gaskets on both joints when refitting and apply some anti-seize compound to the stud threads **(see illustration)**.

11 Tighten the manifold-to-head nuts evenly to the specified torque, then refit the exhaust downpipe.

12 Refit the inlet manifold.

17 Exhaust system - inspection

1 Inspect the system periodically for leaks, corrosion and other damage, and check the security and condition of the mountings. Small leaks are more easily detected if an assistant partly obstructs the tailpipe with a wad of cloth whilst the engine is idling.

2 Proprietary pastes and bandages are available for the repair of holes and splits. They work well in the short term, but renewal of the section concerned will probably prove more satisfactory in the long run.

3 The rubber mountings will crack and split eventually, and should then be renewed. It is sound practice to renew the mountings when renewing other parts of the system.

Chapter 4 Part C: Fuel/exhaust systems - 17D, 17DR & 17DTL engines

Contents

Degrees of difficulty

Easy, suitable for novice with little experience		**Fairly easy,** suitable for beginner with some experience		**Fairly difficult,** suitable for competent DIY mechanic		**Difficult,** suitable for experienced DIY mechanic		**Very difficult,** suitable for expert DIY or professional	

Specifications

General

System type .... Rear-mounted fuel tank, combined lift and injection pump, self-pumping system

Firing order .... 1-3-4-2 (No 1 at pulley end)

Air filter type:
   Astra 1988 to 1991, and Astramax .... Champion U558
   Astra from 1991 .... Champion U599
   Astra with 17DTL engine .... Champion U548
   Cavalier from 1988 .... Champion U554

Fuel filter type:
   Cavalier from 1988, and Astra to 1991 .... Champion L113
   Astra from 1991, and Astramax .... Champion L111
   Astra with 17DTL engine .... Champion L111

Fuel

Fuel type .... Commercial fuel (DERV)

Fuel tank capacity:
   Astra and Cavalier (non turbocharged) .... 42 to 61 litres (9.2 to 13.4 gallons) according to model
   Astra with 17DTL engine
     Saloon .... 52 litres (11.4 gallons)
     Estate .... 50 litres (11.0 gallons)

Injection pump

Manufacturer identification:
   Bosch:
     1989 model year .... VE 4/9F 2300 R 313 MT or VE 4/9F 2300 R 313 - 1 AT
     1991/ 1992 model year .... VE 4/9F 2300 R 443
     1993 model year .... VE 4/9F 2300 R 487
   Lucas/CAV:
     1989 model year .... OP 02 DPC R8443 B55 OA
     1991/ 1992 model year .... OP 02 DPC R8443 B55 OA
     1993 model year .... OP 03 DPC R8443 B85 OC

Drive .... From camshaft drivebelt
Identification of No 1 cylinder union .... D

4C

Injectors

Manufacturer identification:
Bosch .... DN OSD 309
Lucas/CAV .... BDN OSD C 6751 D or RDN OSD C 6751 D
Opening pressure (Bosch and Lucas/CAV):
New .... 135 to 143 bar (1958 to 2073.5 lbf/in2)
Used .... 130 to 138 bar (1885 to 2001 lbf/in2)

Adjustment data

Idle speed:
17D engine .... 820 to 920 rpm
17DR and 17DTL engines:
Below 20°C .... 1200 rpm
Above 20°C .... 850 rpm
Maximum speed .... 5500 to 5600 rpm
Injection commencement at idle .... 2° to 4° BTDC
Pump timing setting:
Bosch .... 0.80 + 0.05 mm
Lucas/CAV .... X - 0.15 mm *(where X = manufacturer's calibration marked on pump)*

Torque wrench settings

	Nm	lbf ft
Air filter		
Filter outlet to inlet manifold	8	6
Fuel filter		
Filter to support bracket	25	18
Fuel line to filter	30	22
Thermoswitch to filter	15	11
Fuel injection pump		
Fuel lines to pump	25	18
Hub to pump	25	18
Sprocket to hub	25	18
Pump to bracket(s)	25	18
Pump to support - M6 bolts	12	9
Vent bolt to pump	25	18
Fuel injectors		
Injector holder to cylinder head	70	52
Injector holder assembly	80	60
EGR system		
Corrugated pipe clamp	4.8	3
Corrugated pipe to exhaust manifold	8	6
Valve to inlet manifold	20	15
Turbocharger		
Turbocharger to exhaust manifold	30	22
Turbocharger support to exhaust manifold	25	18
Turbocharger support to cylinder block	51	38
Turbocharger to exhaust pipe	67	48
Heat shield to turbocharger	8	6
Oil feed line to turbocharger	30	22
Oil return line to turbocharger	20	15
Manifolds		
Inlet manifold to cylinder head	22	16
Safety valve to inlet manifold	49	37
*Exhaust manifold to cylinder head:		
17D, 17DR engines	22	16
17DTL engine	38	30
Exhaust manifold to heat shield	8	6
Exhaust manifold to pipe	25	18
Catalytic converter		
Converter to front exhaust pipe	25	18
Converter to exhaust silencer	25	18
Heat shield to underbody	2	1.5

1 General information and precautions

General information and precautions

The fuel system fitted to the engines covered in this Chapter remains largely unchanged from that described in Chapter 4B, for the 16D and 16DA engines, and the *General information and precautions* listed in the said Chapter are still relevant. However, there are modifications and additions to the system which are described in detail below.

Fuel system faults - general checks

On the fuel system fitted to 17D and 17DR engines, there have been a number of cases where system faults have been incorrectly attributed to injection pump failures, when the real problem was due to leaks in the system in general. In most instances this has become apparent on models fitted with Lucas/CAV injection pumps, but the general checks described here can be applied equally to Bosch-equipped models.

In cases where general rough running or engine misfiring is occurring, check that loose or damaged fuel lines or connections are not allowing air to enter the fuel system. This is most easily done with the vehicle raised on a ramp or axle stands to permit visual inspection of the entire fuel system. Apply low air pressure to the fuel tank. The manufacturer offers no suggestions as to how this might be achieved but one method would be to seal the fuel tank filler then connect a footpump to one of the breather pipe stubs on the fuel tank. Apply gentle pressure to the system, and check carefully for signs of leakage.

Any leakage of fuel discovered should be investigated and the fault rectified. Since the fuel flow line is under slight negative pressure in normal use, fuel leakage while the system is under pressure is likely to equate with air bubbles being drawn into the fuel being delivered to the pump during normal operation. It is also worth remembering that a loose connection on the line from the tank to the pump could also allow surface water to be drawn into the system - check for this if the filter has shown signs of unusually high water contamination.

Exhaust gas recirculation (EGR) system

Fitted to the 17DR and 17DTL engines, the vacuum-operated EGR system reintroduces small amounts of exhaust gas into the combustion cycle so as to reduce the generation of harmful exhaust pollutants.

The system is operational at temperatures above approximately 20°C (68°F) and when the engine is in the idle or part-load mode. A thermo-switch screwed into the thermostat housing operating, in conjunction with a vacuum switch on the injection pump, controls the supply of vacuum to the system components. The vacuum supply is provided by an additional take-off from the vacuum pump. In addition, the thermo-switch also controls the vacuum supplied to the cold start device.

The volume of exhaust gas reintroduced is controlled by the EGR valve mounted on the inlet manifold. When vacuum is supplied to the valve, the diaphragm inside is deflected and a bypass to the exhaust manifold is opened. Exhaust gases are then allowed into the inlet manifold via a corrugated pipe connected between the exhaust and inlet manifolds.

Low pressure turbocharger

Fitted to the 17DTL engine (Astra only), the low pressure turbocharger enables the engine to produce appreciably greater power and torque than its normally-aspirated predecessors.

Mounted between the exhaust manifold and front exhaust pipe, and driven by the exhaust gases, the turbocharger takes its air supply from the filter housing and passes air under pressure to the inlet manifold via a charge air cooler (CAC) which is mounted on the left-hand side of the radiator.

Lubrication for the turbocharger is provided by a dedicated oil supply pipe that runs from the cylinder block. Oil is returned to the sump.

The turbocharger has an integral wastegate valve and vacuum actuator diaphragm, which is used to control the boost pressure applied to the inlet manifold.

The internal components of a turbocharger rotate at very high speed and as such are very sensitive to contamination. A great deal of damage can be caused by small particles of dirt, particularly if they strike the delicate turbine blades. To prevent the ingress of dirt during maintenance, thoroughly clean the area around all connections before disturbing them. Always store dismantled components in a sealed container to prevent contamination. Cover the turbocharger air inlet ducts to prevent the ingress of debris and use lint-free cloths only when cleaning.

Never run the engine with the turbocharger air inlet hose disconnected. Depression at the inlet can build up very suddenly if the engine speed is raised, thereby increasing the risk of foreign objects being sucked in and ejected at very high speed.

Catalytic converter

The exhaust gases of any internal combustion engine (however efficient or well-tuned) which burns hydrocarbon-based fuel consist largely (approximately 99%) of nitrogen (N_2), carbon dioxide (CO_2), oxygen (O_2) and other inert gases and water vapour (H_2O). The remaining 1% is made up of the noxious materials which are currently seen (CO_2) as the major polluters of the environment, ie. carbon monoxide (CO), unburned hydrocarbons (HC), oxides of nitrogen (NO_X) and some solid matter, including a small lead content.

Left to themselves, most of these pollutants are thought eventually to break down naturally (CO and NO_X, for example, break down in the upper atmosphere to release CO_2) having first caused ground-level environmental problems, but the massive increase world-wide in the use of vehicles and the current popular concern for the environment has caused the introduction in most countries of legislation, in varying stages of severity, to combat the problem.

The device most commonly used to clean up vehicle exhausts is the catalytic converter. It is fitted into the vehicle's exhaust system and consists of an element (or substrate) of ceramic honeycomb coated with a combination of precious metals in such a way as to produce a vast surface area over which the exhaust gases must flow; the whole being mounted in a stainless-steel box. The simple oxidation (or two-way) catalytic converter fitted to diesel engines uses platinum and palladium as catalysts to speed up the reaction between the pollutants and the oxygen in the vehicle's exhaust gases, CO and HC being oxidised to form H_2O and CO_2. Note that the catalytic converter is not a filter in the physical sense; its function is to promote a chemical reaction, but it is not itself affected by that reaction.

The catalytic converter is a reliable and simple device which needs no maintenance in itself, but there are some facts of which an owner should be aware if the converter is to function properly for its full service life:

a) *There is no need to worry about using leaded/unleaded fuel in a vehicle equipped with a catalytic converter and a diesel engine - no diesel fuel has added lead.*

b) *Always keep the fuel system well-maintained in accordance with the manufacturer's schedule. Ensure that the air cleaner filter element and the fuel filter are renewed at the correct intervals. If the inlet air/fuel mixture is allowed to become too rich due to neglect, the unburned surplus will enter and burn in the catalytic converter, overheating the element and eventually destroying the converter.*

c) *If the engine develops a misfire, do not drive the vehicle at all (or at least as little as possible) until the fault is cured. A misfire will allow unburned fuel to enter the converter, which will result in its overheating, as noted above. For the same reason do not persist if the engine ever refuses to start. Either trace the problem and cure it yourself or have the vehicle checked immediately by a qualified mechanic. Never allow the vehicle to run out of fuel.*

d) *DO NOT push-or tow-start the vehicle - this will soak the catalytic converter in unburned fuel, causing it to overheat when the engine does start.*

4C

e) Try to avoid repeated successive cold starts with short journeys. If the converter is never allowed to reach its proper working temperature it will gather unburned fuel, allowing some to pass into the atmosphere and the rest to soak the element with unburned fuel thereby causing it to overheat when the engine does start.

f) DO NOT use fuel or engine oil additives as these may contain substances harmful to the catalytic converter.

g) NEVER use silicon-based sealants on any part of the air inlet/inlet manifold, or any kind of sealant on exhaust system joints forward of the catalytic converter. If pieces of sealant (however small) should break off, they will be carried into the converter and cause it to overheat locally.

h) DO NOT continue to use the vehicle if the engine burns oil to the extent of leaving a visible trail of blue smoke. Unburned carbon deposits will clog the converter passages and reduce its efficiency; in severe cases the element will overheat.

i) Remember that the catalytic converter operates at very high temperatures (hence the heat shields on the vehicle's underbody) and the casing will become hot enough to ignite combustible materials which brush against it. DO NOT, therefore, park the vehicle in dry undergrowth, over long grass or piles of dead leaves.

j) Remember that the catalytic converter is FRAGILE - do not strike it with tools during servicing work, take great care when working on the exhaust system, ensure that the converter is well clear of any jacks or other lifting gear used to raise the vehicle and do not drive the vehicle over rough ground, roadhumps, etc., in such a way as to ground the exhaust system.

k) The catalytic converter, used on a well-maintained and well-driven vehicle, should last for between 50 000 and 100 000 miles. From this point on, careful checks should be made at all specified service intervals to ensure that the converter is still operating efficiently. If the converter is no longer effective it must be renewed.

2 Fuel system - contamination

Refer to Section 2, Chapter 4B.

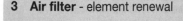

3 Air filter - element renewal

Refer to the appropriate Section of Chapter 2.

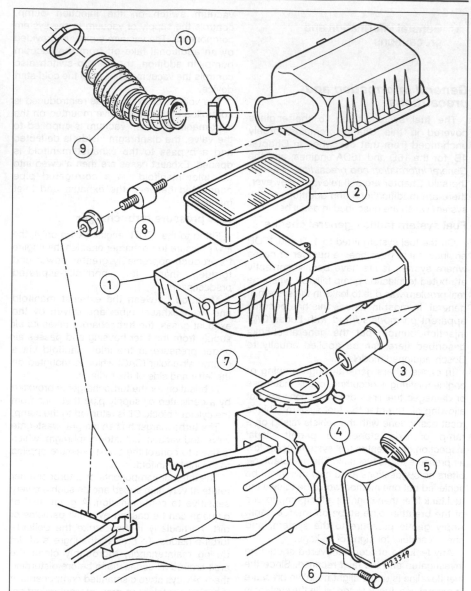

4.2 Exploded view of typical later-type remote air cleaner assembly fitted to Cavalier

1	Air cleaner lower casing	4	Resonator
2	Filter element	5	Sealing ring
3	Air cleaner/resonator tube	6	Screw
		7	Intake gasket

8	Rubber mounting
9	Air inlet hose
10	Hose clips

4 Air cleaner housing - removal and refitting

1 Various later types of remote air cleaner housing are fitted, two typical examples are dealt with below, all other types being similar:

Cavalier - 17D and 17DR engines

2 To remove this type of housing (see illustration), first unclip and withdraw the air cleaner lid and lift out the element.
3 Where fitted, slacken the hose clip and release the air inlet hose from the front of the housing.
4 Undo the mounting screws or slacken the two nuts, according to model, and lift away the housing.
5 On certain models, it may be necessary to remove the headlight unit to allow sufficient clearance to disengage the filter snorkel that runs beneath the headlight unit. Refer to the relevant petrol-engine Manual for details.
6 Refitting is a reversal of removal.

Astra - DTL engine

7 Release the housing inlet scoop from the vehicle front crossmember by removing the

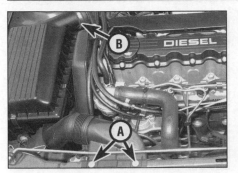

4.7 Remove the air cleaner housing inlet scoop securing screws (A) and outlet tube retaining clamp (B) - DTL engine

two securing screws and manoeuvre it clear of the housing (see illustration).

8 Detach the air filter housing outlet tube retaining clamp.

9 Release the base securing nuts and remove the housing.

10 Refitting is a reversal of removal.

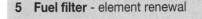

5 Fuel filter - element renewal

Refer to Chapter 2.

6 Fuel filter - draining

Refer to Chapter 2.

7 Heated fuel filter - location and servicing

Refer to Section 6, Chapter 4B.

8 Idle speed - checking and adjustment

Refer to Chapter 2.

9 Maximum speed - checking and adjustment

Refer to Chapter 2.

10 Fuel injection pump timing - checking and adjustment

Bosch and Lucas/CAV pumps

1 The pump timing procedure is generally similar to that given in Chapter 4B, Section 9, whilst noting the following points.

10.3 Flywheel timing marks are visible through clutch housing inspection cover - 17D and 17DR engines

2 With the introduction of the revised camshaft drivebelt inner and outer covers, the timing mark for the injection pump sprocket is now located on the drivebelt inner cover.

3 On 17D and 17DR engines, remove the clutch housing cover plate. With No 1 piston set to TDC on the firing stroke, the TDC mark on the flywheel and the pointer on the clutch housing will be aligned (see illustration).

4 On 17DTL engines, remove the flywheel cover plate. Flywheel position for TDC must be determined by the use of a setting tool (Adjuster KM-851) fitted next to the flywheel as shown (see illustration). With No 1 piston set to TDC on the firing stroke, the TDC mark on the flywheel and the pointer on the setting tool will be aligned.

5 On all engines, the timing mark on the injection pump sprocket will be aligned with the moulded mark on the drivebelt inner cover (see illustration).

Lucas/CAV pump

6 There are also some slight changes to the timing procedure when dealing with the Lucas/CAV injection pump as detailed below.

7 Note that the closing plug is located on the upper surface of the pump rather than at the end of the pump casing as on the Bosch pump. In the absence of the measuring tool KM-690-A and the dial test indicator KM-571-B, you will need a standard dial test indicator (DTI), together with some method of mounting it above the timing hole at the appropriate height. Also required is a headed probe made to the dimensions shown, this being placed in the timing hole before the DTI is mounted in position (see illustrations).

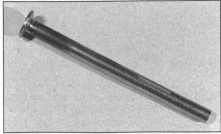

10.7a Home-made probe used for checking Lucas/CAV pump timing

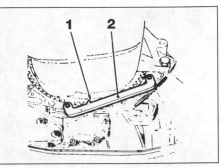

10.4 Determining flywheel position for TDC by the use of a setting tool (Adjuster KM-851) - 17DTL engines
1 Flywheel TDC mark   2 Setting tool

10.5 Fuel injection pump sprocket timing mark aligned with moulded mark on drivebelt inner cover

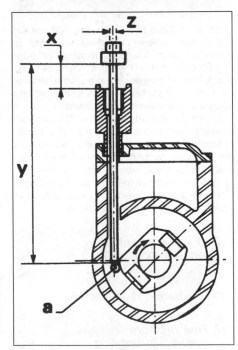

10.7b Special DTI probe shown in position during pump timing check - Lucas/CAV injection pump

a Timing piece
x Timing value (as shown on plate)
y 95.5 ± 0.01 mm
z 7.00 mm shank diameter

4C

10.8 Lucas/CAV pump showing DTI set up for timing check. Individual value for each pump is stamped on plate (arrowed)

8 Check the amount of lift indicated on the DTI when the crankshaft timing marks are brought into alignment. There is no standard specified lift figure for Lucas/CAV pumps. Each pump is calibrated during manufacture and the lift figure marked on a plate which is fitted to the pump lever **(see illustration)**. If the lift figure shown on the DTI does not correspond with that given on the plate, adjust the pump sprocket as described in Chapter 4B, Section 9. Once adjustment is complete, remove the DTI with probe and refit the closing plug.

11 Fuel injection pump - removal, overhaul and refitting

Refer to Section 10, Chapter 4B, whilst noting that where the injection pump is equipped with an EGR system vacuum regulator valve, then the valve setting must be checked and, if necessary, adjusted whenever the pump is disturbed. The same instructions apply if a new valve has been fitted.

Checking and adjustment of the vacuum regulator valve is only possible if a hand-operated vacuum pump/gauge is available. At the time of writing, no information was available for valve adjustment. It is therefore recommended that before carrying out any work on the fuel injection pump, advice is sought from a Vauxhall/Opel dealer.

12 Idle stop solenoid - removal and refitting

Refer to Section 11, Chapter 4B.

13 Fuel injectors - removal, overhaul and refitting

Refer to Section 12, Chapter 4B.

14 Throttle cable - removal and refitting

Refer to Section 13, Chapter 4B.

15 Cold start cable - removal and refitting

Refer to Section 14, Chapter 4B.

16 Vacuum-operated cold start device - removal and refitting (17DR, 17DTL engines)

Bosch fuel injection pump

1 Slacken the lockbolt and remove the clamping sleeve from the end of the cold start device operating cable **(see illustrations)**.
2 Disconnect the vacuum hose, undo the clamping nut and remove the cold start device from its mounting bracket.
3 Refitting is a reversal of removal. On completion, adjust the idle speed.

Lucas/CAV injection pump

4 Undo the two bolts securing the cold start device mounting bracket to the injection pump **(see illustration)**. Note the position of the end of the speed control lever return spring.
5 Release the mounting bracket, then detach the vacuum hoses from the cold start device, noting their locations.
6 Disconnect the cold start device thrust rod and remove the unit complete with mounting bracket. Separate the device from the mounting bracket if necessary, after removal.
7 Refitting is a reversal of removal. On completion, adjust the idle speed.

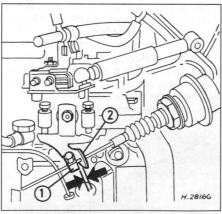

16.1b Checking cold start device free play - Bosch VE injection pump, 17DR and 17DTL engines
1 Clamping sleeve 2 Actuating lever Arrows indicate free play checking point - engine cold

16.1a Vacuum-operated cold start device (arrowed) fitted to Bosch VE injection pump - 17DR and 17DTL engines

17 Fuel tank - removal and refitting

Refer to Section 15, Chapter 4B.

18 Turbocharger - removal and refitting (17DTL engine)

⚠️ *Warning: Never run the engine with the turbocharger air inlet hose disconnected. Depression at the inlet can build up very suddenly if the engine speed is raised thereby increasing the risk of foreign objects being sucked in and ejected at very high speed.*

Note: *Before removing the turbocharger, prevent the ingress of dirt by thoroughly cleaning the area around all unions before disconnection. Store any dismantled components in a sealed container to prevent contamination. Cover the turbocharger air inlet ducts to prevent debris entering and clean with lint-free cloth only.*

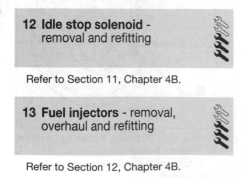

16.4 Lucas/CAV injection pump cold start device attachments - 17DR and 17DTL engines
1 Mounting bracket securing bolts
2 Mounting bracket

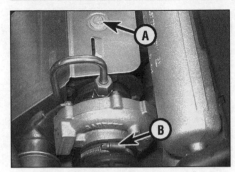

18.2 Remove the turbocharger heat shield (A) and release the air intake hose retaining clamp (B)

Note: *If the wastegate vacuum unit is damaged, then the complete turbocharger unit must be replaced.*

Removal

1 Disconnect the battery earth lead.
2 Remove the heat shield from the top of the turbocharger **(see illustration)**.
3 Release the air inlet hose retaining clamp and pull the hose clear of the turbocharger.
4 Disconnect the charge air cooler hose from the turbocharger.
5 Disconnect the turbocharger oil feed and return pipelines from the cylinder block and sump respectively, catching any escaping oil in a drip tray **(see illustration)**. Note the fitted position of any seals and renew them.
6 Unbolt the exhaust downpipe from the turbocharger. Loosen the pipe mounting bracket nuts **(see illustration)** and move it slightly downwards. Recover the flange gasket.
7 Detach the turbocharger from the exhaust manifold having released its securing bolts. Recover the flange gasket.
8 If required, disconnect the oil feed and return pipelines from the turbocharger, noting the fitted position of any seals and renewing them.

Refitting

9 Reconnect the oil feed and return pipelines to the turbocharger, using new seals and tightening the connections to the specified torque settings.
10 Reattach the turbocharger to the exhaust manifold, fitting a new flange gasket and tightening its securing bolts to the specified torque setting. Take care to avoid damaging the oil feed and return pipelines when installing the turbocharger.
11 Refit the exhaust downpipe to the turbocharger, fitting a new flange gasket and tightening its securing bolts to the specified torque setting. Retighten the pipe mounting bracket nuts.
12 Reconnect the oil feed and return pipelines to the cylinder block and sump respectively, using new seals and tightening the connections to the specified torque settings.

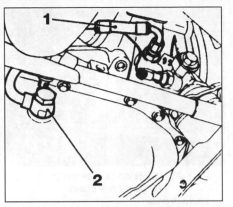

18.5 Disconnect the turbocharger oil feed (A) and return (B) pipelines

13 Reconnect the charge air cooler and air inlet hoses to the turbocharger.
14 Refit the heat shield to the turbocharger, tightening its securing bolts to the specified torque setting.
15 Check, and if necessary replenish, the engine oil.
16 Reconnect the battery and start the engine.
17 Check all disturbed connections for leaks.

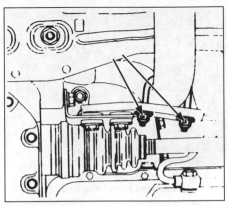

18.6 Unbolt the exhaust downpipe mounting bracket nuts (arrowed)

19 Charge air cooler - removal and refitting (17DTL engine)

1 The charge air cooler (CAC) is mounted on the left-hand side of the radiator and connected to the turbocharger and inlet plenum chamber with hose and pipe assemblies **(see illustration)**.

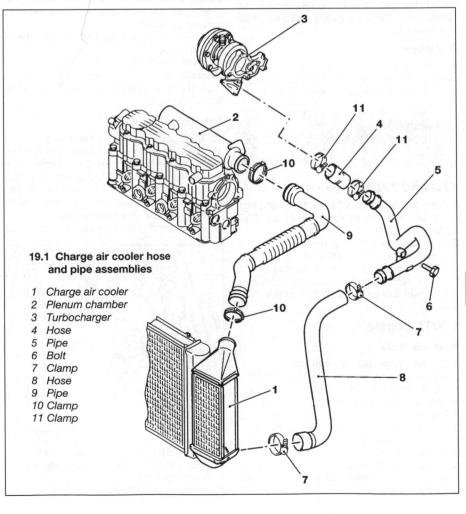

19.1 Charge air cooler hose and pipe assemblies

1 *Charge air cooler*
2 *Plenum chamber*
3 *Turbocharger*
4 *Hose*
5 *Pipe*
6 *Bolt*
7 *Clamp*
8 *Hose*
9 *Pipe*
10 *Clamp*
11 *Clamp*

4C

20.6 Disconnect the manifold wiring harness plug (arrowed)

Removal

2 Commence removal by disconnecting the top (plenum chamber) hose from the cooler.
3 Disconnect the lower (turbocharger) hose from the cooler.
4 Disconnect the wiring harness plug from the cooling fan motor.
5 Detach the coolant hose from its retainer on the fan shroud.
6 Loosen the fan shroud retaining bolts and remove the shroud from the vehicle.
7 Remove the cooler retaining bolts and detach the cooler from its retainer on the radiator end. Ease the cooler upwards, clear of the vehicle.

Refitting

8 Refitting of the cooler is a reversal of removal. Ensure that both hose connections are free of contamination before fitting.

20 Manifolds - removal and refitting

17D and 17DR engines

1 Refer to Section 16, Chapter 4B, noting that on 17DR engines equipped with an EGR system, the following appertain:
2 When removing the inlet manifold, both the vacuum hose of the EGR valve and the corrugated pipe must be disconnected.
3 When removing the exhaust manifold, disconnect the corrugated pipe of the EGR system.

17DTL engine

Inlet manifold

4 Disconnect the battery earth lead.
5 Remove the cover plate from the top of the plenum chamber and detach the wiring looms, moving them clear of the manifold.
6 Disconnect the wiring harness plug mounted on the manifold (see illustration).
7 Pull the vacuum hose from the EGR valve (see illustration).
8 Detach the corrugated pipe of the EGR system from the manifold by releasing its securing clamp.

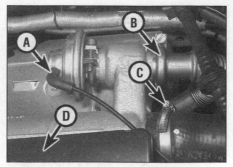

20.7 EGR valve assembly - 17DTL engine shown

A Vacuum hose
B Corrugated pipe clamp.
C Charge air cooler hose clamp
D Plenum chamber cover plate

9 Remove the charge air cooler hose from the plenum chamber.
10 Detach the small diameter charge air hose from the right-hand end of the plenum chamber.
11 Remove the exhaust manifold.
12 Remove the inlet manifold securing bolts, loosening them a little at a time at first whilst working in a diagonal sequence. Remove the manifold and recover the gasket, noting the fitted position of the wiring harness plug mounting bracket.
13 Clean the manifold and cylinder head mating surfaces.
14 Refit the manifold in the reverse order of removal. Use a new gasket and tighten the nuts evenly, in a diagonal sequence, to the specified torque.

Exhaust manifold

15 Disconnect the battery earth lead.
16 Release the breather hose and remove the air cleaner housing to turbocharger hose assembly, noting the fitted positions of the hoses and electrical cables clamped across the hose before releasing them and moving them to one side (see illustration).
17 Disconnect the charge air cooler to

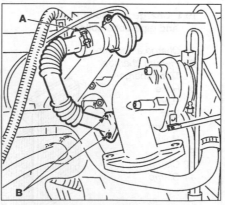

20.19 EGR system corrugated pipe connections - 17DTL engine shown

A Retaining clamp
B flange securing bolts

20.16 Note the fitted position of the hoses and electrical cables clamped across the turbocharger inlet hose before releasing the breather hose (arrowed) and removing the inlet hose assembly

turbocharger hose at the turbocharger, remove the charge air pipe to cylinder head securing bolts and move the pipe/hose assembly clear of the manifold.
18 Unbolt the exhaust downpipe from the turbocharger. Loosen the pipe mounting bracket nuts and move it slightly downwards. Recover the flange gasket.
19 Disconnect the corrugated pipe of the EGR system by removing its retaining clamp and flange securing bolts (see illustration).
20 Disconnect the alternator wiring plug.
21 Loosen the alternator securing bolts and remove the bolt shown (see illustration), noting the fitted position of the earth lead and washers fitted to it. Detach the alternator drivebelt. Release the coolant hose from its mounting bracket on the alternator and secure the alternator to one side against the bulkhead of the engine bay.
22 Remove the two bolts securing the fuel filter assembly to the bulkhead of the engine bay and move the assembly to one side.
23 Disconnect the turbocharger oil feed and return pipelines from the cylinder block and sump respectively, catching any escaping oil in a drip tray. Note the fitted position of any seals and renew them.

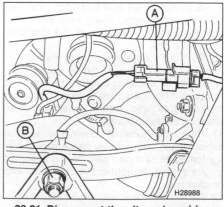

20.21 Disconnect the alternator wiring plug (A) and remove the alternator securing bolt (B)

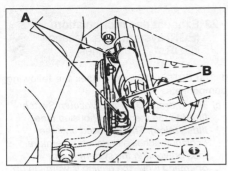

20.24 Remove the turbocharger support securing bolts (A) and the turbocharger support (B)

24 Remove the turbocharger support securing bolts and the turbocharger support (see illustration).

25 Remove the exhaust manifold securing bolts, loosening them a little at a time at first whilst working in a diagonal sequence. Remove the manifold and turbocharger assembly, manoeuvring it carefully upwards. Recover the manifold gasket and note the oil pressure switch wiring connection.

26 Clean the manifold and cylinder head mating surfaces.

27 Refit the manifold in the reverse order of removal, noting the following:

a) Use a new manifold gasket

b) Take care to avoid damaging the turbocharger oil feed and return pipelines when lowering the manifold/turbocharger assembly into position and ensure that they are correctly routed

c) Tighten the manifold retaining nuts evenly, in a diagonal sequence, to the specified torque

d) Use new seals when reconnecting the oil feed and return pipelines to the cylinder block and sump, and tighten their connections to the specified torque settings

e) Ensure that the alternator drivebelt is correctly tensioned after refitting

f) Use a new flange gasket when refitting the corrugated pipe of the EGR system and tighten the pipe securing bolts to the specified torque settings

g) Use a new flange gasket when refitting the exhaust downpipe to the turbocharger and tighten the pipe securing bolts to the specified torque setting

h) Ensure that all turbocharger hose connections are free of oil or grease

I) Check, and if necessary replenish, the engine oil

j) Reconnect the battery and start the engine

k) Check all disturbed connections for leaks

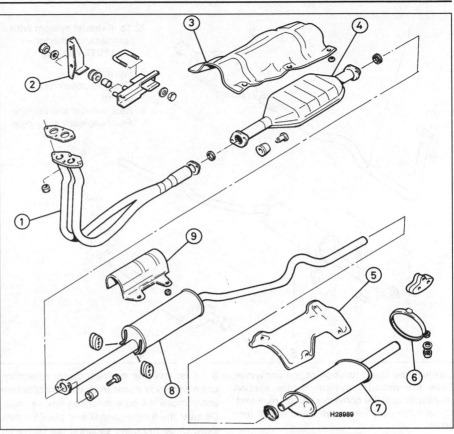

22.1a Exhaust system with catalytic converter - 17D and 17DR engines

1 Front downpipe
2 Front downpipe mounting assembly
3 Heat shield -catalytic converter
4 Catalytic converter
5 Heat shield - rear silencer
6 Clamp
7 Rear silencer and tail pipe
8 Front silencer and centre pipe
9 Heat shield - front silencer

21 Exhaust system - inspection

1 When inspecting the exhaust system, refer to Section 17, Chapter 4B, whilst noting the following appertaining to a system equipped with a catalytic converter.

2 Never use exhaust sealants upstream of a catalytic converter.

3 When renewing rubber mountings, ensure that the mounting nearest the catalytic converter is of the correct type. Due to the converter's high operating temperatures, this mounting must be of high-temperature resistant material.

4 The underbody of the vehicle is protected by heat shields from the very high operating temperatures of a system fitted with a catalytic converter. These shields should be inspected for damage, cracking and security and renewed if necessary.

22 Catalytic converter - removal and refitting

Note: *Never use exhaust sealants upstream of a catalytic converter. Where applicable, ensure that the arrow on the converter's body points to the rear, in line with the exhaust gas flow. In most cases, a converter will fit correctly only one way, as the front and rear flanges will be either of different sizes or have offset studs to prevent incorrect installation.*

Note: *If renewing rubber mountings, ensure that the mounting nearest the catalytic converter is of the correct type. Due to the converter's high operating temperatures, this mounting must be of high-temperature resistant material.*

1 The catalytic converter is located to the rear of the exhaust system front downpipe (see illustrations).

17D and 17DR engines

Removal

2 To remove the converter, undo the bolts securing its front and rear ends whilst noting

4C

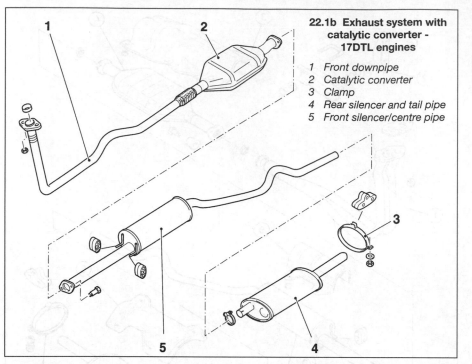

22.1b Exhaust system with catalytic converter - 17DTL engines

1 Front downpipe
2 Catalytic converter
3 Clamp
4 Rear silencer and tail pipe
5 Front silencer/centre pipe

carefully the fitted position of the converter. Ease the exhaust system centre section rearwards until the converter can be removed. Discard the pipe flange seals and obtain new items.

3 Inspect the converter heat shield for damage, cracking and security and renew it if necessary.

Refitting

4 Carefully clean the mating surfaces of the converter and exhaust pipes.

5 Fit the new seals and offer up the converter.

6 Fit and tighten the converter securing bolts to their specified torque wrench settings.

17DTL engine

Removal

7 On this engine the exhaust front downpipe and catalytic converter are one item.

8 To remove the converter/pipe assembly, unbolt the downpipe from the turbocharger and remove the pipe mounting bracket nuts. Discard the flange gasket and obtain a new item. Undo the bolts securing the converter rear end and carefully lower the converter/pipe assembly away from the vehicle.

9 Inspect the converter heat shield for damage, cracking and security and renew it if necessary.

Refitting

10 Carefully clean the mating surfaces of the converter and exhaust pipes.

11 Fit the new flange gasket and offer up the converter/pipe assembly.

12 Fit and tighten the converter/pipe assembly securing bolts to their specified torque wrench settings.

23 Exhaust gas recirculation (EGR) system - maintenance (17DR, 17DTL engines)

1 The EGR system comprises the following components:

a) *The Thermal-Operated Vacuum Switch - fitted to the thermostat housing **(see illustration)**. This is closed until the coolant reaches a certain temperature, thus preventing the system from operating while the engine is warming up*

b) *The Vacuum Regulator Valve - on top of the fuel injection pump. This regulates according to throttle opening the amount of vacuum applied to the EGR valve*

c) *The Vacuum Delay Valve - fitted in the vacuum line to control the rate at which vacuum is applied to the EGR valve*

d) *The EGR valve - mounted on the inlet manifold and connected by a supply pipe to the exhaust manifold **(see illustrations)**. This opens under the control of the vacuum switch, regulator and delay valves, using the depression created by the vacuum pump which allows a proportion of the exhaust gases to flow up into the inlet manifold and into the combustion chamber*

System checking

2 This system is virtually maintenance-free, the only routine operations necessary are checks for condition and security of the component parts.

23.1c EGR valve (arrowed) mounted on inlet manifold - 17DR engine shown

23.1a EGR system thermal - operated vacuum switch (arrowed) fitted to the thermostat housing - 17DR engine shown

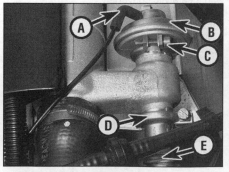

23.1b EGR valve and pipe connections - 17DTL engine shown

A Vacuum hose
B EGR valve
C Valve clamp
D Pipe clamp.
E Corrugated pipe

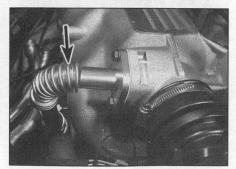

23.1d EGR system corrugated pipe (arrowed) inlet manifold connection - 17DR engine shown

23.7 EGR system vacuum take-off (arrowed) on vacuum pump - 17DR engine shown

3 Whenever the fuel injection pump is removed the vacuum regulator valve setting must be checked and, if necessary, adjusted, refer to Section 11.

4 To check system operation, warm the engine up to normal operating temperature and allow it to idle. Disconnect and reconnect several times the vacuum pipe from the top of the EGR valve. The valve should be heard to operate each time.

5 If the EGR valve does not operate and vacuum can be felt at the pipe end, first check the setting of the vacuum regulator valve.

6 If the vacuum regulator valve is functioning correctly, the fault must be in the EGR valve, which must then be renewed. If the valve is to be renewed, it is always worth first trying the effect of cleaning any carbon build-up from its passages to check whether this is the reason for the failure. If the valve diaphragm has failed, on the other hand, there is no alternative to the renewal of the complete valve unit.

7 If no vacuum can be felt, check back through the system until the leak or blockage is found and rectified. Vacuum supply is provided by an additional take-off from the vacuum pump **(see illustration)**.

Thermal-operated vacuum switch - removal and refitting

8 Drain the cooling system, either completely or down as far as the thermostat.

9 Disconnect the vacuum pipes from the switch, having noted their fitted positions.

10 Unscrew the vacuum switch.

11 On fitting the new switch, ensure that a new sealing washer is used. Tighten the switch securely.

12 Refill the cooling system.

Vacuum regulator valve - removal and refitting

13 Note the fitted position of each valve pipe for reference when refitting.

14 Disconnect each pipe.

15 Unbolt and remove the regulator valve.

16 Refitting is a reversal of removal but if a new valve is being fitted then it must be adjusted, see Section 11.

Vacuum delay valve - removal and refitting

17 At the time of writing, no information was available concerning the precise location of this unit, or whether it is available separately from the vacuum pipes. Consult your local Vauxhall/Opel dealer for details.

18 Note that valves of this type are usually clearly marked to show which way round they are to be fitted. Note any such markings before removing the valve.

19 Refitting is a reversal of removal. Check that all pipe connections are secure.

EGR valve - removal and refitting

20 Disconnect the battery earth (negative) terminal.

21 Disconnect the vacuum pipe from the top of the valve.

22 Release the valve retaining clamp and withdraw the valve from the inlet manifold, tapping it lightly on either side with a soft-faced hammer if it proves difficult to remove.

23 Refitting is a reversal of removal. Do not use undue force when relocating the valve in the inlet manifold .

Supply pipe - removal and refitting

24 Disconnect the corrugated supply pipe by removing its flange securing bolts (17DR engine) or retaining clamp (17DTL engine) from the inlet manifold and its flange securing bolts from the exhaust manifold. Discard the flange gasket(s).

25 Refitting is a reversal of removal. Fit new flange gaskets and tighten the pipe securing bolts to the specified torque settings.

4C

Chapter 4 Part D:
Fuel/exhaust systems - 17DT engine

Contents

Degrees of difficulty

Easy, suitable for novice with little experience	**Fairly easy,** suitable for beginner with some experience	**Fairly difficult,** suitable for competent DIY mechanic	**Difficult,** suitable for experienced DIY mechanic	**Very difficult,** suitable for expert DIY or professional

Specifications

General

System type .... Rear-mounted fuel tank, combined lift and injection pump, self-pumping system

Firing order .... 1-3-4-2 (No 1 at pulley end)

Air filter type .... Champion U548

Fuel filter type .... Champion L111

Fuel

Fuel type .... Commercial diesel fuel (DERV)

Tank capacity:
  Astra:
    Hatchback .... 52 litres (11.4 gallons)
    Estate/Van .... 50 litres (11.0 gallons)
  Cavalier .... 61 litres (13.4 gallons)

Injection pump

Manufacturer identification:
  Bosch .... 9 460 620 007 VE R 365 - 1
  Zexel .... NP - VE 4/10 F 2200 R 365 - 1
Drive .... From camshaft drivebelt

Injectors

Type .... 2 jet - Pintaux
Identification .... NP - DN OPD N 122
Opening pressure .... 142 to 162 bar

Adjustment data

Idle speed .... 780 to 880 rpm
Maximum speed .... 5100 to 5300 rpm
Pump timing setting .... 0.50 to 0.60 mm

4D

Torque wrench settings

	Nm	lbf ft
Fuel injection pump		
Fuel lines to pump	25	18
Pump to bracket	40	30
Pump to cylinder block/flange	23	17
Sprocket to pump	70	51
Central vent bolt	20	15
Fuel injectors		
Injector holder to cylinder head	50	38
Injector nozzle to holder	45	33
Fuel line to nozzle	25	18
Return line to injector nozzle holder	30	22
Turbocharger		
Turbocharger to exhaust manifold	30	22
Turbocharger to exhaust pipe	65	47
Heat shield to turbocharger	8	6
Turbocharger support to cylinder block	51	38
Oil pressure line to turbocharger	15	11
Coolant line to turbocharger	8	6
Return hose connection to turbocharger	10	7
Manifolds		
Inlet manifold to cylinder head	25	18
Charge air safety valve to inlet manifold	50	38
Series resistor to inlet manifold	39	30
Air cleaner to inlet manifold	8	6
Exhaust manifold to cylinder head	40	30
Heat shield to exhaust manifold	8	6
Catalytic converter		
Converter to exhaust pipe	25	18
Converter to exhaust silencer	25	18

---

1 General information and precautions

General information

The fuel and exhaust systems fitted to the 17DT engine follow normal practice for modern passenger diesel vehicles. A combined lift and injection pump, driven from the camshaft drivebelt, draws fuel from the tank and distributes it to each cylinder in turn. The injectors deliver a high pressure spray of fuel into the swirl chambers, where combustion starts. This fuel spray is accompanied by pressurised air supplied by a turbocharger. Excess fuel from the pump and the injectors is returned to the tank. A filter, which also acts as a water trap, protects the pump from contaminated fuel.

Cold starting is assisted by pre-heating the combustion chambers electrically. This system is automatically controlled. A thermostatically-controlled cold start accelerator device attached to the side of the injection pump and interconnected to the engine cooling system, causes the pump to deliver extra fuel and alters the injection timing slightly to improve cold start performance.

Manual bleeding or venting of the fuel system is not necessary even if the fuel tank is run dry. Provided that the battery is in good condition, simply cranking the engine on the starter motor will eventually bleed the system. Note that the starter motor should not be operated for more than ten seconds at a time whilst allowing five seconds between periods of operation.

The fuel injection system is inherently robust and reliable. If the specified maintenance is carried out conscientiously it should give little trouble. Some components can only be overhauled or repaired by specialists and the home mechanic is warned against attempting operations beyond those described in this Chapter, unless qualified to do so.

Turbocharger - operation

The turbocharger fitted as standard to the 17DT engine, enables the engine to produce appreciably greater power and torque than a normally-aspirated unit.

Mounted between the exhaust manifold and front exhaust pipe, and driven by the exhaust gases, the turbocharger takes its air supply from the filter housing and passes air under pressure to the inlet manifold via a charge air cooler (CAC) which is mounted on the left-hand side of the radiator.

Lubrication for the turbocharger is provided by a dedicated oil supply. The turbocharger has an integral wastegate valve and vacuum actuator diaphragm, which is used to control the boost pressure applied to the inlet manifold.

Catalytic converter - function

The exhaust gases of any internal combustion engine (however efficient or well-tuned) which burns hydrocarbon-based fuel consist largely (approximately 99%) of nitrogen (N_2), carbon dioxide (CO_2), oxygen (O_2) and other inert gases and water vapour (H_2O). The remaining 1% is made up of the noxious materials which are currently seen (CO_2) as the major polluters of the environment, ie. carbon monoxide (CO), unburned hydrocarbons (HC), oxides of nitrogen (NO_X) and some solid matter, including a small lead content.

Left to themselves, most of these pollutants are thought eventually to break down naturally (CO and NO_X, for example, break down in the upper atmosphere to release CO_2) having first caused ground-level environmental problems, but the massive increase world-wide in the use of motor vehicles and the current popular concern for the environment has caused the introduction in most countries of legislation, in varying stages of severity, to combat the problem.

The device most commonly used to clean up vehicle exhausts is the catalytic converter. It is fitted into the vehicle's exhaust system and consists of an element (or substrate) of ceramic honeycomb coated with a combination of precious metals in such a way as to produce a vast surface area over which the exhaust gases must flow; the whole being mounted in a stainless-steel box. The simple oxidation (or two-way) catalytic converter fitted to diesel engines uses platinum and palladium as catalysts to speed up the reaction between the pollutants and the oxygen in the vehicle's exhaust gases, CO and HC being oxidised to form H_2O and CO_2. Note that the catalytic converter is not a filter in the physical sense; its function is to promote a chemical reaction, but it is not itself affected by that reaction.

Precautions

Fuel - Warning

Many of the procedures given in this Chapter involve the disconnection of fuel pipes and system components which may result in some fuel spillage. Before carrying out any operation on the fuel system, refer to the precautions given in the "Safety first" Section at the beginning of this Manual and follow them implicitly.

Tamperproof adjustment screws - caution

Certain adjustment points in the fuel system are protected by "tamperproof" caps, plugs or seals. The purpose of this tamperproofing is to discourage adjustment by unqualified operators.

In some EEC countries (though not yet in the UK) it is an offence to drive a vehicle with missing or broken tamperproof seals. Before disturbing a tamperproof seal, satisfy yourself that you will not be breaking local or national anti-pollution regulations by doing so. Fit a new seal when adjustment is complete when this is required by law.

Do not break tamperproof seals on a vehicle which is still under warranty.

Turbocharger

The internal components of a turbocharger rotate at very high speed and as such are very sensitive to contamination. A great deal of damage can be caused by small particles of dirt, particularly if they strike the delicate turbine blades. To prevent the ingress of dirt during maintenance, thoroughly clean the area around all connections before disturbing them. Always store dismantled components in a sealed container to prevent contamination. Cover the turbocharger air inlet ducts to prevent the ingress of debris and use lint-free cloths only when cleaning.

Never run the engine with the turbocharger air inlet hose disconnected. Depression at the inlet can build up very suddenly if the engine speed is raised, thereby increasing the risk of foreign objects being sucked in and ejected at very high speed.

Catalytic converter

The catalytic converter is a reliable and simple device which needs no maintenance in itself, but there are some facts of which an owner should be aware if the converter is to function properly for its full service life.

a) *There is no need to worry about using leaded/unleaded fuel in a vehicle equipped with a catalytic converter and a diesel engine - no diesel fuel has added lead.*

b) *Always keep the fuel system well-maintained in accordance with the manufacturer's schedule. Ensure that the air cleaner filter element and the fuel filter are renewed at the correct intervals. If the inlet air/fuel mixture is allowed to become too rich due to neglect, the unburned surplus will enter and burn in the catalytic converter, overheating the element and eventually destroying the converter.*

c) *If the engine develops a misfire, do not drive the vehicle at all (or at least as little as possible) until the fault is cured. A misfire will allow unburned fuel to enter the converter, which will result in its overheating, as noted above. For the same reason do not persist if the engine ever refuses to start. Either trace the problem and cure it yourself or have the vehicle checked immediately by a qualified mechanic. Never allow the vehicle to run out of fuel.*

d) *DO NOT push-or tow-start the vehicle - this will soak the catalytic converter in unburned fuel, causing it to overheat when the engine does start.*

e) *Try to avoid repeated successive cold starts with short journeys. If the converter is never allowed to reach its proper working temperature it will gather unburned fuel, allowing some to pass into the atmosphere and the rest to soak the element with unburned fuel thereby causing it to overheat when the engine does start.*

f) *DO NOT use fuel or engine oil additives as these may contain substances harmful to the catalytic converter.*

g) *NEVER use silicon-based sealants on any part of the air inlet/inlet manifold, or any kind of sealant on exhaust system joints forward of the catalytic converter. If pieces of sealant (however small) should break off, they will be carried into the converter and cause it to overheat locally.*

h) *DO NOT continue to use the vehicle if the engine burns oil to the extent of leaving a visible trail of blue smoke. Unburned carbon deposits will clog the converter passages and reduce its efficiency; in severe cases the element will overheat.*

i) *Remember that the catalytic converter operates at very high temperatures (hence the heat shields on the vehicle's underbody) and the casing will become hot enough to ignite combustible materials which brush against it. DO NOT, therefore, park the vehicle in dry undergrowth, over long grass or piles of dead leaves.*

j) *Remember that the catalytic converter is FRAGILE - do not strike it with tools during servicing work, take great care when working on the exhaust system, ensure that the converter is well clear of any jacks*

or other lifting gear used to raise the vehicle and do not drive the vehicle over rough ground, roadhumps, etc., in such a way as to ground the exhaust system.

k) *The catalytic converter, used on a well-maintained and well-driven vehicle, should last for between 50 000 and 100 000 miles. From this point on, careful checks should be made at all specified service intervals to ensure that the converter is still operating efficiently. If the converter is no longer effective it must be renewed.*

Working procedures

When working on fuel system components, scrupulous cleanliness must be observed, and care must be taken not to introduce any foreign matter into fuel lines or components. Care should be taken not to disturb any components unnecessarily. Before attempting work, ensure that the relevant spares are available. If persistent problems are encountered, it is recommended that the advice of a Vauxhall/Opel dealer or a Specialist is sought.

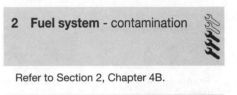
2 Fuel system - contamination

Refer to Section 2, Chapter 4B.

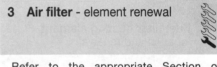
3 Air filter - element renewal

Refer to the appropriate Section of Chapter 2.

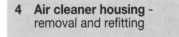
4 Air cleaner housing - removal and refitting

1 The air cleaner housing is bolted to the top of the inlet manifold.
2 To remove the housing, first unscrew its retaining bolts. Release the housing hose clamp and remove the housing with the air filter element **(see illustration)**.
3 Refitting of the housing is a reversal of removal.

4D

4.2 Removing the air cleaner housing with element

7.2 The fuel filter heating element wiring connector (arrowed)

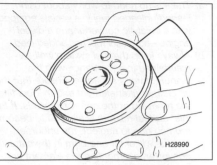

7.3 Lightly smear the sealing ring of the fuel filter heating element with clean diesel fuel before fitting

3 Allow the engine to cool and use a feeler blade to measure the gap between the idle speed stop bolt and the engine speed adjuster lever **(see illustration)**. The gap should be as follows:

Coolant temperature	Gap
- 20ºC	1.7 ± 1.0 mm
+20ºC	0.8 ± 0.3 mm

Adjustment

4 If adjustment is necessary, loosen the stop bolt locknut and turn the bolt until the correct gap is obtained **(see illustration)**. On completion, retighten the locknut.

---

5 Fuel filter - element renewal

Refer to the appropriate Section of Chapter 2.

6 Fuel filter - draining

Refer to the appropriate Section of Chapter 2.

7 Fuel filter heating element - location and renewal

1 An electric heating element is fitted between the fuel filter housing and bowl. A sensor monitors the fuel temperature passing through the filter and if this falls to a point where fuel waxing is likely to occur, the heater is switched on to warm the fuel.
2 To remove the heating element, unplug its wiring connector then remove the filter element followed by the heating element **(see illustration)**.
3 Fitting the heating element is a reversal of the removal procedure. Lightly smear the sealing ring of the element with clean diesel fuel before fitting **(see illustration)**.

8 Idle speed - checking and adjustment

Refer to the appropriate Section of Chapter 2.

9 Maximum speed - checking and adjustment

Refer to the appropriate Section of Chapter 2 .

10 Cold start acceleration - checking and adjustment

Note: *To carry out this operation, it is necessary to obtain a means of accurately measuring the engine coolant temperature. Because of the expense involved in purchasing the necessary instrument and the dangers of possibly exposing oneself to hot coolant, it may be beneficial to leave this operation to a Vauxhall/Opel dealer.*

Checking

1 Refer to the appropriate Section of Chapter 2 and check the engine idle speed.
2 Run the engine until it reaches normal operating temperature.

11 Fuel injection pump timing - checking and adjustment

Note: *The following procedure was carried out with the engine removed from the vehicle. Should the engine be in the vehicle, then access to the injection pump will be restricted. Depending on vehicle type, remove the inlet manifold and/or the starter motor for access to the pump.*
Note: *Ensure that valve timing is correct before checking fuel injection pump timing.*

Checking

1 Timing of the injection pump should only be necessary in the following circumstances:
a) *When fitting a new or overhauled pump*
b) *If the timing is suspected of being wrong*
c) *If the timing belt has been re-tensioned or renewed*
2 Obtain a dial test indicator (DTI) and adapter **(see illustration)**. The manufacturer specifies the use of an adapter which screws into, and seals, the plug hole.
3 Disconnect the battery earth lead.
4 Clean around the injection pipe unions to the pump and cylinder head.
5 Disconnect Nos 1 and 2 injection pipes from the injectors and the pump and remove them from the engine. Be prepared for fuel spillage during subsequent operations.
6 Blank off all exposed pipe connections to prevent the ingress of dirt and moisture.

10.3 Measuring gap between idle speed stop bolt and engine speed adjuster lever - throttle cable removed for clarity

10.4 Adjusting the idle speed stop bolt to engine speed adjuster lever gap

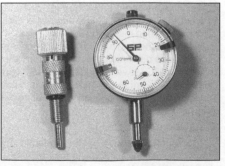

11.2 The dial test indicator and adapter required to set fuel injection pump timing

11.7 Removing the central plug from the injection pump

11.8 The timing mark on the crankshaft pulley aligned with the reference pointer on the engine block

11.9 Deactivating the cold start lever with a screwdriver

11.10 The adapter and dial test indicator fitted to the injection pump

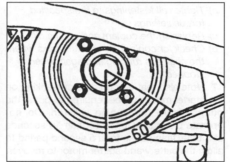

11.11 Turn the crankshaft in the normal direction of rotation to approximately 60° before TDC (No 1 firing)

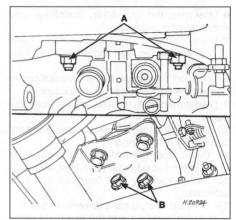

11.14 The fuel injection pump securing nuts (A) and pump bracket bolts (B)

7 Remove the central plug from the injection pump **(see illustration)**.

8 Turn the crankshaft in the normal direction of rotation until the timing mark on its pulley aligns with the reference pointer on the engine block **(see illustration)**. In this position No 1 piston is at TDC on the firing stroke.

9 Deactivate the cold start lever by using a screwdriver as shown **(see illustration)**.

10 Fit the adapter and dial test indicator with the indicator probe entering the central plug hole and contacting the pump piston **(see illustration)**.

11 Turn the crankshaft in the normal direction of rotation to approximately 60° before TDC (No 1 firing) **(see illustration)**.

At this point, the injection pump piston will be at bottom dead centre (BDC).

12 Zero the indicator, checking its adjustment by rotating the crankshaft slightly in either direction to ensure BDC.

13 Bring the engine back to TDC (No 1 firing). When the timing mark on the pulley is aligned with the reference pointer, the dial test indicator should show a lift corresponding to the desired timing setting - see the *Specifications* at the start of this Chapter.

Adjustment

14 If adjustment is necessary, loosen the two nuts which secure the injection pump and the two bolts which secure the pump bracket **(see illustration)**.

15 Loosen Nos 3 and 4 injection pipes at the injectors and pump.

16 Rotate the pump until the dial test indicator shows the desired lift, then tighten the loosened nuts and bolts to the specified torque settings. Rotating the top of the pump towards the engine will lower the lift value, whereas rotating the pump in the opposite direction will raise the lift value.

17 Repeat the checking procedure.

18 With the pump timing correct, remove the DTI and adapter then refit the plug to the pump.

19 Remove any blanking materials and reconnect all injection pipe unions, working in the reverse sequence to removal and tightening them to the specified torque settings.

20 Refit any other disturbed components, start the engine and check for fuel leaks.

12 Fuel injection pump - removal, overhaul and refitting

Removal

1 Disconnect the battery earth lead.

2 Remove the inlet manifold assembly.

3 Refer to Chapter 3 and remove the camshaft drivebelt from the pump sprocket.

4 Using a locking tool similar to that shown, prevent the pump sprocket from turning and remove its securing nut **(see illustration)**.

5 Use a puller to remove the sprocket from the pump shaft and recover the Woodruff key from the shaft **(see illustrations)**.

4D

12.4 Removing the fuel injection pump sprocket securing nut . . .

12.5a . . . and using a puller to remove the sprocket from the pump shaft

12.5b Recovering the Woodruff key from the pump shaft

6 Unscrew the oil filter, catching any escaping oil in a drip tray.
7 Clean around the pipe unions and disconnect the fuel feed and return pipes from the pump.
8 Blank off all exposed pipe connections to prevent the ingress of dirt and moisture.
9 Disconnect the throttle cable from the pump.
10 Drain the cooling system, recovering the coolant if it is fit for re-use.
11 Disconnect the two coolant hoses from the cold start accelerator (see illustration).
12 Disconnect the lead from the idle stop solenoid.
13 Support the pump and remove the two nuts which secure it and the two bolts which secure the pump bracket - **see illustration 11.14**. Remove the pump from the engine.

Overhaul

14 Overhaul of the injection pump should not be attempted. Many tamperproof seals and "Torx" screws will be observed around the pump, these are intended to discourage or detect unauthorised investigation. Do not break any seals if the pump is under warranty or if it is hoped to obtain an exchange unit. Consult a Bosch injection specialist.
15 If a new pump is being fitted, transfer any brackets and other components to it.

Refitting

16 Refit in the reverse order of removal, noting the following points:
  a) With the pump fitted, check its timing

13.5 The idle stop solenoid electrical lead

12.11 The fuel injection pump assembly. Cold start accelerator is arrowed

  b) Tighten all fastenings to the specified torque settings
  c) Replenish the coolant and engine oil
  d) Check for coolant, oil and fuel leaks when the engine is running and again when stopped
17 Note also that a good deal of cranking on the starter motor will be required to prime the pump before the engine will run. Do not operate the starter for more than 10 seconds at a time, then pause for a 5 second period to allow the battery and starter motor to recover.

13 Idle stop solenoid - removal and refitting

Removal

1 Disconnect the battery earth lead.
2 Remove the inlet manifold assembly.
3 Gain access to the solenoid by first cleaning around the pipe unions and then disconnecting the necessary fuel feed and return pipes from the pump.
4 Blank off all exposed pipe connections to prevent the ingress of dirt and moisture.
5 Disconnect the electrical lead from the screw terminal on top of the solenoid (see illustration).
6 Clean around the solenoid, then unscrew it from the pump.
7 Recover the O-ring, spring and plunger (see illustration). Cover the pump orifice to keep dirt out.

13.7 Idle stop solenoid, O-ring, spring and plunger

Refitting

8 Commence refitting by inserting the plunger and spring into the pump orifice.
9 Fit and tighten the solenoid, using a new O-ring. Do not overtighten.
10 Reconnect the solenoid electrical lead.
11 Remove any blanking materials and reconnect all injection pipe unions, working in the reverse sequence to removal and tightening them to the specified torque settings.
12 Refit any other disturbed components, start the engine and check for fuel leaks.

14 Fuel injectors - removal, overhaul and refitting

⚠️ **Warning: Exercise extreme caution when working on the fuel injectors. Never expose the hands or any part of the body to injector spray, as working pressure can cause the fuel to penetrate the skin with possibly fatal results. You are strongly advised to have any work which involves testing the injectors under pressure carried out by a Vauxhall/Opel dealer or fuel injection specialist.**

Removal

1 Remove the inlet manifold assembly.
2 Clean around the injection pipe unions, then remove the pipes from the injectors and pump. Be prepared for fuel spillage.
3 Blank off all exposed pipe connections to prevent the ingress of dirt and moisture.
4 Remove the fuel return line and sealing washer from each injector. Obtain new washers for reassembly.
5 Clean around the base of each injector and unscrew it.
6 Recover the copper sealing ring, corrugated washer and heat sleeve from each injector and obtain new items for reassembly.

Overhaul

7 Injectors can be overhauled, but this is not a DIY job. Consult a Vauxhall/Opel dealer or other reputable specialist.

Refitting

8 Commence refitting by inserting the heat sleeves, corrugated washers and sealing rings into the cylinder head. Note that they must be fitted the right way up, as shown (see illustrations).
9 Screw in the injectors, tightening them to the specified torque setting. Note that the coloured dot or stamp mark on each injector must align with the projection on the cylinder head (see illustration).
10 Place a new sealing washer over each injector and fit the fuel return line, tightening each of its securing nuts to the specified torque setting whilst preventing the injector from turning (see illustrations).

14.8a Refit the injector heat sleeve . . .

14.8b . . . the corrugated washer . . .

14.8c . . . and the sealing ring

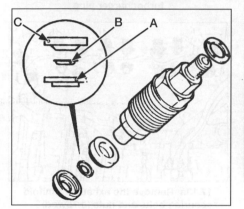

14.8d Correct fitted positions of fuel injector components

A *Heat sleeve*
B *Corrugated washer*
C *Sealing ring*

11 Remove any blanking materials and reconnect all injection pipe unions, tightening them to the specified torque settings.
12 Refit any other disturbed components, start the engine and check for fuel leaks.

15 Throttle cable - removal and refitting

This procedure is similar to that given in Section 13, Chapter 4B. Ignore any references to a throttle damper.

16 Fuel tank - removal and refitting

This procedure is essentially the same as given in the Manual for petrol-engined vehicles, with the bonus that it is much less dangerous. The following points are also to be noted:

a) *Inspect all vent hoses closely and renew them if they have become porous or are in any way suspect. It is possible for water to enter the tank through deteriorated vent hoses*
b) *Ensure all vent hoses are correctly fitted*
c) *Do not confuse the fuel flow (suction) and return connections*

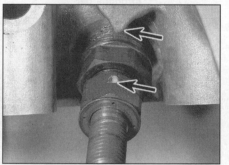

14.9 Coloured dot on injector must align with the projection on cylinder head (arrowed)

17 Turbocharger - removal and refitting

Caution: Never run the engine with the turbocharger air inlet hose disconnected. Depression at the inlet can build up very suddenly if the engine speed is raised thereby increasing the risk of foreign objects being sucked in and ejected at very high speed.
Note: *Before removing the turbocharger, prevent the ingress of dirt by thoroughly cleaning the area around all unions before disconnection. Store any dismantled components in a sealed container to prevent contamination. Cover the turbocharger air inlet ducts to prevent debris entering and clean with lint-free cloth only.*
Note: *If the wastegate vacuum unit is damaged, then the complete turbocharger unit must be replaced.*

Removal

1 If the engine is in the vehicle, it is recommended that the turbocharger and exhaust manifold are removed as one assembly.
2 Disconnect the battery earth lead.
3 Remove the air filter to turbocharger

14.10a Place a new sealing washer over each injector . . .

14.10b . . . and fit the fuel return line

feed hose by disconnecting the following (see illustration):

a) *The feed hose to cylinder head cover breather pipe clip*
b) *The mounting bracket bolts supporting the centre section of feed hose*
c) *The feed hose to turbocharger clamp*

17.3 Removing the air filter to turbocharger feed hose

4D

17.7a Removing the heat shield from the exhaust manifold . . .

17.7b . . . and the heat shield from the turbocharger

17.8 Removing the charge air cooler to turbocharger pipe

17.9 Disconnecting the exhaust downpipe from the turbocharger

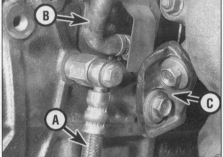

17.10 The turbocharger oil feed pipe (A) oil return pipe (B) and support bracket (C)

17.13a Remove the exhaust manifold securing bolts and nuts (arrowed) . . .

4 Remove the air collector box inlet pipe.

5 Refer to Chapter 6 and remove the cooling fan assembly.

6 Remove the coolant pipe routed from the thermostat housing to the turbocharger, disconnecting it from the front of the cylinder head and catching any escaping coolant in a drip tray.

7 Remove the heat shields from the exhaust manifold and turbocharger. Note that the special insulating washers are retained on each of the shield securing bolts by a retaining plate which should stay in place as long as the bolts are unscrewed only enough for them to disengage from the manifold (see illustrations).

8 Disconnect the pipe routed from the bottom of the charge air cooler to the turbocharger (see illustration).

9 Disconnect the exhaust downpipe from the turbocharger and recover the flange gasket (see illustration).

10 Disconnect the turbocharger oil feed and return pipelines, catching any escaping oil in a drip tray (see illustration). Note the fitted position of any seals and renew them.

11 Disconnect the remaining turbocharger coolant hose(s), catching any escaping coolant in a drip tray.

12 Unbolt the turbocharger support from the cylinder block.

13 Remove the exhaust manifold securing bolts and nuts, loosening them a little at a time at first whilst working in a diagonal sequence (see illustration). Pull the manifold forwards to clear the cylinder head and lift the

17.13b . . . and remove the turbocharger/manifold assembly

turbocharger/manifold assembly out of the engine bay (see illustration). Recover the manifold gasket.

14 Detach the turbocharger from the exhaust manifold, having released its securing bolts. Recover the flange gasket.

15 Clean the manifold, cylinder head and turbocharger mating surfaces.

Refitting

16 Reattach the turbocharger to the exhaust manifold, fitting a new flange gasket and tightening its securing bolts in a diagonal sequence to the specified torque setting.

17 Place a new manifold gasket on the cylinder head (see illustration) and refit the turbocharger/manifold assembly. Take care to avoid damaging any oil and coolant pipelines when lowering the assembly into position. Tighten the manifold retaining bolts and nuts

17.17 Placing a new exhaust manifold gasket on the cylinder head

evenly, in a diagonal sequence, to the specified torque setting.

18 Reattach the turbocharger support to the cylinder block, tightening its retaining bolts to the specified torque setting.

19 Reconnect all except the thermostat housing to turbocharger coolant hose(s).

20 Reconnect the turbocharger oil feed and return pipelines, using new seals and tightening the connections to the specified torque.

21 Refit the exhaust downpipe to the turbocharger, fitting a new flange gasket and tightening its securing bolts to the specified torque setting.

22 Refit the charge air cooler to turbocharger pipe.

23 Refit the heat shields, tightening their securing bolts to the specified torque setting.

24 Refit the coolant pipe routed from the thermostat housing to the turbocharger.

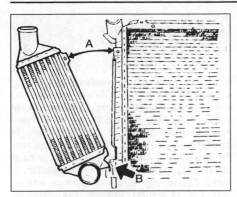

18.3 Removing the charge air cooler from the radiator

A *Upper retaining screw location*
B *Base mounting*

25 Refer to Chapter 6 and refit the cooling fan assembly.
26 Refit the air collector box inlet pipe.
27 Refit the air filter to turbocharger feed hose.
28 Replenish the engine oil and coolant.
29 Reconnect the battery and start the engine.
30 Check all disturbed connections for leaks.

18 Charge air cooler - removal and refitting

1 The charge air cooler (CAC) is mounted on the side of the radiator and connected by hose assemblies to the turbocharger and inlet manifold.

Removal

2 Refer to Chapter 6 and remove the radiator.
3 Remove the cooler upper retaining screws and detach the cooler from the radiator by moving its top away from the radiator so that it detaches from its base mounting (see illustration).

Refitting

4 Refitting of the cooler is a reversal of removal. Ensure that both hose connections are free of contamination before fitting.

19 Charge air safety valve - removal and refitting

To gain access to the charge air safety valve, remove the air cleaner housing (see illustration). The valve can now be unscrewed from the manifold casing.
When fitting the valve, tighten it to the specified torque setting.

19.1 The charge air safety valve (arrowed)

20 Manifolds - removal and refitting

Inlet manifold

Removal

1 Disconnect the battery earth lead.
2 Remove the section of air filter to turbocharger feed hose nearest to the filter housing by disconnecting the following (see illustration):

a) *The hose to cylinder head cover breather pipe clip*
b) *The hose to filter housing securing clamp*
c) *The hose to pipe securing clamp*

3 Remove the hose from between the air inlet collector box and air filter housing. The filter housing can be removed, although this is not strictly necessary.

20.4 Remove the charge air cooler pipe to inlet manifold retaining bolts - upper bolt of two, arrowed

20.7 Disconnecting the inlet manifold to fuel injection pump hose

4 Detach the charge air cooler to manifold pipe from the manifold by removing its two retaining bolts (see illustration). Renew the gasket. Detach the pipe from the side of the cylinder head and move it clear of the manifold.
5 Release the cable-ties from the manifold (see illustration).
6 Disconnect the manifold heater multiplug.
7 Disconnect the manifold to fuel injection pump air hose (see illustration).
8 Loosen the pipe union of No 1 fuel injector to allow movement of the pipe and access to the manifold securing bolt obscured by it (see illustration).

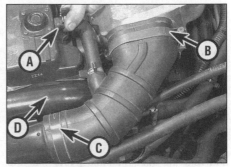

20.2 Removing the section of air filter to turbocharger feed hose nearest to the filter housing

A *Cylinder head cover breather pipe clip*
B *Hose to filter housing securing clamp*
C *Hose to pipe securing clamp*
D *Charge air cooler to manifold pipe*

20.5 Release the cable ties (arrowed) from the inlet manifold
A *Manifold heater*

20.8 Loosening the pipe union of No 1 fuel injector

4D

20.11 The inlet manifold gasket incorporates a sealing ring where it fits over No 2 port

20.13 Fitting a new charge air cooler pipe to inlet manifold gasket

22 Catalytic converter - removal and refitting

9 Remove the five bolts and two nuts which secure the inlet manifold to the cylinder head, working in a diagonal sequence. Take note of the bolt lengths so that they can be refitted to their original positions. Withdraw the manifold and recover the gasket. Note that there is only one securing bolt on No 2 port.

10 Clean the manifold and cylinder head mating surfaces.

Refitting

11 Place a new gasket on the cylinder head and refit the inlet manifold. Note that the gasket incorporates a sealing ring where it fits over No 2 port, this is to offset the missing bolt **(see illustration)**. Tighten the manifold retaining bolts and nuts evenly, in a diagonal sequence, to the specified torque setting.

12 Retighten the pipe union of No 1 fuel injector to the specified torque setting.

13 Reconnect all disturbed hoses, cable-ties and electrical connections **(see illustration)**.

14 Reconnect the battery and start the engine.

15 Check the No 1 fuel injector connection for leaks.

Exhaust manifold

16 With the engine in the vehicle, it is recommended that the exhaust manifold and

turbocharger are removed as one assembly. Refer to Section 17 of this Chapter.

21 Exhaust system - inspection

1 When inspecting the exhaust system, refer to Section 17, Chapter 4B, whilst noting the following appertaining to a system equipped with a catalytic converter.

2 Never use exhaust sealants upstream of a catalytic converter.

3 When renewing rubber mountings, ensure that the mounting nearest the catalytic converter is of the correct type. Due to the converter's high operating temperatures, this mounting must be of high-temperature resistant material.

4 The underbody of the vehicle is protected by heat shields from the very high operating temperatures of a system fitted with a catalytic converter. These shields should be inspected for damage, cracking and security and renewed if necessary.

Note: Never use exhaust sealants upstream of a catalytic converter. Where applicable, ensure that the arrow on the converter's body points to the rear, in line with the exhaust gas flow. In most cases, a converter will fit correctly only one way, as the front and rear flanges will be either of different sizes or have offset studs to prevent incorrect installation.

Note: If renewing rubber mountings, ensure that the mounting nearest the catalytic converter is of the correct type. Due to the converter's high operating temperatures, this mounting must be of high-temperature resistant material.

1 The catalytic converter is located to the rear of the exhaust system front downpipe **(see illustrations)**.

Removal

2 To remove the converter, undo the bolts securing its front and rear ends whilst noting carefully the fitted position of the converter. Ease the exhaust system centre section rearwards until the converter can be removed. Discard the pipe flange seals and obtain new items.

3 Inspect the converter heat shield for damage, cracking and security and renew it if necessary.

Refitting

4 Carefully clean the mating surfaces of the converter and exhaust pipes.

5 Fit the new seals and offer up the converter.

6 Fit and tighten the converter securing bolts to their specified torque wrench settings.

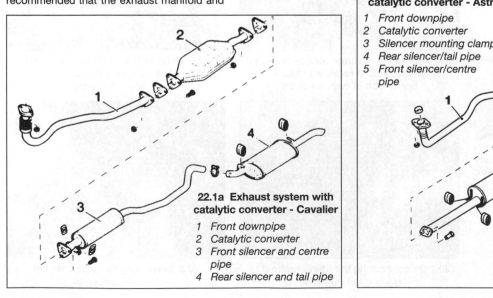

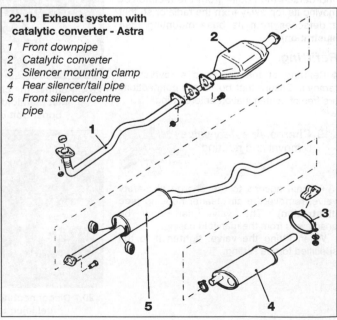

22.1a Exhaust system with catalytic converter - Cavalier

1 *Front downpipe*
2 *Catalytic converter*
3 *Front silencer and centre pipe*
4 *Rear silencer and tail pipe*

22.1b Exhaust system with catalytic converter - Astra

1 *Front downpipe*
2 *Catalytic converter*
3 *Silencer mounting clamp*
4 *Rear silencer/tail pipe*
5 *Front silencer/centre pipe*

Chapter 5 Part A: Engine electrical systems - 16D, 16DA, 17D, 17DR & 17DTL engines

Contents

Degrees of difficulty

Easy, suitable for novice with little experience	Fairly easy, suitable for beginner with some experience	Fairly difficult, suitable for competent DIY mechanic	Difficult, suitable for experienced DIY mechanic	Very difficult, suitable for expert DIY or professional

Specifications

General

System type .... 12V, negative earth

Battery

Capacity (original equipment):
16D and 16DA engines .... 66 Ah
17D, 17DR and 17DTL engines .... 60 Ah

Glow plug type

16D and 16DA engines .... Champion CH-68, or equivalent
17D and 17DR engines .... Champion CH-68, or equivalent
17DTL engine .... Champion CH-158, or equivalent

Starter motor

Make and type .... Bosch GF (pre-engaged) or DW (reduction gear)
Rating .... 12V, 1.7 kW
Commutator minimum diameter:
  Type GF .... 33.5 mm
  Type DW .... 31.2 mm
Brush minimum length:
  Type GF .... 10.0 mm
  Type DW .... 8.0 mm

Fan thermoswitch

16D and 16DA engines:
  Cuts in at .... 97°C
  Cuts out at .... 93°C
17D, 17DR and 17DTL engines:
  Cuts in at .... 100°C
  Cuts out at .... 95°C

5A

Torque wrench settings

	Nm	lbf ft
Starter motor		
Motor to cylinder block:		
Engine side	45	33
Transmission side	75	55
Support:		
To cylinder block	25	18
To motor	7	5
Heat shield to motor	6	4
Glow plugs		
16D and 16DA engines	40	30
17D, 17DR and 17DTL engines	20	15
Cable to plug	4	3
Other components		
Oil pressure switch	30	22

1 General information and precautions

General information

The engine electrical system follows conventional automobile practice, that is, 12 volt negative earth with power being supplied by an alternator. A lead acid battery provides a reserve of power for starting the engine and for situations where the demand on the system temporarily exceeds the alternator output.

Cold starting is assisted by pre-heating the combustion chambers electrically. This system is automatically controlled.

Engines are equipped with two types of starter motor - pre-engaged or reduction gear, the designs of which differ slightly with engine type.

Precautions

It is necessary to take extra care when working on the electrical system to avoid damage to any semi-conductor devices (diodes and transistors) and to avoid the risk of personal injury. In addition to the precautions given in the *Safety first!* Section at the beginning of this Manual, take note of the following points when working on the system.

Always remove rings, watches, etc. before working on the electrical system. Even with the battery disconnected, capacitive discharge could occur if a component live terminal is earthed through a metal object. This could cause a shock or nasty burn.

Do not reverse the battery connections. Components such as the alternator or any other having semi-conductor circuitry could be irreparably damaged.

If the engine is being started using jump leads and a slave battery, connect the batteries *positive to positive* and *negative to negative*. This also applies when connecting a battery charger.

Never disconnect the battery terminals, or alternator multi-plug connector, when the engine is running.

The battery leads and alternator multi-plug must be disconnected before carrying out any electric welding on the vehicle.

Never use an ohmmeter of the type incorporating a hand cranked generator for circuit or continuity testing.

2 Battery - maintenance

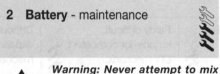

 Warning: Never attempt to mix or replenish battery electrolyte at home. Even in its dilute state, electrolyte is poisonous and corrosive.

Caution: Never reverse the battery connections, as components having semi-conductor circuitry could be irreparably damaged.

Routine maintenance

1 Refer to the appropriate Section of Chapter 2 for routine battery maintenance.

Charge check

2 If a battery hydrometer is available, it is instructive occasionally to check the state of charge of the battery. Use the hydrometer in accordance with the manufacturer's instructions. Variation between cells is more significant than the overall state of charge. One cell reading which differs greatly from the others suggests either an incorrect electrolyte mix in that cell or possible cell failure.

Electrolyte replenishment

3 If it appears that acid has been lost from one or more cells at some time and the deficiency made good with water, consult a Vauxhall/Opel dealer or battery specialist. Do not attempt to mix or replenish electrolyte at home. Even in its dilute state, electrolyte is poisonous and corrosive.

Charging

4 Many batteries nowadays are of the "maintenance-free" type, requiring no inspection or topping-up throughout their life. Sometimes they incorporate a charge indicator (**see illustration**). Follow the instructions on the outside of the battery, as applicable. Note particularly that rapid or "boost" charging is usually forbidden due to the risk of explosion.

5 Charging of the battery from an external source should not normally be necessary. In extreme conditions (mainly short journeys with much electrical equipment in use) or to revive a flagging battery, assistance from a domestic charger may be useful. Disconnect the battery from the vehicle, and preferably remove it completely, before charging. The charge rate (in Amps) should not exceed one-tenth of the battery capacity (in Amp-hours), except under carefully controlled conditions. Remember that the battery gives off hydrogen gas, which is inflammable and potentially explosive during charging.

3 Starter motor - removal and refitting

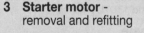

Note: *Depending on vehicle type, access to the starter motor in situ is generally very poor but may be improved slightly by removing the exhaust downpipe, or a good deal by removing both manifolds.*

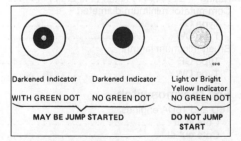

2.4 Charge condition indicator found on original equipment maintenance-free batteries. Green dot denotes full charge

3.3 Starter motor upper retaining bolt (arrowed)

3.4 Starter motor tail bracket to cylinder block bolt (arrowed)

3.6 Starter motor with heat shield removed, showing correct fitting of supply lead terminal (arrowed)

16D and 16DA engines

Removal

1 Disconnect the battery earth lead.
2 Disconnect the starter motor supply lead from the battery positive terminal. Separate the command lead connector at the same point.
3 Remove the upper retaining bolt, which also secures a cable bracket **(see illustration)**.
4 From below, remove the lower retaining bolt and the bolt(s) securing the tail bracket to the cylinder block **(see illustration)**.
5 Remove the starter motor complete with heat shield, leads and tail bracket.

Refitting

6 If a new starter motor is to be fitted, transfer the accessories to it. Pay attention to the supply lead, which must be fitted so that no metal part of it will touch the heat shield or block **(see illustration)**.
7 Fit the assembled motor, with bracket, leads and heat shield, and secure it by nipping up the lower retaining bolt.
8 Fit the tail bracket-to-block bolt(s). If the bracket is under strain, slacken the bracket-to-starter nuts while tightening the bolt(s) then retighten them on completion.
9 Fit the upper retaining bolt and tighten it to the specified torque. Do not forget the cable bracket.
10 Tighten the lower retaining bolt to the specified torque.
11 Reconnect the starter motor leads and the battery earth lead.

17D, 17DR and 17DTL engines

Removal

12 Note that on 17DTL engines, it is necessary to detach the turbocharger oil return line from the sump in order to facilitate starter motor removal. Be prepared to catch any escaping oil in a drip tray and note the fitted position of the union seals. The seals must be renewed. See Chapter 4 for illustrations.
13 Disconnect the battery earth lead.
14 Remove the starter motor support from the motor and cylinder block.

15 Detach the heat shield from the motor.
16 Disconnect the electrical supply lead from the motor terminal.
17 Remove the motor to cylinder block securing bolt on the transmission side and then the securing bolt on the engine side.
18 Remove the starter motor

Refitting

19 Position the starter motor and fit its securing bolts, tightening them to the specified torque settings.
20 Reconnect the electrical supply lead to the motor terminal. This must be fitted so that no metal part of it touches the heat shield or cylinder block.
21 Refit the heat shield to the motor.
22 Refit the starter motor support, tightening its securing bolts to the specified torque settings.
23 On 17DTL engines, reconnect the turbocharger oil return line, using new seals and tightening the union to the specified torque setting. Check the connection for leaks after the engine is started.
24 Reconnect the battery earth lead.
25 Check, and if necessary replenish, the engine oil.

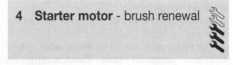

4 Starter motor - brush renewal

All engines - reduction gear type motor

Caution: The permanent magnets which are used in this motor instead of field coils are sensitive to impact and pressure. Do not drop the motor or grip its body in a vice.

Note: *The later types of motor fitted to 17D, 17DR and 17DTL engines, differ slightly in brushholder design to earlier motors, the following procedure is however relevant to all motor types.*

Removal

1 If not already done, remove the heat shield, tail bracket and leads from the motor.
2 Remove the two screws which secure the commutator end cap. Remove the cap and sealing washer.
3 Remove the C-washer and plain washer(s) from the end of the armature shaft **(see illustration)**.
4 Remove the two through-bolts from the commutator end shield. In the absence of the deep 7 mm box spanner needed to deal with these, lock two nuts onto the protruding threaded section of each bolt and unscrew them with a spanner on the nuts **(see illustration)**.

4.3 With the end cap removed, detach the C-washer (arrowed) from the end of the armature shaft

4.4 Undoing a through-bolt with two nuts locked together

5A

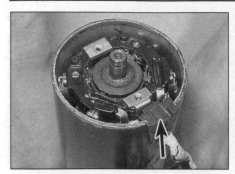

4.7 Prise out the grommet (arrowed) to remove the brushgear

4.9 Fitting a pair of brushes with clips and leads to the carrier plate

4.10 Keeping the brushes retracted with a tube - in this case a large socket

5 Remove the commutator end shield from the field frame.

6 Disconnect the brushgear feed lead at the solenoid.

7 The brushgear can be removed after prising out the grommet **(see illustration)**. Be prepared for the sudden release of the brushes and springs.

Overhaul

8 Clean the commutator with a cloth moistened in petrol or another suitable solvent to remove any burn marks from its contact surface with the brushes.

9 Clean and inspect the brush assemblies. If any of the brushes have worn down to, or beyond, the specified minimum length they must be renewed as a set. Solder new brushes to the old brush leads if necessary, or fit new brushes complete with clips and leads. Make sure that all the springs are present and that the brushes are free to move in their holders **(see illustration)**.

10 Prepare the brushgear for fitting by retracting the brushes with a tube of diameter equal to the commutator **(see illustration)**.

Refitting

11 Fit the brushgear over the commutator so that the tube is displaced and the brushes fall onto the commutator. Make sure that the feed lead grommet is correctly positioned.

12 Reconnect the feed lead to the solenoid.

13 Refit the commutator end shield and secure it with the throughbolts.

14 Refit the plain washer(s) and C-washer to the end of the armature shaft.

15 Press some grease into the commutator end cap, then fit the cap and its sealing washer **(see illustration)**. Secure the cap with the two screws.

16 Refit the supply leads, tail bracket and heat shield,

16D and 16DA engines - Pre-engaged type motor

Removal

17 Remove the heat shield, tail bracket and supply leads (if not already done).

18 Remove the two nuts and washers from the commutator end cover **(see illustration)**.

19 Remove the two brushgear mounting screws from the commutator end cover and carefully remove the cover to expose the brushgear **(see illustrations)**.

20 Disconnect the motor feed lead from the solenoid.

21 Withdraw the field (positive) brushes from their holders, noting the arrangement of the springs. Remove the brushgear from the armature shaft. Recover and note the position of any shims and brake washers.

Overhaul

22 Clean the commutator with a cloth moistened in petrol or another suitable solvent to remove any burn marks from its contact surface with the brushes.

23 Clean and inspect the brush assemblies. If any of the brushes have worn down to, or beyond, the specified minimum length they must be renewed as a set. To renew the brushes, cut off the old ones and solder the

4.15 Grease and fit the commutator end cap and sealing washer

4.19a .. and brushgear mounting screw

new brush leads to the old tails. Do not allow solder to run into the flexible parts of the leads near the brushes.

Refitting

24 If removed, refit the brake washers and shims in the positions noted during brush removal.

25 Refit the brushgear. Make sure that the brushes move freely in their holders and that (when installed) the springs bear on the brushes.

26 Reconnect the feed lead to the solenoid.

27 Refit the commutator end cover, aligning the brushgear securing holes when doing so. Fit and tighten the two brushgear mounting screws.

28 Refit the two washers and nuts which secure the end cover.

29 Refit the supply leads, tail bracket and heat shield.

4.18 Removing the commutator end cover nut . . .

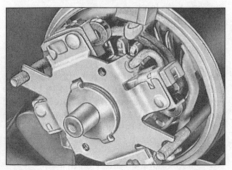

4.19b Brushgear exposed by removal of end cover

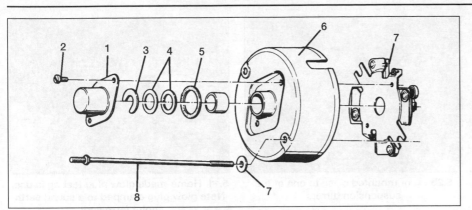

4.31 Pre-engaged type starter motor brush and end cover assembly - 17D and 17DR engines

1 Commutator end cap   4 Plain washers   7 Brush assembly
2 Screws (2 off)   5 Sealing washer   8 Through-bolts (2 off)
3 C-washer   6 Commutator end shield 9 Washer

17D and 17DR engines - Pre-engaged type motor

Removal

30 If not already done, remove the heat shield, tail bracket and leads from the motor.

31 Remove the commutator end cap securing screws then remove the cap and sealing washer **(see illustration)**.

32 Remove the C-washer and plain washer(s) from the end of the armature shaft.

33 Remove the two through-bolts from the commutator end shield. If necessary, lock two nuts onto the protruding threaded section of each bolt and unscrew them with a spanner on the nuts.

34 Remove the commutator end shield.

35 Disconnect the brushgear feed lead at the solenoid.

36 The brushgear can now be withdrawn. Be prepared for the sudden release of the brushes and springs.

Overhaul

37 Clean the commutator with a cloth moistened in petrol or another suitable solvent to remove any burn marks from its contact surface with the brushes.

38 Clean and inspect the brush assemblies. If any of the brushes have worn down to, or beyond, the specified minimum length they must be renewed as a set. To renew the brushes, cut off the old ones and solder the new brush leads to the old tails. Do not allow solder to run into the flexible parts of the leads near the brushes. Refit the brushes in their holders, making sure that they move freely and that their springs are in direct contact.

Refitting

39 Relocate the brushgear over the commutator, making sure that the feed lead grommet is correctly positioned.

40 Reconnect the feed lead to the solenoid.

41 Refit the commutator end shield and secure it with the throughbolts.

42 Refit the plain washer(s) and C-washer to the end of the armature shaft.

43 Press some grease into the commutator end cap, then fit the cap and its sealing washer. Secure the cap with the two screws.

44 Refit the supply leads, tail bracket and heat shield,

5 Preheating system - description and testing

⚠️ *Warning: Glow plug tips become very hot during testing. Take care to avoid burns, especially from plugs which have only just stopped glowing*

Description

1 The engine swirl chambers are heated immediately before start-up by electrical heater plugs, which are usually called glow plugs. When the ignition key is turned to the "ON" position, a warning light illuminates to inform the driver that preheating is in progress. When the light goes out, the engine is ready to be started **(see illustration)**.

2 Switching of the high current needed to heat the glow plugs is carried out by a relay mounted either on the bulkhead of the engine bay or on or near one of the suspension turrets, depending on vehicle type **(see illustrations)**. This relay also determines the time for which the current needs to be applied.

Testing

16D, 16DA and early 17D engines

Note: *The following information is applicable only to the 11-volt glow plugs fitted these engines. Later engines have a 5-volt preheating system, which cannot be tested without specialist equipment. Ensure that 11-volt glow plugs are fitted to your engine before carrying out the following tests.*

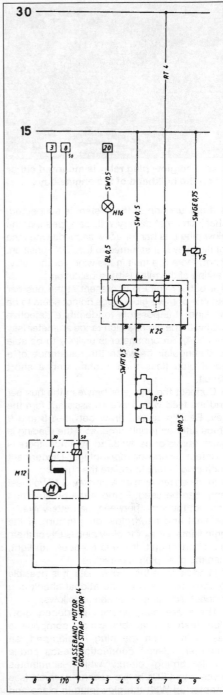

5.1 Typical wiring diagram for preheating system

H16	Warning light	20	Front
K25	Glow plug relay		instrument fuse
M12	Starter motor	30	Live rail
R5	Glow plugs		(full-time)
Y5	Idle stop		**Colour code**
	solenoid	BL	Blue
3	From battery	BR	Brown
8	From starter	GE	Yellow
	switch	RT	Red
15	Live rail (ignition	SW	Black
	controlled)	VI	Violet

5A

5.2a The glow plug relay is mounted either on the bulkhead of the engine bay . . .

5.2b . . . or mounted close to one of the suspension turrets

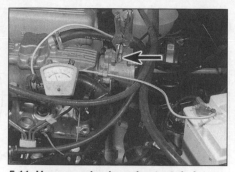

5.11 Home-made glow plug test rig in use. Note glow plug clamped to a sound earth point (arrowed)

3 If malfunction of the system is suspected, check first that battery voltage appears at the glow plug bus bar for a few seconds when the ignition key is first turned to the "ON" position. If not, there is a fault in the wiring or the relay. Testing of the relay is by substitution.

4 If battery voltage is present at the bus bar but one or more glow plugs do not seem to be working, it is possible to identify a defective plug with the aid of a high range ammeter (say 0 to 50A). An ohmmeter is unlikely to be able to distinguish between the resistance of a good plug (less than 1 ohm) and a short circuit.

5 Connect the ammeter between the bus bar and the feed wire. Have an assistant turn the key. Each plug will draw between 8 and 9 amps after an initial surge, so if the reading is much above or below 32 to 36 amps, there is a defect in one or more plugs. Disconnect each plug in turn to isolate the culprit.

6 In the absence of an ammeter, a 12 volt test lamp can be used. Remove the bus bar and connect the lamp between the battery live (+) terminal and each glow plug in turn. If the lamp lights, either the glow plug is OK or there is a short-circuit. If the lamp does not light, then the glow plug is defective.

7 In addition to the above tests, it is possible to carry out a visual operational check of a suspect glow plug. Proceed as follows:

8 There are commercially-produced glow plug testers available which comprise a casing in which the plug is clamped, an ammeter, 12-volt connection leads and a simple timing circuit which illuminates successive LEDs in five-second intervals (see Chapter 8). With the glow plug in place and the leads connected to a 12-volt battery, note the time taken before the tip of the plug begins to glow and the current drops.

9 Whilst such equipment is available in a commercial workshop, it is too infrequently needed by most owners to justify the purchase price. However, an equivalent test rig can be made up at home at little cost.

10 Using an ammeter with a range of at least 30A, connect a lead to each terminal, fitting a crocodile clip at each end. In the interests of safety, fit an in-line fuseholder to one of the leads, using a 30A fuse.

11 With the suspect glow plug removed from the cylinder head, clamp it with self-locking pliers against its metal body to a sound earth point on the engine. Connect the lead from the positive (+) terminal on the ammeter to the glow plug terminal **(see illustration)**. Have an assistant ready with a watch so that a running count of seconds elapsed can be made while you watch the glow plug tip.

12 Connect the remaining crocodile clip from the ammeter negative (-) terminal to the battery positive terminal and start the count. Watch the ammeter needle and the glow plug tip closely. The glow plug tip should start to glow red after about five seconds. After about fifteen seconds, the current reading should drop from around 25A to about 12A.

13 Note that the above timings and current figures are not precise. If the glow plug under test performs reasonably closely to the above sequence, it is likely to be alright. An abnormally high or low current reading (or a blown fuse) indicates the need for renewal, as does a failure of the tip to glow at all.

17DR and later 17D engines

14 These engines have a 5-volt preheating system, which cannot be tested without specialist equipment. Refer to a Vauxhall/Opel dealer or diesel specialist.

6 Glow plugs - removal and refitting

Refer to Chapter 2.

7.1 The oil pressure warning light switch is screwed into the rear of the oil pump

7 Engine oil pressure warning light switch - removal and refitting

1 The oil pressure warning light switch is screwed into the rear of the oil pump **(see illustration)**. If it is suspected of being defective it should be renewed immediately.

Removal

2 To remove the switch, unplug it from the wiring harness and unscrew it from the pump.
3 If a new switch is not to be fitted immediately, fit a blanking plug - this is essential if the engine is to be run.

Refitting

4 Fit the new switch with sealing washer to the pump, tightening it to the specified torque setting. Connect the wiring harness plug.
5 Switch on the ignition and check for correct operation.

8 Cooling fan thermoswitch - testing, removal and refitting

Testing

1 If the cooling fan runs all the time with the ignition on, or does not run even though the coolant is boiling, the thermoswitch may be at fault **(see illustration)**.

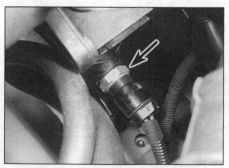
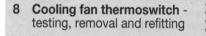

8.1 The cooling fan thermoswitch (arrowed)

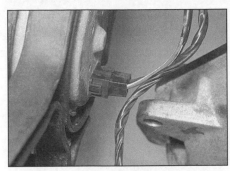

9.2 The cooling fan wiring connector

10.1 The coolant temperature gauge sensor (arrowed) is screwed into the thermostat housing

2 Before condemning the thermoswitch, be sure that the coolant is really hot enough to trip the switch and that the problem is not (for instance) a faulty temperature gauge. A defective switch must be renewed.

Removal

3 To remove the switch, first drain the cooling system whilst taking precautions against scalding if the coolant is hot.
Save the coolant if it is fit for re-use.
4 Unplug the switch and unscrew it from its location in the radiator.

Refitting

5 Coat the switch threads with a little sealant and screw the new switch into its housing. Plug in the switch connector.
6 Refill the cooling system.

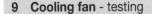

9 Cooling fan - testing

1 If the fan does not operate even though the coolant is boiling, disconnect the leads from the thermoswitch and join them together with a wire link. Do not allow the link to touch other metal. With the ignition on and the switch leads joined, the fan should run continuously. This test determines, in cases of fan malfunction, whether it is the fan or the thermoswitch which is at fault.
2 If the fan will not run as just described, unplug its wiring connector (see illustration) and use a test lamp or meter to check for voltage across the connector terminals. If no voltage is present, check the fuse and wiring. If voltage is present but the fan does not turn, it is defective and should be removed.
3 To remove the fan, refer to Chapter 6A.

10 Coolant temperature gauge sensor - removal and refitting

1 The temperature gauge sensor is screwed into the thermostat housing (see illustration). If it malfunctions it must be renewed.

Removal

2 Disconnect the battery earth lead.
3 Place a thick cloth over the expansion tank cap. Turn the cap anti-clockwise to allow any pressure to escape, then remove and refit the cap. This will depressurise the system and minimise coolant loss.
4 Disconnect the electrical wire from the sensor.
5 Apply a little sealant to the threads of the new sensor and have it ready for installation. Unscrew and remove the old sensor.

Refitting

6 Screw in and tighten the new sensor.
7 Reconnect the wire to the sensor.
8 Reconnect the battery earth lead.
9 Run the engine to operating temperature and check the gauge for correct operation.

11.1 The fuel temperature sensor is combined with the hose union banjo bolt

10 Stop the engine and allow it to cool. Check the coolant level and top-up if necessary.

11 Fuel filter temperature sensor - location and testing

Location

1 The temperature sensor for the heated fuel filter is combined in a modified banjo bolt which passes through one of the fuel line unions and secures it to the filter head (see illustration).
2 The heater is switched by a relay, which is housed together with its 30A supply fuse in the electrical ancillary box mounted on the engine bay bulkhead (see illustration).

Testing

3 No details of test procedures or specifications are supplied by the manufacturer but in the event of a suspected fault, check the sensor, relay and the heater unit by substitution of new units.
4 Whenever removing the temperature sensor for testing, note the fitted position of the union seals and renew the seals when refitting. Check the connection for leaks after the engine is started.

12 Wiring diagrams

Vauxhall/Opel wiring diagrams are "universal", so no separate diagrams are published for diesel models. Refer to the appropriate Manual for petrol-engined models.

11.2 The filter heater is switched by this relay. Note fuse in background (arrowed)

5A

Chapter 5 Part B: Engine electrical systems - 15D, 15DT & 17DT engines

Contents

Degrees of difficulty

Easy, suitable for novice with little experience	**Fairly easy,** suitable for beginner with some experience	**Fairly difficult,** suitable for competent DIY mechanic	**Difficult,** suitable for experienced DIY mechanic	**Very difficult,** suitable for expert DIY or professional

Specifications

General
System type .... 12V, negative earth

Battery
Capacity .... 60 Ah

Starter motor
Make and type .... Hitachi - Reduction gear
Identification:
  15D and 15DT engines .... Vauxhall/Opel Part No 94 386 328
  17DT engine .... Vauxhall/Opel Part No 94 332 586
Commutator minimum diameter:
  15D and 15DT engines .... 29.0 mm
  17DT engine .... 30.0 mm
Brush minimum length .... 10.0 mm

Glow plugs
15D engine:
  5 volt system only .... Champion CH-110, or equivalent
  11 volt system only .... Champion CH-157, or equivalent
15DT engine:
  11 volt system only .... Champion CH-158, or equivalent
17DT engine .... Champion CH-158, or equivalent

Fan thermoswitch
Cuts in at .... 100°C
Cuts out at .... 95°C

5B

Torque wrench settings

	Nm	lbf ft
Starter motor		
Motor to cylinder block:		
15D and 15DT engines:		
Lower bolt - to engine	45	33
Upper bolt - to transmission	75	55
17DT engine	40	30
Housing through-bolts	7	5
Field winding cable connector	9	7
Glow plugs		
Plug to cylinder head	20	15
Cable to plug	4	3
Other components		
Oil pressure switch	20	15
Fan thermoswitch	10	7
Coolant temperature gauge sensor	8	6

1 General information and precautions

General information

The engine electrical system follows conventional automobile practice, that is, 12 volt negative earth with power being supplied by an alternator. A lead acid battery provides a reserve of power for starting the engine and for situations where the demand on the system temporarily exceeds the alternator output.

Cold starting is assisted by pre-heating the combustion chambers electrically. This system is automatically controlled.

All engines are equipped with a reduction gear type of starter motor, a similar design being fitted to all engine types.

Precautions

It is necessary to take extra care when working on the electrical system to avoid damage to any semi-conductor devices (diodes and transistors) and to avoid the risk of personal injury. In addition to the precautions given in the *Safety first!* Section at the beginning of this Manual, take note of the following points when working on the system.

Always remove rings, watches, etc. before working on the electrical system.

Even with the battery disconnected, capacitive discharge could occur if a component live terminal is earthed through a metal object. This could cause a shock or nasty burn.

Do not reverse the battery connections. Components such as the alternator or any other having semi-conductor circuitry could be irreparably damaged.

If the engine is being started using jump leads and a slave battery, connect the batteries positive to positive and negative to negative. This also applies when connecting a battery charger.

Never disconnect the battery terminals, or alternator multi-plug connector, when the engine is running.

The battery leads and alternator multi-plug must be disconnected before carrying out any electric welding on the vehicle.

Never use an ohmmeter of the type incorporating a hand cranked generator for circuit or continuity testing.

2 Battery - maintenance

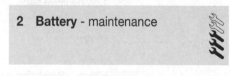

Routine maintenance

Refer to the appropriate Section of Chapter 2 for routine battery maintenance.

Charge check, electrolyte replenishment and charging

Refer to Section 2 in Part A of this Chapter.

3 Starter motor - removal and refitting

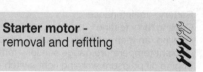

15D and 15DT engines

Removal

1 Disconnect the battery earth lead.

2 Engage first gear. This will allow clearance for the starter motor to pass between the fuel injection pump and gearchange linkage.

3 Jack up the front left-hand side of the vehicle and support it on axle stands. Remove the front left-hand side wheel.

4 Remove the starter motor upper retaining bolt (see illustration). This bolt is approached through the transmission cutout in the front left-hand side wheel well. Note the fitted position of the clutch cable bracket located beneath the bolt head.

5 Disconnect the starter motor supply lead from the solenoid switch terminal. Disconnect the small lead also (see illustration).

6 Remove the starter motor lower retaining bolt and lower the starter motor away from the engine (see illustration).

3.4 The starter motor upper retaining bolt (arrowed)

3.5 Disconnect the starter motor supply lead (A) and small lead (B) from solenoid

3.6 The starter motor lower retaining bolt (arrowed). Driveshaft removed for clarity

Refitting

7 Refitting the starter motor is the reverse of the removal procedure, noting the following points:

a) *Ensure that the starter motor leads are correctly routed so that they do not touch the cylinder block*

b) *Tighten all fasteners to the torque wrench settings specified*

17DT engine

Removal

8 Disconnect the battery earth lead.

9 Jack up the front of the vehicle and support it on axle stands.

10 Remove the starter motor upper retaining bolt (see illustration 3.4).

11 Disconnect the starter motor supply lead from the solenoid switch terminal. Disconnect the small lead also (see illustration 3.5).

12 Remove the starter motor lower retaining bolt and lower the starter motor away from the engine (see illustration 3.6).

Refitting

13 Refitting the starter motor is the reverse of the removal procedure, noting the following points:

a) *Ensure that the starter motor leads are correctly routed so that they do not touch the cylinder block*

b) *Tighten all fasteners to the torque wrench settings specified*

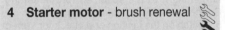

| 4 | Starter motor - brush renewal |

Dismantling

1 Disconnect the field winding connection at the solenoid (see illustration).

2 Remove the two solenoid retaining bolts and detach the solenoid from the starter motor (see illustration).

3 Remove the two through-bolts from the commutator end shield and detach the end shield from the field frame (see illustration).

4 Separate the field frame with rotor and brush holder from the motor body (see illustration).

5 The brushes can now be removed from their holder by releasing their retaining springs with the flat of a small screwdriver as shown.

Overhaul

6 Clean the rotor commutator with a cloth moistened in petrol or another suitable solvent to remove any burn marks from its contact surface with the brushes.

7 Clean and inspect the brush assemblies. If any of the brushes have worn down to, or beyond, the specified minimum length they must be renewed as a set. To renew the brushes, unsolder their leads from the brushholder terminals then solder the new brush leads in their place (see illustration).

8 Refit the brushes in their holders, making sure that they move freely and that their retaining springs are in direct contact with the brush ends.

9 Renew the field frame end sealing ring and, immediately before assembly, apply sealing compound (GM spec. 15 03 166) to the edge of the mating face (see illustration).

Reassembly

10 Reassembly is the reverse of the dismantling procedure, noting the following points:

a) *Tighten all fasteners to the torque wrench settings specified*

b) *Make sure that the feed lead grommet is correctly positioned (see illustration)*

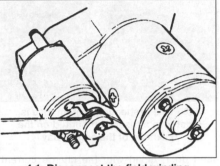

4.1 Disconnect the field winding connection at the solenoid . . .

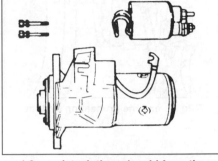

4.2 . . . detach the solenoid from the starter motor . . .

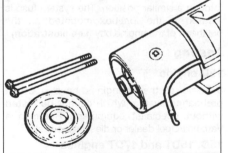

4.3 . . . remove the through-bolts, detach the commutator end shield . . .

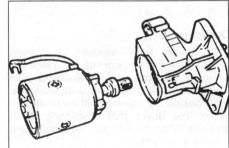

4.4 . . . and separate the field frame with rotor and brush holder from the motor body

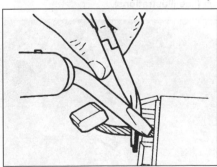

4.7 Soldering a new brush lead to its brushholder terminal

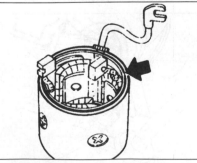

4.9 Renew the field frame end sealing ring (arrowed) and apply sealing compound to the edge of the mating face

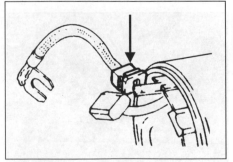

4.10 Ensure that the feed lead grommet (arrowed) is correctly positioned

5B

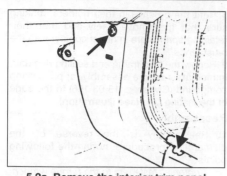

5.2a Remove the interior trim panel forward of the front right-hand door . . .

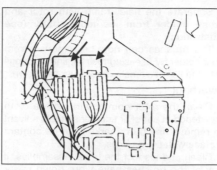

5.2b . . . to expose the preheating system relays (arrowed) . . .

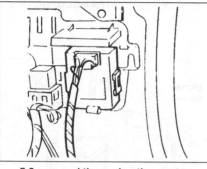

5.2c . . . and the preheating system control unit

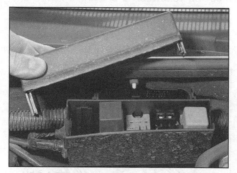

5.2d The preheating system fuse is located in a fusebox mounted on the bulkhead of the engine bay

tested without specialist equipment. Ensure that 11-volt glow plugs are fitted to your engine before carrying out the following tests.
4 Testing of the system relays and control unit is by substitution.
5 Refer to Section 5, Part A of this Chapter for testing of the glow plugs.

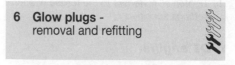

6 Glow plugs -
removal and refitting

Refer to the appropriate Section of Chapter 2.

7 Engine oil pressure warning light switch - removal and refitting

1 The oil pressure warning light switch is screwed into the cylinder block, adjacent to the oil cooler **(see illustration)**. If it is suspected of being defective it should be renewed immediately.

Removal

2 To remove the switch, unplug it from the wiring harness and unscrew it from the cylinder block.
3 If a new switch is not to be fitted immediately, fit a blanking plug - this is essential if the engine is to be run.

Refitting

4 Fit the new switch with sealing washer, tightening it to the specified torque setting. Connect the wiring harness plug.
5 Switch on the ignition and check for correct operation.

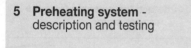

5 Preheating system -
description and testing

Description

1 The engine swirl chambers are heated immediately before start-up by electrical heater plugs, which are usually called glow plugs. When the ignition key is turned to the "ON" position, a warning light illuminates to inform the driver that preheating is in progress. When the light goes out, the engine is ready to be started.
2 Switching of the high current needed to heat the glow plugs is carried out by a relay. On Corsa models fitted with the 15D and 15DT engines, this relay is located behind the interior trim panel forward of the front right-

hand door, along with the charge current control relay and the control unit **(see illustrations)**. Astra and Cavalier models fitted with the 17DT engine have the relay fitted in a similar position. The system fuse is located in the fusebox mounted on the bulkhead of the engine bay **(see illustration)**.

Testing

15D engine

3 Some of these engines have a 5-volt preheating system which cannot be tested without specialist equipment. Refer to a Vauxhall/Opel dealer or diesel specialist.

15D, 15DT and 17DT engines

Note: *The following information is applicable only to the 11-volt glow plugs fitted these engines. Those 15D engines which have a 5-volt preheating system fitted, cannot be*

8 Cooling fan thermoswitch -
testing, removal and refitting

Testing

1 If the cooling fan runs all the time with the ignition on, or does not run even though the coolant is boiling, the thermoswitch may be at fault **(see illustrations)**.

7.1 The oil pressure warning light switch (arrowed) is adjacent to the oil cooler

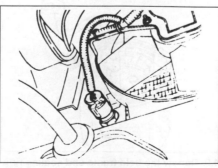

8.1a Cooling fan thermoswitch location - Corsa

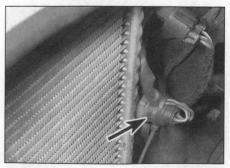

8.1b Cooling fan thermoswitch location - Cavalier

9.2 The cooling fan wiring connector

2 Before condemning the thermoswitch, be sure that the coolant is really hot enough to trip the switch and that the problem is not (for instance) a faulty temperature gauge. A defective switch must be renewed.

Removal

3 To remove the switch, first drain the cooling system whilst taking precautions against scalding if the coolant is hot.
Save the coolant if it is fit for re-use.
4 Unplug the switch and unscrew it from its location in the radiator. Renew the switch sealing ring, where fitted.

Refitting

5 Coat the switch threads with a little sealant and screw the new switch into its housing. Plug in the switch connector.
6 Refill the cooling system.

9 Cooling fan - testing

1 If the fan does not operate even though the coolant is boiling, disconnect the leads from the thermoswitch and join them together with a wire link. Do not allow the link to touch other metal. With the ignition on and the switch

10.1 The coolant temperature gauge sensor (arrowed)

leads joined, the fan should run continuously. This test determines, in cases of fan malfunction, whether it is the fan or the thermoswitch which is at fault.
2 If the fan will not run as just described, unplug its wiring connector **(see illustration)** and use a test lamp or meter to check for voltage across the connector terminals. If no voltage is present, check the fuse and wiring. If voltage is present but the fan does not turn, it is defective and should be removed.
3 To remove the fan, refer to Chapter 6B.

10 Coolant temperature gauge sensor - removal and refitting

The temperature gauge sensor is screwed into the thermostat housing **(see illustration)**. If it malfunctions it must be renewed.
Refer to Section 10 in Part A of this Chapter for the removal and refitting procedures.

11 Fuel filter temperature sensor - location and testing

Refer to Section 11 in Part A of this Chapter.

12 Wiring loom - removal and refitting (17DT engine, Cavalier)

Removal

When removing the 17DT engine from Cavalier models, the engine wiring loom will remain attached to the engine. To detach the loom, disconnect it from the following:

a) *Gearbox reverse lamp switch and oil pressure warning light switch* **(see illustration)**
b) *Coolant temperature gauge sensor and connector at adjacent clamp* **(see illustration)**
c) *Bracket at thermostat housing*
d) *Tie adjacent to thermostat housing bracket*
e) *Speedometer drive sensor plug* **(see illustration)**
f) *Starter motor solenoid, see Chapter 5*
g) *Fuel injection pump stop solenoid, see Chapter 4*
h) *Any remaining clamps or ties*

Refitting

Refitting the loom is the reverse of the removal procedure. Ensure that all parts of the loom are correctly routed so that they do not touch any moving parts.

13 Wiring diagrams

Vauxhall/Opel wiring diagrams are "universal", so no separate diagrams are published for diesel models. Refer to the appropriate Manual for petrol-engined models.

5B

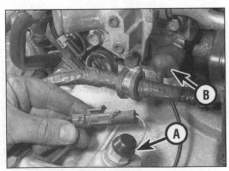

12.1a Disconnect the gearbox reverse lamp switch (A) the oil pressure warning light switch (B) . . .

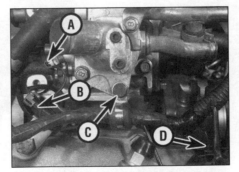

12.1b . . . the coolant temperature gauge sensor (A), connector (B), thermostat housing bracket (C), loom tie (D) . . .

12.1c . . . and the speedometer drive sensor plug

Chapter 6 Part A: Ancillary components - 16D, 16DA, 17D, 17DR & 17DTL engines

Contents

Degrees of difficulty

| **Easy,** suitable for novice with little experience | ⚒ | **Fairly easy,** suitable for beginner with some experience | ⚒ | **Fairly difficult,** suitable for competent DIY mechanic | ⚒ | **Difficult,** suitable for experienced DIY mechanic | ⚒ | **Very difficult,** suitable for expert DIY or professional | ⚒ |

Specifications

Alternator drivebelt

Type . . . . V-belt
Tension (using tension gauge):
   New . . . . 450 N
   Used . . . . 250 to 400 N

Power steering pump drivebelt

Type . . . . V-belt
Tension (using tension gauge):
   New . . . . 450 N
   Used . . . . 250 to 300 N

Torque wrench settings

	Nm	lbf ft
Vacuum pump		
Pump to camshaft housing	28	21
Power steering pump		
Drivebelt tensioner to pump	40	30
Pressure line to pump connections	28	21
Pump support to main bracket	25	18
Pump mounting bracket to cylinder block	40	30
Alternator		
Pivot bolt	25	18
Adjuster strap nuts and bolts	25	18

6A

1.1 Disconnecting the servo vacuum pipe from the vacuum pump

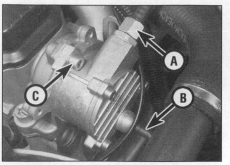

1.2 Vacuum pump connections - 17DR and 17DTL engines

A *Servo vacuum pipe*
B *EGR system vacuum supply hose*
C *Pump securing screws (2 off)*

1.3a Remove the two pump securing screws . . .

1.3b . . . and withdraw the vacuum pump from the camshaft housing

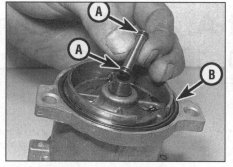

1.5 Renew the O-rings fitted to the central oil pipe (A) and the pump body to camshaft housing seal (B)

1.7 Refitting the central oil pipe with driving dog to the vacuum pump

1 Vacuum pump - removal and refitting

Removal

1 Disconnect the servo vacuum pipe from the pump. Do this by counterholding the large union nut and unscrewing the small one **(see illustration)**.
2 On 17DR and 17DTL engines, disconnect the EGR system vacuum supply hose from the pump **(see illustration)**.
3 Remove the two pump securing screws and withdraw the pump from the camshaft housing **(see illustrations)**. Be prepared for some oil spillage.
4 Recover the small central oil pipe and the driving dog.
5 Discard the two O-rings fitted to the central oil pipe and also the pump body to camshaft housing seal **(see illustration)**.

Refitting

6 Fit new sealing rings to the pump assembly.
7 Refit the central oil pipe and the driving dog to the pump **(see illustration)**.
8 Offer the pump to the camshaft housing, making sure that the teeth of the driving dog engage with the slot in the camshaft end. Fit

the pump securing screws and tighten them to the specified torque.
9 Reconnect and secure the vacuum pipe connection(s).

2 Power steering pump - removal and refitting

> ⚠ **Warning: At no time during system bleeding should the power steering pump be allowed to run dry of fluid.**

Removal

1 The power steering pump is mounted on a bracket which is bolted to the front right-hand end of the cylinder block.
2 Before the pump can be removed, adequate access must first be gained by jacking up the front right-hand side of the vehicle and supporting it securely on axle stands.
3 Disconnect the battery earth (negative) lead.
4 Release tension on the pump drivebelt and remove it.
5 Disconnect the fluid pressure and return hoses **(see illustration)** from the pump and

allow the fluid to drain into a suitable container. Plug or cap all hoses and unions to keep dirt out.
6 Remove the pump to mounting bracket bolt and pump to tensioner bolt.
7 Unscrew the bolt located behind the pump pulley **(see illustration)** and lower the pump away from the engine.

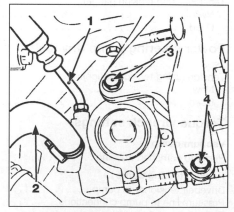

2.5 Power steering pump connections

1 *Fluid pressure hose*
2 *Fluid return hose*
3 *Pump to mounting bracket bolt*
4 *Pump to tensioner bolt*

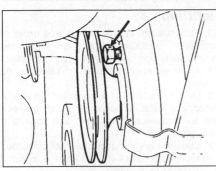

2.7 Unscrew the bolt (arrowed) located behind the pump pulley to release the pump

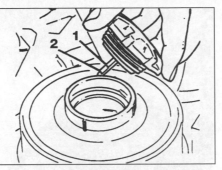

2.10 Remove the power steering fluid reservoir cap to expose the fluid level dipstick

1 Fluid level "MAX" mark
2 Fluid level "MIN" mark

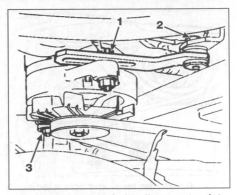

3.3 Alternator drivebelt adjustment points

1 Alternator to adjuster strap bolt
2 Adjuster strap pivot bolt
3 Alternator pivot bolt

Refitting

8 Refitting is the reverse of the removal procedure, noting the following points:
  a) *Tighten all fasteners to the torque wrench settings specified*
  b) *Remove any plugs when reconnecting hoses. Ensure no dirt is allowed to enter the hydraulic system and check that both hoses are correctly routed, well clear of any adjacent components*
  c) *Refit and adjust the pump drivebelt*
  d) *Refill the system with the specified type of fluid, then bleed any air from it as described in the following sub Section*

System bleeding

9 Bleeding of the hydraulic system will normally only be required if any part of it has been disconnected.
10 Remove the fluid reservoir filler cap to expose the fluid level dipstick attached to its underside **(see illustration)**.
11 Top-up the fluid level to the "MAX" mark on the dipstick, using only that fluid specified in *"Lubricants, fluids and capacities"*.
12 Start the engine and immediately top-up the level in the fluid reservoir to the "MIN" mark on the dipstick.
13 Slowly move the steering wheel 2 to 3 times from left to right, approximately 45°. Now slowly move the steering wheel from lock-to-lock twice to purge out the air, then top-up the level in the fluid reservoir to the "MIN" mark on the dipstick. Add fluid slowly to prevent the possibility of aeration of the fluid in the circuit.
14 Switch off the engine, then recheck the fluid level in the reservoir. The level must be as follows:

  Fluid level at "MAX" mark Fluid at operating temperature (approx. 80°C)
  Fluid level at "MIN" mark Fluid cold (approx. 20°C)

15 Finally, check the system hoses and connections for any signs of fluid leaks, which if found, must be rectified.

3 Auxiliary drivebelts - inspection, renewal and adjustment

Alternator

Inspection

1 Refer to the appropriate Section of Chapter 2.

Renewal

2 Gain full access to the drivebelt by removing the air cleaner housing assembly.
3 To remove the drivebelt, first slacken the alternator pivot and adjuster strap nuts and bolts **(see illustration)**.
4 Where fitted, remove the power steering pump drivebelt.
5 Move the alternator towards the engine and slip the drivebelt off its pulleys.
6 Fit the new drivebelt in position over the pulleys and adjust it as follows:

Adjustment

7 Tighten the alternator fastening slightly, so that the alternator can just be moved by hand.
8 Move the alternator away from the engine until the belt tension is correct.
9 Vauxhall recommend the use of a special tool (KM-128-A) for tensioning the belt to the specified amount **(see illustration)**. In the absence of this tool, aim for a tension such that the belt can be deflected about 12 mm by

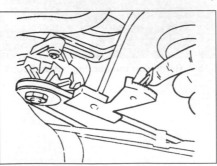

3.9 Using special tool KM-128-A to tension the alternator drivebelt

firm finger pressure in the middle of its run. The belt tension must, however, be checked with the special tool as soon as possible. If using a lever to move the alternator, only use a wooden or plastic one and only lever at the pulley end.
10 Tighten the alternator fastenings to the specified torque setting once the belt tension is correct.
11 Where applicable, refit and tension the steering pump drivebelt.
12 Refit the air cleaner housing assembly.
13 The tension of a new drivebelt should be rechecked after a few hundred miles.

Power steering pump

Inspection

14 Refer to the appropriate Section of Chapter 2.

Renewal

15 Gain full access to the drivebelt by jacking up the front right-hand side of the vehicle and supporting it on axle stands.
16 To remove the drivebelt, first loosen the pump mounting and tensioner bolts shown **(see illustration)**. Release the tensioner

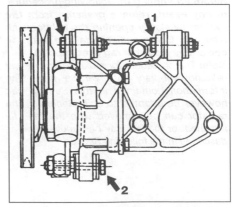

3.16a Power steering pump drivebelt adjustment points

1 Pump mounting bolts
2 Tensioner bolt

6A

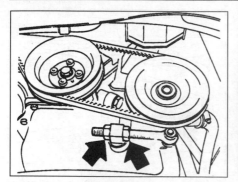

3.16b Rotate the tensioner screw locknuts (arrowed) to adjust drivebelt tension

screw locknuts and rotate them to allow the drivebelt to slacken **(see illustration)**. Slip the drivebelt off its pulleys.

17 Fit the new drivebelt in position over the pulleys and adjust it as follows:

Adjustment

18 Rotate the tensioner screw locknuts until the belt tension is correct.

19 Vauxhall recommend the use of a special tool (KM-128-A) for tensioning the belt to the specified amount. In the absence of this tool, aim for a tension such that the belt can be deflected approximately 12 mm by firm finger pressure in the middle of its run. The belt tension must, however, be checked with the special tool as soon as possible.

20 Once belt tension is correct, tighten the tensioner screw locknuts and lower the vehicle.

21 The tension of a new drivebelt should be rechecked after a few hundred miles.

4 Radiator - removal and refitting

⚠️ **Warning: If the engine has recently been run, then wait for the cooling system to cool before attempting the following procedure. In any event, release pressure from the system by slowly opening the header tank filler cap. Guard against scalding from the coolant by placing a rag over the cap.**

Note: *The procedure for radiator removal and refitting will vary with vehicle type. The information contained in this Section can however be adapted to suit. Generally, the radiator can be removed with the fan still attached, or the fan may be removed first as described in the following Section.*

4.8 Releasing a radiator mounting clip

Removal

1 Disconnect the battery earth (negative) lead.

2 Drain the cooling system, saving the coolant if it is fit for re-use.

3 Disconnect the top and bottom coolant hoses from the radiator and, if applicable, any vent hoses.

4 On automatic transmission models, disconnect and plug the fluid cooler pipes. Be prepared for fluid spillage.

5 On turbocharged models, refer to Chapter 4 and remove the charge air cooler.

6 Disconnect the fan and thermoswitch wiring, if not already done.

7 If obstructing radiator removal, remove the air cleaner housing inlet hose or pipe.

8 Release the radiator from its mountings. Typically there are two bolts or clips at the top and two rubber blocks to receive pegs at the bottom **(see illustration)**.

9 Carefully lift out the radiator (with fan if not already removed). Remember that the matrix is easily damaged.

5.3 Removing the cooling fan and cowl

Refitting

10 Refit the radiator in the reverse order of removal, ensuring that all mounting components and hoses are in good condition.

11 On completion of fitting, refill the cooling system.

12 On automatic transmission models, reconnect the fluid cooler pipes, then check the transmission fluid level and top-up if necessary.

13 Start the engine and check all disturbed connections for signs of fluid leakage, which if found, must be rectified.

14 Recheck the coolant level and if necessary, replenish the system.

5 Cooling fan - removal and refitting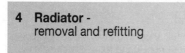

Removal

1 Disconnect the battery earth (negative) lead.

2 On turbocharged models, refer to Chapter 4 and remove the charge air cooler.

3 If not already done, unplug the wiring connector from the fan motor, then remove the two screws which secure the top corners of the fan cowl. Disengage the bottom corners of the cowl from their mountings and carefully remove the fan and cowl **(see illustration)**.

4 The fan with motor can be removed from the cowl after undoing the three retaining nuts **(see illustration)**.

5 It is not recommended that dismantling of the motor be attempted; spares are not available in any case.

Refitting

6 Refit the cooling fan and cowl in the reverse order of removal.

5.4 Fan to cowl retaining nuts (arrowed)

Chapter 6 Part B: Ancillary components - 15D, 15DT & 17DT engines

Contents

Degrees of difficulty

Easy, suitable for novice with little experience	✎	**Fairly easy,** suitable for beginner with some experience	✎	**Fairly difficult,** suitable for competent DIY mechanic	✎	**Difficult,** suitable for experienced DIY mechanic	✎	**Very difficult,** suitable for expert DIY or professional	✎

Specifications

Alternator drivebelt

Type	V-belt
Tension (using tension gauge):	
New	440 to 540 N
Used	320 to 390 N

Power steering pump drivebelt

Type	V-belt
Tension (using tension gauge):	
New	450 N
Used	250 to 300 N

Vacuum pump

Impeller vane minimum length	13 mm
Pump housing maximum inner diameter	57.10 mm

Torque wrench settings

	Nm	lbf ft
Vacuum pump		
Pump to alternator	7	5
Oil feed pipeline to pump	22	16
Power steering pump		
Pump to support	25	18
Pump support to mounting bracket	25	18
Pump mounting bracket to cylinder block	60	44
Drivebelt tensioner to bracket	25	18
Drivebelt tensioner to pump	18	13
Pressure line to pump connections	28	21
Alternator		
Alternator to mounting bracket:		
M8 bolt	24	18
M10 bolt	48	35
Radiator		
15D and 15DT engines:		
Radiator mounting bracket to deflector panel	4	3
Cowl to radiator	4	3
Fan motor to cowl	4	3

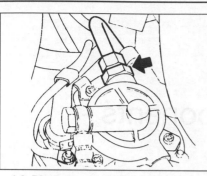

1.3 Disconnect the servo vacuum pipe (arrowed) from the vacuum pump

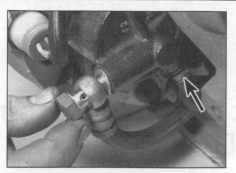

1.4 Disconnecting oil feed pipeline from vacuum pump. Return pipeline arrowed

1.5 Removing the vacuum pump from the alternator

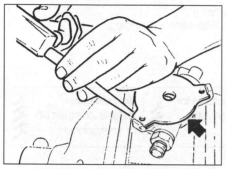

1.6 Using a drift to release the vacuum pump impeller cover

1.7a Remove the impeller cover . . .

1.7b . . . to expose the impeller and its vanes
A Impeller vane   B O-ring

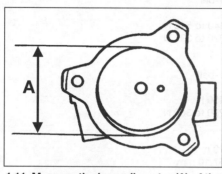

1.11 Measure the inner diameter (A) of the vacuum pump housing

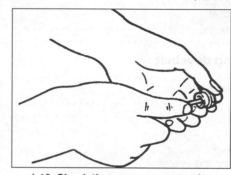

1.12 Check the vacuum pump valve functions correctly by testing it for free movement with a screwdriver

1 Vacuum pump - removal, inspection and refitting

Removal

1 The vacuum pump is mounted on the alternator casing. Access to the pump with the alternator in the vehicle is restricted but can be improved by removal of the exhaust pipe heatshield adjacent to it. Alternatively, remove the alternator from the vehicle.
2 Gain access to the pump by jacking up the front of the vehicle and supporting it on axle stands.
3 Commence removal by disconnecting the servo vacuum pipe from the pump. Do this by counterholding the large union nut and unscrewing the small one **(see illustration)**.
4 Disconnect the oil feed and return pipelines from the pump **(see illustration)**. Allow any oil to drain into a suitable container and plug or cap all hoses and unions to keep dirt out.
5 Remove the pump securing screws, taking note of any cable clips fitted beneath them, and pull the pump from the alternator drive spline **(see illustration)**.

Dismantling

6 Mark the fitted position of the pump impeller cover and then remove it by placing the pump in a vice and using a drift to rotate the cover free of its holding slots **(see illustration)**.
7 Remove the impeller cover to expose the impeller and its vanes **(see illustrations)**.
8 Separate the impeller and vanes from their housing and carefully clean each component part of the pump.

Inspection

9 Inspect the impeller and its housing for signs of scoring or overheating. If either is present, then renew the pump and investigate the reason for the fault having appeared.
10 Measure the length of the impeller vanes. If the length is below the specified minimum, then renew the vanes as a set.
11 Measure the inner diameter of the pump housing at various points **(see illustration)**. If the diameter is greater than the specified maximum, then renew the pump.
12 Unscrew the valve from the pump housing and check that it functions correctly by testing it for free movement with a screwdriver **(see illustration)**. Renew the valve if suspect.

1.13 Renew the O-ring (arrowed) in the alternator casing

Reassembly

13 Renew the O-rings in the pump housing and alternator casing **(see illustration)**.

14 Renew all pipeline union sealing washers.

15 Insert the vanes in the pump impeller so that their rounded ends are in contact with the bearing surface of the housing. Note that the grooves of the impeller should face the bottom of the housing.

16 Refit the impeller cover in its previously noted position.

Refitting

17 Refitting the pump is the reverse of the removal procedure, noting the following points:

a) With the pump refitted to the alternator, ensure that the alternator pulley can be turned easily by hand

b) Ensure that the alternator electrical cables are correctly routed around the pump and then properly secured **(see illustration)**

c) Tighten all fasteners to the torque wrench settings specified

d) Remove any blanking materials when reconnecting pipelines

e) Ensure no dirt is allowed to enter the pump

f) Pour approximately 5 cc of clean engine oil into the pump oil feed aperture before connecting the pipeline

g) Once fitted, check that pipelines are correctly routed, well clear of any adjacent components

2 Power steering pump -
removal and refitting

⚠️ **Warning: Never allow the power steering pump to run dry of fluid during system bleeding**

Removal

1 The power steering pump is mounted on a support which is itself attached to a mounting bracket bolted to the front right-hand end of the cylinder block.

2 Before the pump can be removed, adequate access must first be gained by removing the air cleaner housing assembly.

1.17 Ensure that the electrical cables are correctly routed around the vacuum pump

3 Disconnect the battery earth (negative) lead.

4 Release tension on the pump drivebelt and remove it.

5 Disconnect the fluid pressure and return hoses from the pump **(see illustration)** and allow the fluid to drain into a suitable container. Plug or cap all hoses and unions to keep dirt out.

6 The pump and mounting bracket can be removed as a complete assembly by removing the mounting bracket to cylinder block securing bolts and lifting the assembly clear of the engine **(see illustrations)**.

7 If renewing the pump, remove the mounting brackets from the old item and transfer them directly onto the replacement pump.

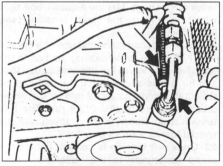

2.5 Disconnect the fluid pressure and return hoses (arrowed) from the power steering pump

2.6b . . . and lift the pump assembly clear of the engine

Refitting

8 Refitting is the reverse of the removal procedure, noting the following points:

a) Tighten all fasteners to the torque wrench settings specified

b) Remove any plugs when reconnecting hoses. Ensure no dirt is allowed to enter the hydraulic system and check that both hoses are correctly routed, well clear of any adjacent components

c) Refit and adjust the pump drivebelt

d) Refill the system with the specified type of fluid, then bleed any air from it as described in the following sub Section

System bleeding

9 Bleeding of the hydraulic system will normally only be required if any part of it has been disconnected.

10 Remove the fluid reservoir filler cap to expose the fluid level dipstick attached to its underside **(see illustration)**.

11 Top-up the fluid level to the "MAX" mark on the dipstick, using only that fluid specified in *"Lubricants, fluids and capacities"*.

12 Start the engine and immediately top-up the level in the fluid reservoir to the "MIN" mark on the dipstick.

13 Slowly move the steering wheel 2 to 3 times from left to right, approximately 45°. Now slowly move the steering wheel from lock-to-lock twice to purge out the air, then top-up the level in the fluid reservoir to the "MIN" mark on the

2.6a Remove the power steering pump mounting bracket to cylinder block securing bolts . . .

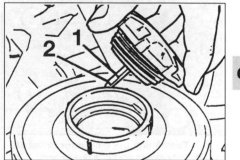

2.10 Remove the power steering fluid reservoir filler cap to expose the dipstick
1 "MAX" mark   2 "MIN" mark

dipstick. Add fluid slowly to prevent the possibility of aeration of the fluid in the circuit.

14 Switch off the engine, then recheck the fluid level in the reservoir. The level must be as follows:

Fluid level at "MAX" mark Fluid at operating temperature (approx. 80°C) Fluid level at "MIN" mark Fluid cold (approx. 20°C)

15 Finally, check the system hoses and connections for any signs of fluid leaks, which if found, must be rectified.

3 Auxiliary drivebelts - inspection, renewal and adjustment

Alternator

Inspection

1 Refer to the appropriate Section of Chapter 2.

Renewal

2 Gain full access to the alternator by jacking up the front right-hand side of the vehicle and supporting it on axle stands.

3 To remove the drivebelt, first slacken the alternator pivot and adjuster bolts.

4 Where fitted, remove the power steering pump drivebelt.

5 Move the alternator towards the engine and slip the drivebelt off its pulleys.

6 Fit the new drivebelt in position over the pulleys and adjust it as follows:

Adjustment

7 Tighten the alternator fastenings slightly, so that the alternator can just be moved by hand.

8 Insert a socket drive in the end of the adjuster arm and use it as a lever to move the alternator away from the engine until the belt tension is correct. Nip the adjuster bolt tight whilst checking the belt tension **(see illustration)**.

9 Vauxhall recommend the use of a special tool (KM-128-A) for tensioning the belt to the specified amount **(see illustration)**. In the

absence of this tool, aim for a tension such that the belt can be deflected about 12 mm by firm finger pressure in the middle of its run. The belt tension must, however, be checked with the special tool as soon as possible.

10 Tighten the alternator fastenings to the specified torque setting once the belt tension is correct.

11 Where applicable, refit and tension the steering pump drivebelt.

12 Lower the front of the vehicle, removing the axle stands and jack.

13 The tension of a new drivebelt should be rechecked after a few hundred miles.

Power steering pump

Inspection

14 Refer to the appropriate Section of Chapter 2.

Renewal

15 Gain access to the drivebelt by removing the air cleaner housing assembly.

16 To remove the drivebelt, first loosen the pump pivot and adjuster bolts.

17 Move the pump towards the engine and slip the drivebelt off its pulleys.

18 Fit the new drivebelt in position over the pulleys and adjust it as follows:

Adjustment

19 Tighten the pump fastenings slightly, so that the pump can just be moved by hand.

20 Insert a socket drive in the end of the adjuster arm and use it as a lever to move the pump away from the engine until the belt tension is correct. Nip the adjuster bolt tight whilst checking the belt tension **(see illustration)**.

21 Vauxhall recommend the use of a special tool (KM-128-A) for tensioning the belt to the specified amount. In the absence of this tool, aim for a tension such that the belt can be deflected approximately 12 mm by firm finger pressure in the middle of its run. The belt tension must, however, be checked with the special tool as soon as possible.

22 Once belt tension is correct, tighten the pump fastenings to the specified torque setting.

23 Refit the air cleaner housing assembly.

24 The tension of a new drivebelt should be rechecked after a few hundred miles.

4 Radiator - removal and refitting

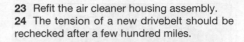

> ⚠ *Warning: If the engine has recently been run, then wait for the cooling system to cool before attempting the following procedure. In any event, release pressure from the system by slowly opening the header tank filler cap. Guard against scalding from the coolant by placing a rag over the cap.*

Note: *The procedures given in this Section may vary with vehicle type. The information contained in this Section can, however, be adapted to suit.*

15D and 15DT engines

Removal

1 Disconnect the battery earth (negative) lead.

2 Drain the cooling system, saving the coolant if it is fit for re-use.

3 If obstructing radiator removal, remove the air cleaner housing inlet hose or pipe.

4 Refer to the following Section and remove the fan cowl with motor

5 Disconnect the thermoswitch wiring connector.

6 Disconnect the top and bottom coolant hoses from the radiator and, if applicable, any vent hoses **(see illustration)**.

7 Unbolt the radiator upper mounting brackets from the air deflector panel.

8 Carefully lift out the radiator, detaching it from its lower rubber mountings. Remember that the matrix is easily damaged.

Refitting

9 Refit the radiator in the reverse order of removal, ensuring that all mounting components and hoses are in good condition and that all fastenings are tightened to the specified torque settings.

3.8 Tensioning the alternator drivebelt
A Socket drive in end of adjuster arm
B Adjuster strap bolt
C Pivot bolt

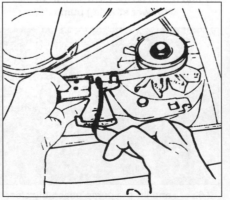

3.9 Using special tool KM-128-A to tension the alternator drivebelt

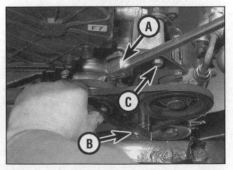

3.20 Tensioning the power steering pump drivebelt
A Socket drive in end of adjuster arm
B Adjuster strap bolt
C Pivot bolt

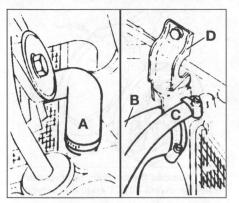

4.6 Details of radiator mounting bracket and hose connections - 15D and 15DT engines

A Bottom coolant hose
B Top coolant hose
C Vent hose
D Upper mounting bracket

10 On completion of fitting, refill the cooling system.
11 Start the engine and check all disturbed connections for signs of coolant leakage, which if found, must be rectified.
12 Recheck the coolant level and if necessary, replenish the system.

17DT engine - Astra

13 Refer to the removal and refitting procedure given in Part A of this Chapter for the 17DTL engine.

17DT engine - Cavalier

Removal

14 Disconnect the battery earth (negative) lead.
15 Drain the cooling system, saving the coolant if it is fit for re-use.
16 If obstructing radiator removal, remove the air cleaner housing inlet hose or pipe.
17 Disconnect the top (plenum chamber) hose and bottom (turbocharger) hose from the charge air cooler (CAC) which is mounted on the left-hand side of the radiator.
18 Disconnect the fan and thermoswitch wiring connectors.

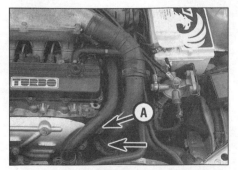

5.4a Remove the plenum chamber to turbocharger feed hose (arrowed)
A Oil dipstick tube

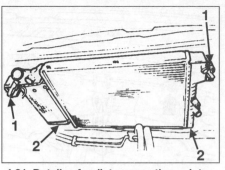

4.21 Details of radiator mounting points - 17DT engine in Cavalier

1 Top mounting clips
2 Bottom mounting pegs

19 Refer to the following Section and remove the fan cowl with motor
20 Disconnect the top and bottom coolant hoses from the radiator and, if applicable, any vent hoses.
21 Release the radiator from its upper mountings. Typically there are two clips at the top and two rubber blocks to receive pegs at the bottom **(see illustration)**.
22 Carefully lift out the radiator and charge air cooler assembly. Remember that the matrix is easily damaged.

Refitting

23 Refit the radiator and CAC assembly in the reverse order of removal, ensuring all mountings and hoses are in good condition.
24 On completion of fitting, refill the cooling system.
25 Start the engine and check all disturbed connections for signs of fluid leakage, which if found, must be rectified.
26 Recheck the coolant level and if necessary, replenish the system.

5 Cooling fan - removal and refitting

Note: The procedures given in this Section may vary with vehicle type. The information contained in this Section can, however, be adapted to suit.

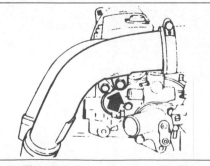

5.4b The plenum chamber to turbocharger feed hose cylinder head mounting bolt (arrowed)

15D engine

Removal

1 Disconnect the battery earth (negative) lead.
2 Where it interferes with cowl removal, remove the air cleaner housing inlet pipe.

15DT engine

Removal

3 Disconnect the battery earth (negative) lead.
4 Gain the necessary clearance for fan removal by first removing the plenum chamber to turbocharger feed hose, see Chapter 3 **(see illustrations)**.
5 Unbolt the oil dipstick tube from the cylinder block and remove it.
6 Remove the air cleaner housing inlet pipe.
7 With the engine cold, release pressure from the cooling system by slowly opening the header tank filler cap. Guard against possible scalding from the coolant by placing a rag over the cap.
8 Disconnect the top coolant hose and vent hose from the radiator, catching any spilt coolant.
9 On vehicles equipped with power steering, release the fluid reservoir mounting strap bolt and remove the reservoir from its mounting. Keeping it upright, secure the reservoir to one side, clear of the fan cowl.
10 Unbolt the radiator upper mounting brackets from the air deflector panel and carefully push the radiator forwards.

15D and 15DT engines

Removal

11 Unplug the wiring connector from the fan motor and detach the wiring harness from the cowl.
12 Remove the two bolts which secure the top of the cowl **(see illustration)**.
13 Disengage the bottom corners of the cowl from their mountings and carefully lift the fan and cowl assembly away from the radiator **(see illustration)**.
14 Remove the fan assembly from the motor by detaching its retaining clip from the motor shaft.

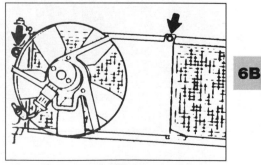

5.12 The fan cowl securing bolts (arrowed) - 15D and 15DT engines

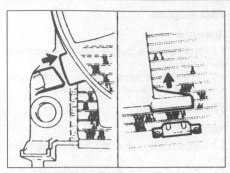

5.13 The fan cowl bottom mountings - 15D and 15DT engines

5.22 The fan cowl securing bolts (arrowed) - 17DT engine in Cavalier

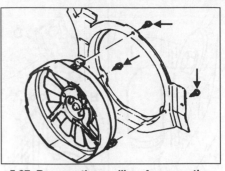

5.27 Remove the auxiliary fan mounting bolts (arrowed) - 17DT engine in Cavalier

15 The motor can now be removed from the cowl after undoing its retaining nuts.

16 It is not recommended that dismantling of the motor be attempted; spares are not available in any case.

Refitting

17 Refit the cooling fan and cowl in the reverse order of removal, noting the following:

a) *Tighten all fasteners to the specified torque wrench settings*
b) *Check that the tang on the motor shaft aligns with the groove of the fan*
c) *Check that the fan retaining clip is tight on the motor shaft*
d) *Route the wiring harness correctly, so that it cannot be damaged by the fan*
e) *Where the radiator has been disturbed, refill the cooling system and with the engine running, check all disturbed connections for leaks*

17DT engine - Astra

18 Refer to the removal and refitting procedure given in Part A of this Chapter for the 17DTL engine.

17DT engine - Cavalier

Removal - main fan and cowl

19 Disconnect the battery earth (negative) lead.

20 Where it interferes with cowl removal, remove the air inlet collector box inlet pipe.

21 Unplug the wiring connector from the fan motor and where necessary, detach the wiring harness from the cowl.

22 Remove the two bolts which secure the top of the cowl **(see illustration)**.

23 Disengage the bottom corners of the cowl from their mountings and carefully lift the fan and cowl assembly away from the radiator.

24 Remove the fan assembly from the motor by detaching its retaining clip from the motor shaft.

25 The motor can now be removed from the cowl after undoing its retaining nuts.

26 It is not recommended that dismantling of the motor be attempted; spares are not available in any case.

Removal - auxiliary fan

27 With the radiator removed, detach the auxiliary fan from its mounting on the crossmember by removing its forward-facing retaining bolts **(see illustration)**.

28 The motor can be removed from its mounting after undoing its retaining nuts. Note that the fan to motor securing nut has a left-hand thread.

Refitting

29 Refit the main fan and cowl in the reverse order of removal, noting the following:

a) *Tighten all fasteners to the torque wrench settings specified*
b) *Check that the tang on the motor shaft aligns with the groove of the fan*
c) *Check that the fan retaining clip is tight on the motor shaft*
d) *Route the wiring harness correctly, so that it cannot be damaged by the fan*

Chapter 7
Fault diagnosis

Contents

1 Introduction

The majority of starting problems on small diesel engines are electrical in origin. The mechanic who is familiar with petrol engines but less so with diesel may be inclined to view the diesel's injectors and pump in the same light as the spark plugs and distributor, but this is generally a mistake.

When investigating complaints of difficult starting for someone else, make sure that the correct starting procedure is understood and is being followed. Some drivers are unaware of the significance of the preheating warning light - many modern engines are sufficiently forgiving for this not to matter in mild weather, but with the onset of winter problems begin.

As a rule of thumb, if the engine is difficult to start but runs well when it has finally got going, the problem is electrical (battery, starter motor or preheating system). If poor performance is combined with difficult starting, the problem is likely to be in the fuel system. The low pressure (supply) side of the fuel system should be checked before suspecting the injectors and injection pump. Normally the pump is the last item to suspect, since unless it has been tampered with there is no reason for it to be at fault.

The table overleaf lists various possible causes of faults. Further discussion of some faults will be found in the Sections indicated.

7

2 Fault diagnosis -
symptoms and reasons

Engine turns but will not start (cold)

- ☐ Incorrect use of preheating system (Chapter 5)
- ☐ Preheating system fault (Chapter 5)
- ☐ Fuel waxing (in very cold weather) (Section 5)
- ☐ Overfuelling/cold start advance mechanism defective (Chapter 4)

Engine turns but will not start (hot or cold)

- ☐ Low cranking speed (see below)
- ☐ Poor compression (Section 3)
- ☐ No fuel in tank
- ☐ Air in fuel system (Section 4)
- ☐ Fuel feed restriction (Section 5)
- ☐ Fuel contaminated (Chapter 4)
- ☐ Stop solenoid defective (Section 17)
- ☐ Major mechanical failure (Chapter 3)
- ☐ Injection pump internal fault (Chapter 4)

Low cranking speed

- ☐ Inadequate battery capacity (Chapter 2)
- ☐ Incorrect grade of oil (*Lubricants, fluids and capacities*)
- ☐ High resistance in starter motor circuit (Chapter 5)
- ☐ Starter motor internal fault (Chapter 5)

Engine is difficult to start

- ☐ Incorrect starting procedure
- ☐ Battery or starter motor fault (Chapters 2 and 5)
- ☐ Preheating system fault (Chapter 5)
- ☐ Air in fuel system (Section 4)
- ☐ Fuel feed restriction (Section 5)
- ☐ Poor compression (Section 3)
- ☐ Valve clearances incorrect (Chapter 3)
- ☐ Valves sticking (Chapter 3)
- ☐ Blockage in exhaust system
- ☐ Valve timing incorrect (Chapter 3)
- ☐ Injector(s) faulty (Chapter 4)
- ☐ Injection pump timing incorrect (Chapter 4)
- ☐ Injection pump internal fault (Chapter 4)

Engine starts but stops again

- ☐ Fuel very low in tank
- ☐ Air in fuel system (Section 4)
- ☐ Idle adjustment incorrect (Chapter 2)
- ☐ Fuel feed restriction (Section 5)
- ☐ Fuel return restriction (Chapter 4)
- ☐ Air cleaner dirty (Chapter 2)
- ☐ Blockage in induction system (Chapter 4)
- ☐ Blockage in exhaust system
- ☐ Injector(s) faulty (Chapter 4)

Engine will not stop when switched off

- ☐ Stop solenoid defective (Section 17)

Misfiring/rough idle

- ☐ Air cleaner dirty (Chapter 2)
- ☐ Blockage in induction system (Chapter 4)

- ☐ Air in fuel system (Section 4)
- ☐ Fuel feed restriction (Section 5)
- ☐ Valve clearances incorrect (Chapter 3)
- ☐ Valve(s) sticking (Chapter 3)
- ☐ Valve spring(s) weak or broken (Chapter 3)
- ☐ Poor compression (Section 3)
- ☐ Overheating (Section 15)
- ☐ Injector pipe(s) wrongly connected or wrong type (Chapter 4)
- ☐ Valve timing incorrect (Chapter 3)
- ☐ Injector(s) faulty or wrong type (Chapter 4)
- ☐ Injection pump timing incorrect (Chapter 4)
- ☐ Injection pump faulty or wrong type (Chapter 4)

Lack of power (Section 6)

- ☐ Accelerator linkage not moving through full travel (cable slack or pedal obstructed) (Chapter 4)
- ☐ Injection pump control linkages sticking or maladjusted (Chapter 4)
- ☐ Air cleaner dirty (Chapter 2)
- ☐ Blockage in induction system (Chapter 4)
- ☐ Air in fuel system (Section 4)
- ☐ Fuel feed restriction (Section 5)
- ☐ Valve timing incorrect (Chapter 3)
- ☐ Injection pump timing incorrect (Chapter 4)
- ☐ Blockage in exhaust system
- ☐ Turbo boost pressure inadequate, when applicable (Section 7)
- ☐ Valve clearances incorrect (Chapter 3)
- ☐ Poor compression (Section 3)
- ☐ Injector(s) faulty or wrong type (Chapter 4)
- ☐ Injection pump faulty (Chapter 4)

Fuel consumption excessive (Section 8)

- ☐ External leakage
- ☐ Fuel passing into sump (Section 9)
- ☐ Air cleaner dirty (Chapter 2)
- ☐ Blockage in induction system (Chapter 4)
- ☐ Valve clearances incorrect (Chapter 3)
- ☐ Valve(s) sticking (Chapter 3)
- ☐ Valve spring(s) weak (Chapter 3)
- ☐ Poor compression (Section 3)
- ☐ Valve timing incorrect (Chapter 3)
- ☐ Injection pump timing incorrect (Chapter 4)
- ☐ Injector(s) faulty or wrong type (Chapter 4)
- ☐ Injection pump faulty (Chapter 4)

Engine knocks (Section 10)

- ☐ Air in fuel system (Section 4)
- ☐ Incorrect fuel grade or quality poor (*Lubricants, fluids and capacities*)
- ☐ Injector(s) faulty or wrong type (Section 10)
- ☐ Valve spring(s) weak or broken (Chapter 3)
- ☐ Valve(s) sticking (Chapter 3)
- ☐ Valve clearances incorrect (Chapter 3)
- ☐ Valve timing incorrect (Chapter 3)

- ☐ Injection pump timing incorrect (Chapter 4)
- ☐ Piston protrusion excessive/head gasket thickness inadequate (after repair) (Chapter 3)
- ☐ Valve recess incorrect (after repair) (Chapter 3)
- ☐ Piston rings broken or worn (Chapter 3)
- ☐ Pistons and/or bores worn (Chapter 3)
- ☐ Crankshaft bearings worn or damaged (Chapter 3)
- ☐ Small-end bearings worn (Chapter 3)
- ☐ Camshaft worn (Chapter 3)

Black smoke in exhaust (Section 11)

- ☐ Air cleaner dirty (Chapter 2)
- ☐ Blockage in induction system (Chapter 4)
- ☐ Valve clearances incorrect (Chapter 3)
- ☐ Poor compression (Section 3)
- ☐ Turbo boost pressure inadequate, when applicable (Section 7)
- ☐ Blockage in exhaust system
- ☐ Valve timing incorrect (Chapter 3)
- ☐ Injector(s) faulty or wrong type (Chapter 4)
- ☐ Injection pump timing incorrect (Chapter 4)
- ☐ Injection pump faulty (Chapter 4)

Blue or white smoke in exhaust (Section 11)

- ☐ Engine oil incorrect grade or poor quality (Lubricants, fluids and capacities)
- ☐ Glow plug(s) defective, or controller faulty (smoke at start-up only) (Chapter 5)
- ☐ Air cleaner dirty(Chapter 2)
- ☐ Blockage in induction system (Chapter 4)
- ☐ Valve timing incorrect (Chapter 3)
- ☐ Injection pump timing incorrect (Chapter 4)
- ☐ Injector(s) defective, or heat shields damaged or missing (Chapter 4)
- ☐ Engine running too cool
- ☐ Oil entering via valve stems (Section 12)
- ☐ Poor compression (Section 3)
- ☐ Head gasket blown (Chapter 3)
- ☐ Piston rings broken or worn (Chapter 3)
- ☐ Pistons and/or bores worn (Chapter 3)

Oil consumption excessive (Section 13)

- ☐ External leakage (standing or running)
- ☐ New engine not yet run-in
- ☐ Engine oil incorrect grade or poor quality (Lubricants, fluids and capacities)
- ☐ Oil level too high (Chapter 2)
- ☐ Crankcase ventilation system obstructed (Chapter 2)
- ☐ Oil leaking from oil feed pipe into fuel feed pipe (Chapter 4)
- ☐ Oil leakage from ancillary component (vacuum pump etc.) (Chapter 6)
- ☐ Oil leaking into coolant (Chapter 4)
- ☐ Oil leaking into injection pump (Chapter 4)
- ☐ Air cleaner dirty (Chapter 2)
- ☐ Blockage in induction system (Chapter 4)
- ☐ Cylinder bores glazed (Section 14)
- ☐ Piston rings broken or worn (Chapter 3)
- ☐ Pistons and/or bores worn (Chapter 3)
- ☐ Valve stems or guides worn (Chapter 3)
- ☐ Valve stem oil seals worn (Chapter 3)

Overheating (Section 15)

- ☐ Coolant leakage (Chapter 2)
- ☐ Engine oil level too high (Chapter 2)
- ☐ Electric cooling fan malfunctioning (Chapter 5)
- ☐ Coolant pump defective (Chapter 3)
- ☐ Radiator clogged externally
- ☐ Radiator clogged internally
- ☐ Coolant hoses blocked or collapsed
- ☐ Coolant reservoir pressure cap defective or incorrect
- ☐ Coolant thermostat defective or incorrect (Chapter 3)
- ☐ Thermostat missing (Chapter 3)
- ☐ Air cleaner dirty (Chapter 2)
- ☐ Blockage in induction system (Chapter 4)
- ☐ Blockage in exhaust system
- ☐ Head gasket blown (Chapter 3)
- ☐ Cylinder head cracked or warped (Chapter 3)
- ☐ Valve timing incorrect (Chapter 3)
- ☐ Injection pump timing incorrect (over-advanced) (Chapter 4)
- ☐ Injector(s) faulty or wrong type (Chapter 4)
- ☐ Injection pump faulty (Chapter 4)
- ☐ Imminent seizure (piston pick-up)

Crankcase pressure excessive (oil being blown out)

- ☐ Blockage in crankcase ventilation system (Chapter 2)
- ☐ Leakage in vacuum pump or exhauster (Chapter 6)
- ☐ Piston rings broken or sticking (Chapter 3)
- ☐ Pistons or bores worn (Chapter 3)
- ☐ Head gasket blown (Chapter 3)

Erratic running

- ☐ Operating temperature incorrect
- ☐ Accelerator linkage maladjusted or sticking (Chapter 4)
- ☐ Air cleaner dirty (Chapter 2)
- ☐ Blockage in induction system (Chapter 4)
- ☐ Air in fuel system (Section 4)
- ☐ Injector pipe(s) wrongly connected or wrong type (Chapter 4)
- ☐ Fuel feed restriction (Section 5)
- ☐ Fuel return restriction
- ☐ Valve clearances incorrect (Chapter 3)
- ☐ Valve(s) sticking (Chapter 3)
- ☐ Valve spring(s) broken or weak (Chapter 3)
- ☐ Valve timing incorrect (Chapter 3)
- ☐ Poor compression (Section 3)
- ☐ Injector(s) faulty or wrong type (Chapter 4)
- ☐ Injection pump mountings loose (Chapter 4)
- ☐ Injection pump timing incorrect (Chapter 4)
- ☐ Injection pump faulty (Chapter 4)

Vibration

- ☐ Accelerator linkage sticking (Chapter 4)
- ☐ Engine mountings loose or worn (Chapter 3)
- ☐ Cooling fan damaged or loose
- ☐ Crankshaft pulley/damper damaged or loose (Chapter 3)
- ☐ Injector pipe(s) wrongly connected or wrong type (Chapter 4)
- ☐ Valve(s) sticking (Chapter 3)
- ☐ Flywheel or (when applicable) flywheel housing loose (Chapter 3)
- ☐ Poor (uneven) compression (Section 3)

7

Low oil pressure

- ☐ Oil level low (Chapter 2)
- ☐ Oil grade or quality incorrect (*Lubricants, fluids and capacities*)
- ☐ Oil filter clogged (Chapter 2)
- ☐ Overheating (Section 15)
- ☐ Oil contaminated (Section 16)
- ☐ Gauge or warning light sender inaccurate (Chapter 5)
- ☐ Oil pump pick-up strainer clogged (Chapter 3)
- ☐ Oil pump suction pipe loose or cracked (Chapter 3)
- ☐ Oil pressure relief valve defective or stuck open (Chapter 3)
- ☐ Oil pump worn (Chapter 3)
- ☐ Crankshaft bearings worn (Chapter 3)

High oil pressure

- ☐ Oil grade or quality incorrect (*Lubricants, fluids and capacities*)
- ☐ Gauge inaccurate
- ☐ Oil pressure relief valve stuck shut (Chapter 3)

Injector pipe(s) break or split repeatedly

- ☐ Missing or wrongly located clamps (Chapter 4)
- ☐ Wrong type or length of pipe (Chapter 4)
- ☐ Faulty injector (Chapter 4)
- ☐ Faulty delivery valve (Chapter 4)

3 Poor compression

1 Poor compression may give rise to a number of faults, including difficult starting, loss of power, misfiring or uneven running and smoke in the exhaust.

2 Before looking for mechanical reasons for compression loss, check that the problem is not on the induction side. A dirty air cleaner or some other blockage in the induction system can restrict air inlet to the point where compression suffers.

3 Mechanical reasons for low compression include :

a) *Incorrect valve clearances*
b) *Sticking valves*
c) *Weak or broken valve springs*
d) *Incorrect valve timing*
e) *Worn or burnt valve heads and seats*
f) *Worn valve stems and guides*
g) *Head gasket blown*
h) *Piston rings broken or sticking*
j) *Pistons or bores worn*
k) *Head gasket thickness incorrect (after rebuild)*

4 Compression loss on one cylinder alone can be due to a defective or badly seated glow plug, or a leaking injector sealing washer. Some engines also have a cylinder head plug for the insertion of a dial test indicator probe when determining TDC and this should not be overlooked.

5 Compression loss on two adjacent cylinders is almost certainly due to the head gasket blowing between them. Sometimes the fault will be corrected by renewing the gasket but a blown gasket can also be an indication that the cylinder head itself is warped. Always check the head mating face for distortion when renewing the gasket. On wet liner engines also check liner protrusion.

Compression test

6 A compression tester specifically intended for diesel engines must be used, because of the higher pressures involved - see Chapter 3. The tester is connected to an adapter which screws into the glow plug or injector hole. Normally sealing washers must be used on both sides of the adapter.

7 Unless specific instructions to the contrary are supplied with the tester, observe the following points :

a) *The battery must be in a good state of charge, the air cleaner element must be clean and the engine should be at normal operating temperature*
b) *All the injectors or glow plugs should be removed before starting the test. If removing the injectors, also remove their heat shields (when fitted), otherwise they may be blown out*
c) *The stop control lever on the injection pump must be operated, or the stop solenoid disconnected, to prevent the engine from running or fuel from being discharged*

8 There is no need to hold the accelerator pedal down during the test because the diesel engine air inlet is not throttled. There are rare exceptions to this case, when a throttle valve is used to produce vacuum for servo or governor operation.

9 The actual compression pressures measured are not so important as the balance between cylinders. Typical values at cranking speed are:

Good condition - 25 to 30 bar (363 to 435 lbf/in2)
Minimum - 18 bar (261 lbf/in2)
Maximum difference between cylinders - 5 bar (73 lbf/in2)

10 The cause of poor compression is less easy to establish on a diesel engine than on a petrol one. The effect of introducing oil into the cylinders (wet testing) is not conclusive, because there is a risk that the oil will sit in the bowl in the piston crown (direct injection engines) or in the swirl chamber (indirect) instead of passing to the rings.

Leakdown test

11 A leakdown test measures the rate at which compressed air fed into the cylinder is lost. It is an alternative to a compression test and in many ways it is better, since it provides easy identification of where pressure loss is occurring (piston rings, valves or head gasket). However, it does require a source of compressed air.

12 Before beginning the test, remove the cooling system pressure cap. This is necessary because if there is a leak into the cooling system, the introduction of compressed air may damage the radiator. Similarly, it is advisable to remove the dipstick or the oil filler cap to prevent excessive crankcase pressurisation.

13 Connect the tester to a compressed air line and adjust the reading to 100% as instructed by the manufacturer.

14 Remove the glow plugs or injectors and screw the appropriate adapter into a glow plug or injector hole. Fit the whistle to the adapter and turn the crankshaft. When the whistle begins to sound, the piston in question is rising on compression. When the whistle stops, TDC has been reached **(see illustrations)**.

15 Engage a gear and apply the handbrake to stop the engine turning. Remove the whistle and connect the tester to the adapter. Note the tester reading, which indicates the rate at which the air escapes. Repeat the test on the other cylinders **(see illustration)**.

16 The tester reading is in the form of a percentage, where 100% is perfect. Readings of 80% or better are to be expected from an engine in good condition. The actual reading is less important than the balance between cylinders, which should be within 5%.

17 The areas from which escaping air emerges show where a fault lies, as follows :

Air escaping from	Probable cause
Oil filler cap or or dipstick tube	Worn piston rings cylinder bores
Exhaust pipe	Worn or burnt exhaust valve
Air cleaner/inlet manifold	Worn or burnt inlet valve
Cooling system	Blown head gasket or cracked cylinder head

18 Bear in mind that if the head gasket is blown between two adjacent cylinders, air escaping from the cylinder under test may emerge via an open valve in the cylinder adjacent.

3.14a Leakdown test adapter being fitted to a glow plug hole

3.14b Whistle fitted to adapter to find TDC

3.15 Leakdown tester in use

4 Air in fuel system

1 The diesel engine will not run at all, or at best will run erratically, if there is air in the fuel lines. If the fuel tank has been allowed to run dry, or after operations in which the fuel supply lines have been opened, the fuel system must be bled before the engine will run.

2 Unlike some older systems, manual bleeding or venting of the fuel system fitted to the engines covered in this Manual is not necessary, even if the fuel tank is run dry. Provided that the battery is in good condition, simply cranking the engine on the starter motor will eventually bleed the system. Note that the starter motor should not be operated for more than ten seconds at a time whilst allowing five seconds between periods of operation.

3 Air will also enter the fuel lines through any leaking joint or seal, since the supply side is under negative pressure all the time that the engine is running.

5 Fuel feed restricted

1 Restriction in the fuel feed from the tank to the pump may be caused by any of the following faults :
a) Fuel filter blocked
b) Tank vent blocked
c) Feed pipe blocked or collapsed
d Fuel waxing (in very cold weather)

Fuel waxing

2 In the case of fuel waxing, the wax normally builds up first in the filter. If the filter can be warmed this will often allow the engine to run. *Caution : Do not use a naked flame for this. Only in exceptionally severe weather will waxing prevent winter grade fuel from being pumped out of the tank*

Microbiological contamination

3 Under certain conditions it is possible for micro-organisms to colonise the fuel tank and supply lines. These micro-organisms produce a black sludge or slime which can block the filter and cause corrosion of metal parts. The problem normally shows up first as an unexpected blockage of the filter.

4 If such contamination is found, drain the fuel tank and discard the drained fuel. Flush the tank and fuel lines with clean fuel and renew the fuel filter - in bad cases steam clean the tank as well. If there is evidence that the contamination has passed the fuel filter, have the injection pump cleaned by a specialist.

5 Further trouble may be avoided by only using fuel from reputable outlets with a high turnover. Proprietary additives are also available to inhibit the growth of micro-organisms in storage tanks or in the vehicle fuel tank.

6 Lack of power

Complaints of lack of power are not always justified. If necessary, perform a road or dynamometer test to verify the condition. Even if power is definitely down, the complaint is not necessarily due to an engine or injection system fault.

Before commencing detailed investigation, check that the accelerator linkage is moving through its full travel. Also make sure that an apparent power loss is not caused by items such as binding brakes, under-inflated tyres, overloading of the vehicle, or some particular feature of operation.

7 Turbo boost pressure inadequate

If boost pressure is low, power will be down and too much fuel may be delivered at high engine speeds (depending on the method of pump control). Possible reasons for low boost pressure include :
a) Air cleaner dirty
b) Leaks in induction system
c) Blockage in exhaust system
d) Turbo control fault (wastegate or actuator)
e) Turbo mechanical fault

8 Fuel consumption excessive

Complaints of excessive fuel consumption, as with lack of power, may not mean that a fault exists. If the complaint is justified and there are no obvious fuel leaks, check the same external factors as for lack of power before turning to the engine and injection system.

9 Fuel in sump

If fuel oil is found to be diluting the oil in the sump, this can only have arrived by passing down the cylinder bores. Assuming that the problem is not one of excessive fuel delivery, piston and bore wear is indicated.

Fuel contamination of the oil can be detected by smell, and in bad cases by an obvious reduction in viscosity.

10 Knocking caused by injector fault

1 A faulty injector which is causing knocking noises can be identified as follows.

2 Clean around the injector fuel pipe unions. Run the engine at a fast idle so that the knock can be heard. Using for preference a split ring spanner, slacken and retighten each injector union in turn

 Warning: Protect yourself against contact with diesel fuel by covering each union with a piece of rag to absorb the fuel which will spray out.

3 When the union supplying the defective injector is slackened, the knock will disappear. Stop the engine and remove the injector for inspection.

7

11 Excessive exhaust smoke

1 Check first that the smoke is still excessive when the engine has reached normal operating temperature. A cold engine may produce some blue or white smoke until it has warmed up; this is not necessarily a fault.

Black smoke

2 This is produced by incomplete combustion of the fuel in such a way that carbon particles (soot) are formed. Incomplete combustion shows that there is a lack of oxygen, either because too much fuel is being delivered or because not enough air is being drawn into the cylinders. A dirty air cleaner is an obvious cause of air starvation; incorrect valve clearances should also be considered. Combustion may also be incomplete because the injection timing is incorrect (too far retarded) or because the injector spray pattern is poor.

Blue smoke

3 This is produced either by incomplete combustion of the fuel or by burning lubricating oil. This type of incomplete combustion may be caused by incorrect injection timing (too far advanced), by defective injectors or by damaged or missing injector heat shields.
4 All engines burn a certain amount of oil, especially when cold, but if enough is being burnt to cause excessive exhaust smoke this suggests that there is a significant degree of wear or some other problem.

White smoke

5 Not to be confused with steam, this is produced by unburnt or partially burnt fuel appearing in the exhaust gases. Some white smoke is normal during and immediately after start-up, especially in cold conditions. Excessive amounts of white smoke can be caused by a preheating system fault, by incorrect injection pump timing, or by too much fuel being delivered by the injection pump (overfuelling device malfunctioning). The use of poor quality fuel with a low cetane number, and thus a long ignition delay, can also increase emissions of white smoke.
6 Accurate measurement of exhaust smoke requires the use of a smoke meter. This is not a DIY job, but any garage which carries out diesel MoT tests will have such a meter.

12 Oil entering engine via valve stems

Excessive oil consumption due to oil passing down the valve stems can have three causes :
a) Valve stem wear
b) Valve guide wear
c) Valve stem oil seal wear

In the first two cases the cylinder head must be removed and dismantled so that the valves and guides can be inspected and measured for wear.

13 Oil consumption excessive

When investigating complaints of excessive oil consumption, make sure that the correct level checking procedure is being followed. If insufficient time is allowed for the oil to drain down after stopping the engine, or if the level is checked while the vehicle is standing on a slope, a false low reading may result. The unnecessary topping-up which follows may of itself cause increased oil consumption as a result of the level being too high.

14 Cylinder bore glazing

Engines which spend long periods idling can suffer from glazing of the cylinder bores, leading to high oil consumption although no significant wear has taken place. The same effect can be produced by incorrect running-in procedures, or by the use of the incorrect grade of oil during running-in. The remedy is to remove the pistons, deglaze the bores with a hone or 'glaze buster' tool and to fit new piston rings.

15 Overheating

Any modern engine will certainly suffer serious damage if overheating is allowed to occur. The importance of regular and conscientious cooling system maintenance cannot be overstressed. Always use a good quality antifreeze and renew it regularly. When refilling the cooling system, follow the specified procedures carefully in order to eliminate any airlocks.

If overheating does occur, do not continue to drive. Stop at once and do not proceed until the problem is fixed.

16 Oil contamination

1 Oil contamination falls into three categories - dirt, sludge and dilution.

Dirt

2 Dirt or soot builds up in the oil in normal operation. It is not a problem if regular oil and filter changes are carried out. If it gets to the stage where it is causing low oil pressure, change the oil and filter immediately.

Sludge

3 This occurs when inferior grades of oil are used, or when regular oil changing has been neglected. It is more likely to occur on engines which rarely reach operating temperature. If sludge is found when draining, a flushing oil may be used if the engine manufacturer allows it. The engine should then be refilled with fresh oil of the correct grade and a new oil filter be fitted.
Caution : Some engine manufacturers forbid the use of flushing oil, because it cannot all be drained afterwards. If in doubt, consult a dealer or specialist

Dilution

4 This is of two kinds - fuel and coolant. In either case if the dilution is bad enough the engine oil level will appear to rise with use.
5 Coolant dilution of the oil is indicated by the 'mayonnaise' appearance of the oil and water mixture. Sometimes oil will also appear in the coolant. Possible reasons are :
a) Blown head gasket
b) Cracked or porous cylinder head or block
c) Cylinder liner seal failure (on wet liner engines)
d) Leaking oil-to-coolant oil cooler (when fitted)
6 With either type of dilution, the cause must be dealt with and the oil and filter changed.

17 Engine stop (fuel cut-off) solenoid - emergency repair

1 The solenoid valve cuts off the supply of fuel to the high pressure side of the injection pump when the ignition is switched off. If the solenoid fails electrically or mechanically so that its plunger is in the shut position, the engine will not run. One possible reason for such a failure is that the ignition has been switched off while engine speed is still high. In such a case the plunger will be sucked onto its seat with considerable force, and perhaps jam.
2 Should the valve fail on the road and a spare not be immediately available, the following procedure will serve to get the engine running again.
Caution : It is important that no dirt is allowed to enter the injection pump via the solenoid hole.
3 With the ignition off, disconnect the wire from the solenoid. Thoroughly clean around the solenoid where it screws into the pump (see illustration).
4 Unscrew the solenoid and remove it. If a hand priming pump is fitted, operate the pump a few times while lifting out the solenoid to wash away any particles of dirt. Do not lose the sealing washer.
5 Remove the plunger from the solenoid (or from the recess in the pump, if it is stuck inside) (see illustrations). Refit the solenoid

17.3 Stop solenoid wire secured by nut (arrowed)

17.5a Removing the stop solenoid plunger from the pump

17.5b Stop solenoid components

body, making sure the sealing washer is in place, again operating the priming pump at the same time to flush away dirt.

6 Tape up the end of the solenoid wire so that it cannot touch bare metal.

7 The engine will now start and run as usual, but it will not stop when the ignition is switched off. It will be necessary to use the manual stop lever (if fitted) on the injection pump, or to stall the engine in gear.

8 Fit a new solenoid and sealing washer at the earliest opportunity.

7

Chapter 8
Tools and equipment

Contents

1 Normal workshop tools

1 The decision as to what range of tools is necessary will depend on the work to be done, the range of vehicles which it is expected to encounter, and not least the financial resources available. The tools in the following list, with additions as necessary from the various categories of diesel-specific tools described later, should be sufficient for carrying out most routine maintenance and repair operations.

Combination spanners (see below)
Socket spanners (see below)
Ratchet, extension piece and universal joint (for use with sockets)
Torque wrench
Angle tightening indicator (see below)
Adjustable spanner
Set of sump drain plug keys
Strap or chain wrench (for fuel and oil filters)
Oil drain tray
Feeler gauges
Combination pliers
Long-nosed pliers
Self-locking pliers (Mole wrench)
Screwdrivers (large and small, flat blade and cross blade)
Set of Allen keys
Set of splined and Torx keys and sockets (see below)
Ball pein hammer
Soft-faced hammer
Puller (universal type, with interchangeable jaws)
Cold chisel
Scriber
Scraper
Centre punch
Hacksaw
File
Steel rule/straight-edge
Axle stands and/or ramps

Trolley jack
Inspection light
Inspection mirror
Telescopic magnet/pick-up tool

Socket and spanner size

2 A good range of open-ended, ring and socket spanners will be required. Most vehicles use metric size fastenings throughout but some earlier UK-built machines will have Imperial fastenings - or a mixture of both.
3 Split ring spanners (also known as flare nut spanners) are particularly useful for dealing with fuel pipe unions, on which a conventional ring or socket cannot be used because the pipe is in the way. The most common sizes are 17 mm and 19 mm on metric systems, and ⅝ in and ¾ in on Imperial.
4 Sockets are available in various drive sizes. The half inch square drive size is most widely used and accepts most torque wrenches. Smaller drive sizes (⅜ or ¼ in) are useful for working in confined spaces, while for large high-torque fastenings (driveshaft or hub nuts, crankshaft pulley bolts) ¾ inch drive is most satisfactory.
5 The humble box spanner should not be overlooked. Box spanners are cheap and will sometimes serve as a substitute for a deep socket, though they cannot be used with a torque wrench and are easily deformed.

Angle tightening

6 For fastenings such as cylinder head bolts, many manufacturers now specify tightening in terms of angular rotation rather than an absolute torque. After an initial 'snug' torque wrench setting, subsequent tightening stages are specified as angles through which each bolt must be turned. Variations in tightening torque which could be caused by the presence or absence of dirt, oil etc. on the bolt threads thus have no effect. A further benefit is that there is no need for a high-range torque wrench.
7 The owner-mechanic who expects to use this method of tightening only once or twice in

the life of the vehicle may be content to make up a cardboard template, or mark the bolt heads with paint spots, to indicate the angle required. Greater speed and accuracy will result from using one of the many angle tightening indicators commercially available. Most of them are intended for use with ½ in drive sockets or keys **(see illustration)**.

Splined bolt heads

8 The conventional hexagon head bolt is being replaced in many areas by the splined or 'Torx' head bolt. This type of bolt has multiple splines in place of the hexagon. A set of splined or Torx keys will be needed to deal with female splined heads. Torx bolts with male heads also exist, and for these Torx sockets will be needed. Both keys and sockets are available to accept ½ in square drives.

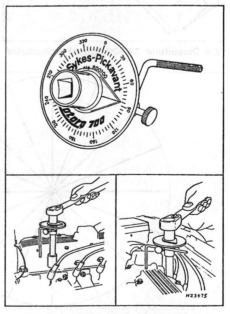

1.7 Sykes-Pickavant 800700 angle tightening gear

2 Diesel-specific tools

Basic tune-up and service

1 Besides the normal range of spanners, screwdrivers and so on, the following tools and equipment will be needed for basic tune-up and service operations on most models :

Deep socket for removing and tightening screw-in injectors
Injector puller for removing clamp type injectors
Optical or pulse-sensitive tachometer
Electrical multi-meter, or dedicated glow plug tester
Compression or leakdown tester
Vacuum pump and/or gauge

Injector socket

2 The size most commonly required is 27 mm or 1¹⁄₁₆ in AF. Some Japanese injectors require 22 mm or ⅞ in AF. The socket needs to be deep in order not to foul the injector body. On some engines it also needs to be thin-walled.

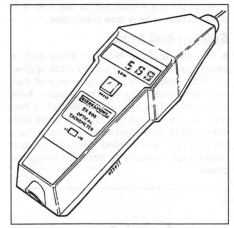

2.5 Dieseltune DX.800 optical tachometer

Suitable sockets are sold by Dieseltune, Sykes-Pickavant and Snap-On, among others.

Tachometer

3 The type of tachometer which senses ignition system HT pulses via an inductive pick-up cannot be used on diesel engines, unless a device such as the Sykes-Pickavant timing light adapter is available.

4 If an engine is fitted with a TDC sensor and a diagnostic socket, an electronic tachometer which reads the signals from the TDC sensor can be used.

5 Not all engines have TDC sensors. On those which do not, the use of an optical or pulse-sensitive tachometer is necessary **(see illustration)**.

6 The optical tachometer registers the passage of a paint mark or (more usually) a strip of reflective foil placed on the crankshaft pulley. It is not so convenient to use as the electronic or pulse-sensitive types, since it has to be held so that it can 'see' the pulley, but it has the advantage that it can be used on any engine, petrol or diesel, with or without a diagnostic socket.

7 The pulse-sensitive tachometer uses a transducer similar to that needed for a timing light. The transducer converts hydraulic or mechanical impulses in an injector pipe into electrical signals, which are displayed on the tachometer as engine speed.

8 Some dynamic timing equipment for diesel engines incorporates a means of displaying engine speed. If this equipment is available, a separate tachometer will not be required.

9 Both optical and pulse-sensitive tachometers are sold by A. M. Test Systems and Kent-Moore. Optical tachometers are sold by (inter alia) Dieseltune, and pulse-sensitive by Souriau and Bosch.

DIY alternative tachometer

10 The owner-mechanic who only wishes to check the idle speed of one engine occasionally may well feel that the purchase of a special

tachometer is not justified. Assuming that mains electric light is available, the use of a stroboscopic disc is a cheap alternative. The principle will be familiar to anyone who has used such a disc to check the speed of a record-player turntable.

11 A disc must be constructed of stiff paper or card to fit onto the crankshaft pulley (or camshaft pulley, if appropriate - but remember that this rotates at half speed). The disc should be white or light-coloured, and divided using a protractor into regular segments with heavy black lines **(see illustration)**. The number of segments required will depend on the desired idle speed and the frequency of the alternating current supply. For the 50 Hz supply used in the UK and most of Europe the figures are as follows:

Speed (rpm)	No of segments	Angle per segment
706	17	21° 11'
750	16	22° 30'
800	15	24°
857	14	25° 43'
923	13	27° 42'

12 Attach the disc to the crankshaft pulley and position the car so that the disc can be viewed using only artificial light. A fluorescent tube is best. Failing this a low-wattage incandescent bulb will give better results than a high-wattage one. Run the engine at idle and observe the disc.

 Warning : Do not run the engine in a confined space without some means of extracting the exhaust fumes.

13 If the engine speed corresponds to the calculated disc speed, the disc segments will appear to be stationary. If the speed is different, the segments will appear to drift in the direction of engine rotation (too fast) or against it (too slow). The segments will also appear to be stationary at multiples or sub-multiples of the calculated speed - twice or half the speed, and so on - so some common sense must be used.

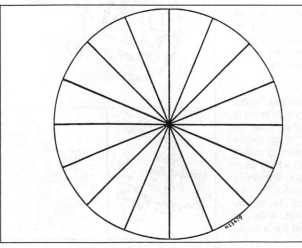

2.11 Home-made tachometer disc

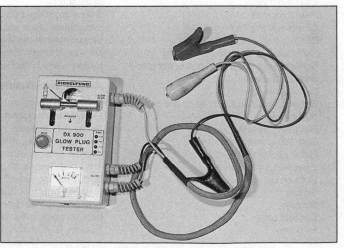

2.14 Dieseltune DX.900 glow plug tester

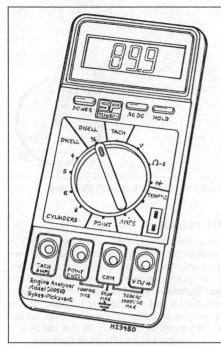

2.15 Sykes-Pickavant 300510 engine analyser/multi-meter

Electrical multi-meter or glow plug tester

14 It is possible to test glow plugs and their control circuitry with a multi-meter, or even (to a limited extent) with a 12 volt test lamp. A purpose-made glow plug tester will do the job faster and is much easier to use, but on the other hand it will not do anything else **(see illustration)**.

15 If it is decided to purchase a multi-meter, make sure that it has a high current range - ideally 0 to 100 amps - for checking glow plug current draw. Some meters require an external shunt to be fitted for this. An inductive clamp connection is preferred for high current measurement since it can be used without breaking into the circuit. Other ranges required are dc voltage (0 to 20 or 30 volts is suitable for most applications) and resistance. Some meters have a continuity buzzer in addition to a resistance scale ; the buzzer is particularly useful when working single-handed **(see illustration)**.

16 Glow plug testers are available from makers such as Beru, Dieseltune and Kent-Moore. Some incorporate a 'hot test chamber' in which the heating of individual plugs can be observed.

Compression tester

17 A tester specifically intended for diesel engines must be used **(see illustration)**. The push-in connectors used with some petrol engine compression testers cannot be used for diesel engines because of the higher pressures involved. Instead, the diesel engine compression tester screws into an injector or glow plug hole, using one of the adapters supplied with the tester.

18 Most compression testers are used while cranking the engine on the starter motor. A few, such as the Dieseltune DX 511, can be used with the engine idling. This gives more reliable results, since it is hard to guarantee that cranking speed will not fall in the course of testing all four cylinders, whereas idle speed will remain constant.

19 Recording testers, which produce a pen-and-ink trace for each cylinder, are available from A. M. Test Systems and Kent-Moore. Non-recording testers are more common and are available from Dieseltune and Sykes-Pickavant as well as the makers previously mentioned.

Leak-down tester

20 The leak-down tester measures the rate at which air pressure is lost from each cylinder, and can also be used to pinpoint the source of pressure loss (valves, head gasket or bores). It depends on the availability of a supply of compressed air, typically at 5 to 10 bar (73 to

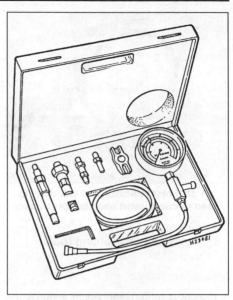

2.17 Dieseltune DX.511 compression tester

145 lbf/in2). The same tester (with different adapters) can be used on both petrol and diesel engines **(see illustration)**.

21 In use, the tester is connected to an air line and to an adapter screwed into the injector or glow plug hole, with the piston concerned at TDC on the compression stroke. Leak-down testers are offered by Dieseltune, Sykes-Pickavant and others.

Vacuum pump and/or gauge

22 A vacuum gauge, with suitable adapters, is useful for locating blockages or air leaks in the supply side of the fuel system. A simple gauge is used with the engine running to create vacuum in the supply lines. A hand-held vacuum pump with its own gauge can be used without running the engine, and is also useful for bleeding the fuel system when a hand priming pump is not fitted **(see illustration)**.

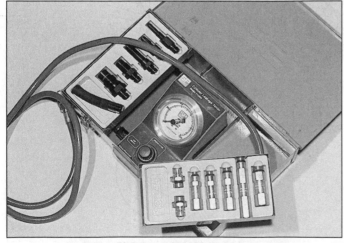

2.20 Sykes-Pickavant 013800 leak-down tester

2.22 Dieseltune DX 760 'Mityvac' test kit

8

3.4 Dial test indicator and stand being used to check swirl chamber protrusion

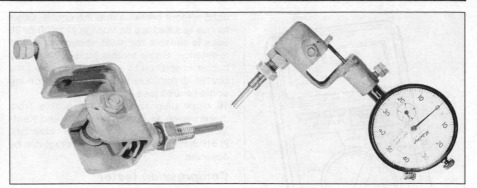

3.6a DTI and locally-made bellcrank adapter for timing a Bosch VE pump

3 Injection pump timing tools

1 If work is undertaken which disturbs the position of the fuel injection pump, certain tools will be needed to check the injection timing on reassembly. This also applies if the pump drive is disturbed - including renewal of the timing belt on some models. Checking of the timing is also a necessary part of fault diagnosis when investigating complaints such as power loss, knock and smoke.

Static timing tool

2 Static timing is still the most widely-used method of setting diesel injection pumps. It is time-consuming and sometimes messy. Precision measuring instruments are often needed for dealing with distributor pumps. Good results depend on the skill and patience of the operator.

3 The owner-mechanic who will only be dealing with one engine should refer to the appropriate text to find out what tools will be required. The diesel tune-up specialist will typically need the following :

Dial test indicators (DTI) with magnetic stand
DTI adapters and probes for Bosch and CAV distributor pumps
Spill tube for in-line pumps
Timing gear pins or pegs
Crankshaft or flywheel locking pins

Dial test indicator and magnetic stand

4 This is a useful workshop tool for many operations besides timing. It is the most accurate means of checking the protrusion or recession of swirl chambers, pistons and liners when renewing cylinder head gaskets. If major overhauls are undertaken it can also be used for measuring values such as crankshaft endfloat **(see illustration)**.

5 Two DTIs may be needed for setting the timing on some engines - one to measure the pump plunger or rotor movement and one to measure engine piston position.

DTI adapters

6 Adapters and probes for fitting the DTI to the distributor pump are of various patterns, due partly to the need to be able to use them in conditions of poor access on the vehicle **(see illustrations)**. This means that the same adapter cannot necessarily be used on the same type of pump and engine if the under-bonnet layout is different. On the bench it is often possible to use simpler equipment.

7 A spring-loaded probe is used on some CAV/RotoDiesel pumps to find the timing groove in the pump rotor **(see illustration)**.

Timing gear pins or pegs

8 Pins or pegs are used on some engines to lock the pump and/or the camshaft in a particular position. They are generally specific to a particular engine or manufacturer. It is sometimes possible to use suitably sized dowel rods, drill shanks or bolts instead.

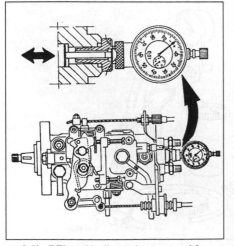

3.6b DTI and in-line adapter used for timing a Bosch VE pump

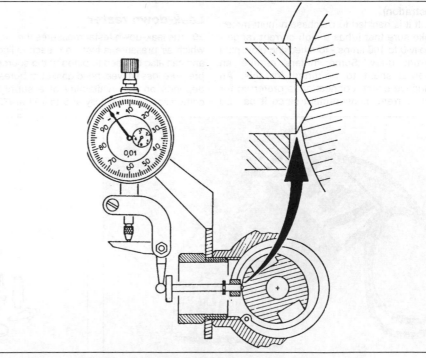

3.7 DTI and adapter used for timing Lucas/CAV pump

3.14 Clamping a timing light transducer onto an injector pipe

3.22a Sykes-Pickavant 300540 diesel timing light adapter

Crankshaft or flywheel locking pins

9 These are used for locking the crankshaft at TDC (or at the injection point on some models).
10 The crankshaft locking pin is inserted through a hole in the side of the crankcase after removal of a plug, and enters a slot in a crankshaft counterweight or web. The flywheel pin passes through a hole in the flywheel end of the crankcase and enters a hole in the flywheel. Again, suitably sized rods or bolts can sometimes be used instead.

Dynamic timing tools

11 Dynamic timing on diesel engines has not yet become widespread, due no doubt in part to the relatively expensive equipment required. Additionally, not all vehicle manufacturers provide dynamic timing values. In principle it makes possible much faster and more accurate checking of the injection timing, just as on petrol engines. It can also be used to verify the operation of cold start advance systems.
12 Most dynamic timing equipment depends on converting mechanical or hydraulic impulses in the injection system into electrical signals. An alternative approach is adopted by

one or two manufacturers who use an optical-to-electrical conversion, with a sensor which screws into a glow plug hole and 'sees' the light of combustion. The electrical signals are used to trigger a timing light, or as part of the information fed into a diagnostic analyser.
13 Not all diesel engines have ready-made timing marks. If the engine has a TDC sensor (or provision for fitting one) and the timing equipment can read the sensor output, this is not a problem. Some engines have neither timing marks nor TDC sensors. In such cases there is no choice but to establish TDC accurately and make marks on the flywheel or crankshaft pulley.

Timing lights

14 The simplest dynamic timing equipment uses a transducer to convert the pressure pulse in the injector pipe into an electrical signal which triggers a timing light. Such transducers are of two types - in-line and clamp-on **(see illustration)**.
15 The in-line transducer is connected into No 1 injector pipe using adapters to suit the fuel pipe unions. The electrical connection from the transducer goes to the timing light,

which will also require a 12 volt or mains supply to energise its tube.
16 The clamp-on transducer is used in a similar way but instead of actually tapping into the injector pipe it clamps onto it. The transducer must be of the right size for the pipe concerned and any dirt, rust or protective coating on the pipe must be removed.
17 The position of the clamp-on transducer on the pipe is important. The injection pulse takes a finite amount of time to travel from one end of the pipe to the other. If the transducer is in the wrong place, a false result will be obtained. Place the transducer as directed by the equipment or engine manufacturer.
18 The timing light itself may be an existing inductive type light normally used on petrol engines, if the transducer output is suitable. Other types of transducer can only be used with their own timing light.

Diagnostic analysers

19 Diagnostic engine analysers (Crypton, AVL, Souriau etc.) will display timing and speed information with the aid of diesel adapters or interface units. These will normally be specific to the equipment concerned; consult the manufacturers for details.
20 The output from the Sykes-Pickavant diesel adapter can be used to drive the inductive HT pick-up on a diagnostic analyser.

Injection testers

21 Injection testers are halfway between simple timing light/tachometer combinations and full-blown diagnostic analysers. They interpret the transducer output to provide a 'start-of-injection' signal, enabling comparison to be made between all the injectors on an engine, so that defective injectors can be identified.
22 The diesel adapter sold by Sykes-Pickavant for use with a conventional inductive timing light has an injection testing facility **(see illustration)**. More sophisticated equipment, such as the AVL Diesel Injection Tester 873 **(see illustration)**, accepts an input from the engine's TDC sensor (if fitted) as well, giving a digital read-out of injection timing without the need for a stroboscope.

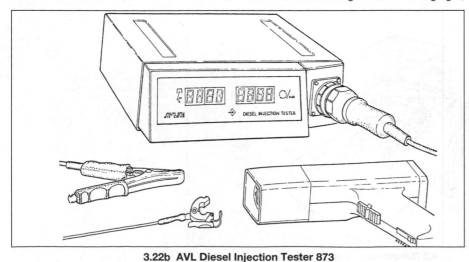

3.22b AVL Diesel Injection Tester 873

8

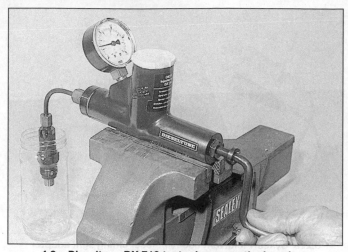

4.3a Dieseltune DX 710 tester in use on the bench. . .

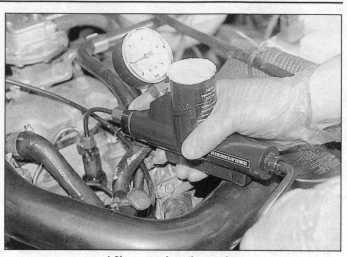

4.3b . . . and on the engine

4 Injector testing equipment

Warning : Never expose the hands, face or any other part of the body to injector spray. The high working pressure can penetrate the skin, with potentially fatal results. When possible use injector test oil rather than fuel for testing. Take precautions to avoid inhaling the vaporised fuel or injector test fluid. Remember that even diesel fuel is inflammable when vaporised.

1 Some kind of injector tester will be needed if it is wished to identify defective injectors, or to test them after cleaning or prolonged storage. Various makes and models are available, but the essential components of all of them are a high pressure hand-operated pump and a pressure gauge.

2 For safety reasons, injector test or calibration fluid should be used for bench testing rather than diesel fuel or paraffin. Use the fluid specified by the maker of the test equipment if possible.

3 One of the simplest testers currently available is Dieseltune's DX 710 **(see illustrations)**. This has the advantage that (access permitting) it can be used to test opening pressure and back leakage without removing the injectors from the engine. Its small reservoir makes it of limited use for bench testing, but good results can be obtained with practice.

4 Another method of testing injectors on the engine is to connect a pressure gauge into the line between the injection pump and the injector. This test can also detect faults caused by the injection pump high pressure piston or delivery valve.

5 The workshop which tests or calibrates injectors regularly will need a bench-mounted tester. These testers have a lever-operated pump, and a larger fluid reservoir than the hand-held tester. The best models also incorporate a transparent chamber for safe viewing of the injector spray pattern and perhaps a test fluid recirculation system **(see illustration)**.

6 Some means of extracting the vapour produced when testing, such as a hood connected to the workshop's fume extraction system, is desirable. Although injector test fluid is relatively non-toxic, its vapour is not particularly pleasant to inhale.

5 Injection pump testing and calibration equipment

The equipment needed for testing and calibration of injection pumps is beyond the scope of this book. Any such work should be entrusted to the pump manufacturer's agent - though the opportunity is taken to say yet again that the injection pump is often blamed for faults when in fact the trouble lies elsewhere.

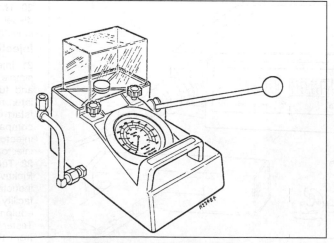

4.5 Dieseltune 111 injector tester

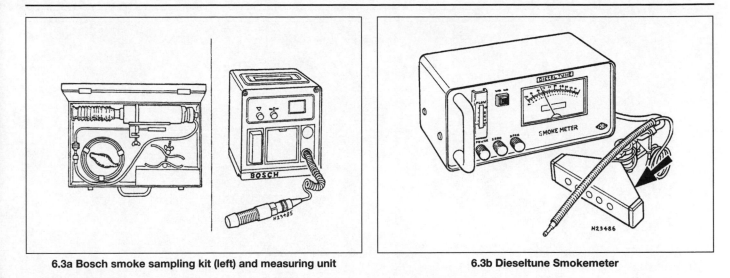

6.3a Bosch smoke sampling kit (left) and measuring unit

6.3b Dieseltune Smokemeter

6 Smoke testing equipment

1 Smoke emission testing is already mandatory for heavy goods vehicles and is likely to become so, probably as part of the MOT test, for cars and light commercial vehicles.

2 Smoke testing equipment falls into two categories - indirect and direct reading. With the indirect systems, a sample of exhaust gas is passed over a filter paper and the change in opacity of the paper is measured using a separate machine. With the direct systems, an optically sensitive probe measures the opacity of the exhaust gas and an immediate read-out is available.

3 The smoke sampling kit from Bosch is an example of the indirect reading system and is used in conjunction with a photoelectric measuring unit. Dieseltune's Smokemeter is an example of the direct reading machine **(see illustrations)**.

8

Dimensions and weights

Note: *All figures are approximate, and may vary according to model. Refer to manufacturer's data for exact figures.*

Weights (typical)

Kerb weights:
Nova/Corsa	840 to 1059 kg
Astra/Belmont/Kadett	1050 to 1209 kg
Cavalier	1044 to 1240 kg

Gross vehicle weights:
Nova/Corsa	1315 to 1650 kg (Up to 1834 kg - option on Combo models)
Astra/Belmont/Kadett	1555 to 1710 kg
Cavalier	1545 to 1740 kg

Trailer weights:
Nova/Corsa (up to 03/93):	
Trailer without brakes	400 kg
Trailer with brakes	800 kg
Corsa (from 04/93):	
Trailer without brakes	450 kg
Trailer with brakes	800 kg
Astra/Belmont/Kadett:	
Trailer without brakes	425 ± 25 kg
Trailer with brakes	975 ± 225 kg
Cavalier	
Trailer without brakes	500 kg
Trailer with brakes	1100 ± 400 kg

Dimensions (typical)

Overall length:
Nova/Corsa (up to 03/93)	3652 to 3986 mm
Corsa (from 04/93)	3279 to 4230 mm
Astra/Belmont/Kadett	4051 to 4278 mm
Cavalier	4264 to 4432 mm

Overall width:
Nova/Corsa (up to 03/93)	1535 to 1542 mm
Corsa (from 04/93)	1768 to 2060 mm
Astra/Belmont/Kadett	1795 mm
Cavalier	1668 to 1876 mm

Overall height:
Nova/Corsa (up to 03/93)	1360 to 1365 mm
Corsa (from 04/93)	1420 to 1805 mm
Astra/Belmont/Kadett	1410 to 1490 mm
Cavalier	1368 to 1400 mm

Wheelbase:
Nova/Corsa (up to 03/93)	2343 mm
Corsa (from 04/93)	2443 to 2480 mm
Astra/Belmont/Kadett	2517 mm
Cavalier	2574 to 2600 mm

Length (distance)

Inches (in)	x 25.4	= Millimetres (mm)	x 0.0394	= Inches (in)	
Feet (ft)	x 0.305	= Metres (m)	x 3.281	= Feet (ft)	
Miles	x 1.609	= Kilometres (km)	x 0.621	= Miles	

Volume (capacity)

Cubic inches (cu in; in³)	x 16.387	= Cubic centimetres (cc; cm³)	x 0.061	= Cubic inches (cu in; in³)	
Imperial pints (Imp pt)	x 0.568	= Litres (l)	x 1.76	= Imperial pints (Imp pt)	
Imperial quarts (Imp qt)	x 1.137	= Litres (l)	x 0.88	= Imperial quarts (Imp qt)	
Imperial quarts (Imp qt)	x 1.201	= US quarts (US qt)	x 0.833	= Imperial quarts (Imp qt)	
US quarts (US qt)	x 0.946	= Litres (l)	x 1.057	= US quarts (US qt)	
Imperial gallons (Imp gal)	x 4.546	= Litres (l)	x 0.22	= Imperial gallons (Imp gal)	
Imperial gallons (Imp gal)	x 1.201	= US gallons (US gal)	x 0.833	= Imperial gallons (Imp gal)	
US gallons (US gal)	x 3.785	= Litres (l)	x 0.264	= US gallons (US gal)	

Mass (weight)

Ounces (oz)	x 28.35	= Grams (g)	x 0.035	= Ounces (oz)	
Pounds (lb)	x 0.454	= Kilograms (kg)	x 2.205	= Pounds (lb)	

Force

Ounces-force (ozf; oz)	x 0.278	= Newtons (N)	x 3.6	= Ounces-force (ozf; oz)	
Pounds-force (lbf; lb)	x 4.448	= Newtons (N)	x 0.225	= Pounds-force (lbf; lb)	
Newtons (N)	x 0.1	= Kilograms-force (kgf; kg)	x 9.81	= Newtons (N)	

Pressure

Pounds-force per square inch (psi; lbf/in²; lb/in²)	x 0.070	= Kilograms-force per square centimetre (kgf/cm²; kg/cm²)	x 14.223	= Pounds-force per square inch (psi; lbf/in²; lb/in²)	
Pounds-force per square inch (psi; lbf/in²; lb/in²)	x 0.068	= Atmospheres (atm)	x 14.696	= Pounds-force per square inch (psi; lbf/in²; lb/in²)	
Pounds-force per square inch (psi; lbf/in²; lb/in²)	x 0.069	= Bars	x 14.5	= Pounds-force per square inch (psi; lbf/in²; lb/in²)	
Pounds-force per square inch (psi; lbf/in²; lb/in²)	x 6.895	= Kilopascals (kPa)	x 0.145	= Pounds-force per square inch (psi; lbf/in²; lb/in²)	
Kilopascals (kPa)	x 0.01	= Kilograms-force per square centimetre (kgf/cm²; kg/cm²)	x 98.1	= Kilopascals (kPa)	
Millibar (mbar)	x 100	= Pascals (Pa)	x 0.01	= Millibar (mbar)	
Millibar (mbar)	x 0.0145	= Pounds-force per square inch (psi; lbf/in²; lb/in²)	x 68.947	= Millibar (mbar)	
Millibar (mbar)	x 0.75	= Millimetres of mercury (mmHg)	x 1.333	= Millibar (mbar)	
Millibar (mbar)	x 0.401	= Inches of water (inH₂O)	x 2.491	= Millibar (mbar)	
Millimetres of mercury (mmHg)	x 0.535	= Inches of water (inH₂O)	x 1.868	= Millimetres of mercury (mmHg)	
Inches of water (inH₂O)	x 0.036	= Pounds-force per square inch (psi; lbf/in²; lb/in²)	x 27.68	= Inches of water (inH₂O)	

Torque (moment of force)

Pounds-force inches (lbf in; lb in)	x 1.152	= Kilograms-force centimetre (kgf cm; kg cm)	x 0.868	= Pounds-force inches (lbf in; lb in)	
Pounds-force inches (lbf in; lb in)	x 0.113	= Newton metres (Nm)	x 8.85	= Pounds-force inches (lbf in; lb in)	
Pounds-force inches (lbf in; lb in)	x 0.083	= Pounds-force feet (lbf ft; lb ft)	x 12	= Pounds-force inches (lbf in; lb in)	
Pounds-force feet (lbf ft; lb ft)	x 0.138	= Kilograms-force metres (kgf m; kg m)	x 7.233	= Pounds-force feet (lbf ft; lb ft)	
Pounds-force feet (lbf ft; lb ft)	x 1.356	= Newton metres (Nm)	x 0.738	= Pounds-force feet (lbf ft; lb ft)	
Newton metres (Nm)	x 0.102	= Kilograms-force metres (kgf m; kg m)	x 9.804	= Newton metres (Nm)	

Power

Horsepower (hp)	x 745.7	= Watts (W)	x 0.0013	= Horsepower (hp)	

Velocity (speed)

Miles per hour (miles/hr; mph)	x 1.609	= Kilometres per hour (km/hr; kph)	x 0.621	= Miles per hour (miles/hr; mph)	

Fuel consumption*

Miles per gallon (mpg)	x 0.354	= Kilometres per litre (km/l)	x 2.825	= Miles per gallon (mpg)	

Temperature

Degrees Fahrenheit = (°C x 1.8) + 32   Degrees Celsius (Degrees Centigrade; °C) = (°F - 32) x 0.56

It is common practice to convert from miles per gallon (mpg) to litres/100 kilometres (l/100km), where mpg x l/100 km = 282

Spare parts are available from many sources, including maker's appointed garages, accessory shops, and motor factors. To be sure of obtaining the correct parts, it may sometimes be necessary to quote the vehicle identification number. If possible, it can also be useful to take the old parts along for positive identification. Items such as starter motors and alternators may be available under a service exchange scheme - any parts returned should always be clean.

Our advice regarding spare part sources is as follows:

Officially-appointed garages

This is the best source of parts which are peculiar to your car, and are not otherwise generally available (eg badges, interior trim, certain body panels, etc). It is also the only place at which you should buy parts if the vehicle is still under warranty.

Accessory shops

These are very good places to buy materials and components needed for the maintenance of your car (oil, air and fuel filters, spark plugs, light bulbs, drivebelts, oils and greases, brake pads, touch-up paint, etc). Parts like this sold by a reputable shop are of the same standard as those used by the car manufacturer.

Motor factors

Good factors will stock all the more important components which wear out comparatively quickly and can sometimes supply individual components needed for the overhaul of a larger assembly. They may also handle work such as cylinder block reboring, crankshaft regrinding and balancing, etc.

Tyre and exhaust specialists

These outlets may be independent or members of a local or national chain. They frequently offer competitive prices when compared with a main dealer or local garage, but it will pay to obtain several quotes before making a decision. Also ask what 'extras' may be added to the quote - for instance, fitting a new valve and balancing the wheel are both often charged on top of the price of a new tyre.

Other sources

Beware of parts of materials obtained from market stalls, car boot sales or similar outlets. Such items are not invariably sub-standard, but there is little chance of compensation if they do prove unsatisfactory. In the case of safety-critical components such as brake pads there is the risk not only of financial loss but also of an accident causing injury or death.

Vehicle identification

Modifications are a continuing and unpublished process in vehicle manufacture, quite apart from major model changes. Spare parts manuals and lists are compiled upon a numerical basis, the individual numbers being essential to correct identification of the component required.

When ordering spare parts, always give as much information as possible. Quote the car model, year of manufacture and vehicle identification and/or engine numbers as appropriate.

The *vehicle identification plate* is riveted on top of the front body panel and includes the Vehicle Identification Number (VIN), vehicle weight information and paint and trim colour codes.

The *Vehicle Identification Number (VIN)* is given on the vehicle identification plate. It is also stamped into the body floor panel, between the driver's seat and the door sill panel, under a flap in the carpet.

The *engine number* is stamped on a horizontal flat located on the cylinder block, below the cylinder head at the front of the engine. From model year 1993, the engine number can be found on the cylinder block next to the transmission **(see illustrations)**.

Engine number location - 16D engine

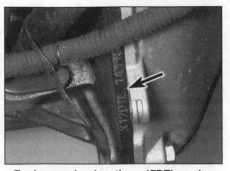

Engine number location - 17DTL engine

VAUXHALL MOTORS Ltd.		
TA NO	055007011	
VIN	XXXXXXXXXXXXXXX	
GVW	1445	kg
GCW	2395	kg
AXLE 1-	720	kg
AXLE 2-	725	kg
COLOR	15L 801	
MADE IN UNITED KINGDOM.		

Vehicle identification number (VIN) plate - typical

Whenever servicing, repair or overhaul work is carried out on the car or its components, it is necessary to observe the following procedures and instructions. This will assist in carrying out the operation efficiently and to a professional standard of workmanship.

Joint mating faces and gaskets

When separating components at their mating faces, never insert screwdrivers or similar implements into the joint between the faces in order to prise them apart. This can cause severe damage which results in oil leaks, coolant leaks, etc upon reassembly. Separation is usually achieved by tapping along the joint with a soft-faced hammer in order to break the seal. However, note that this method may not be suitable where dowels are used for component location.

Where a gasket is used between the mating faces of two components, ensure that it is renewed on reassembly, and fit it dry unless otherwise stated in the repair procedure. Make sure that the mating faces are clean and dry, with all traces of old gasket removed. When cleaning a joint face, use a tool which is not likely to score or damage the face, and remove any burrs or nicks with an oilstone or fine file.

Make sure that tapped holes are cleaned with a pipe cleaner, and keep them free of jointing compound, if this is being used, unless specifically instructed otherwise.

Ensure that all orifices, channels or pipes are clear, and blow through them, preferably using compressed air.

Oil seals

Oil seals can be removed by levering them out with a wide flat-bladed screwdriver or similar tool. Alternatively, a number of self-tapping screws may be screwed into the seal, and these used as a purchase for pliers or similar in order to pull the seal free.

Whenever an oil seal is removed from its working location, either individually or as part of an assembly, it should be renewed.

The very fine sealing lip of the seal is easily damaged, and will not seal if the surface it contacts is not completely clean and free from scratches, nicks or grooves. If the original sealing surface of the component cannot be restored, and the manufacturer has not made provision for slight relocation of the seal relative to the sealing surface, the component should be renewed.

Protect the lips of the seal from any surface which may damage them in the course of fitting. Use tape or a conical sleeve where possible. Lubricate the seal lips with oil before fitting and, on dual-lipped seals, fill the space between the lips with grease.

Unless otherwise stated, oil seals must be fitted with their sealing lips toward the lubricant to be sealed.

Use a tubular drift or block of wood of the appropriate size to install the seal and, if the seal housing is shouldered, drive the seal down to the shoulder. If the seal housing is unshouldered, the seal should be fitted with its face flush with the housing top face (unless otherwise instructed).

Screw threads and fastenings

Seized nuts, bolts and screws are quite a common occurrence where corrosion has set in, and the use of penetrating oil or releasing fluid will often overcome this problem if the offending item is soaked for a while before attempting to release it. The use of an impact driver may also provide a means of releasing such stubborn fastening devices, when used in conjunction with the appropriate screwdriver bit or socket. If none of these methods works, it may be necessary to resort to the careful application of heat, or the use of a hacksaw or nut splitter device.

Studs are usually removed by locking two nuts together on the threaded part, and then using a spanner on the lower nut to unscrew the stud. Studs or bolts which have broken off below the surface of the component in which they are mounted can sometimes be removed using a stud extractor. Always ensure that a blind tapped hole is completely free from oil, grease, water or other fluid before installing the bolt or stud. Failure to do this could cause the housing to crack due to the hydraulic action of the bolt or stud as it is screwed in.

When tightening a castellated nut to accept a split pin, tighten the nut to the specified torque, where applicable, and then tighten further to the next split pin hole. Never slacken the nut to align the split pin hole, unless stated in the repair procedure.

When checking or retightening a nut or bolt to a specified torque setting, slacken the nut or bolt by a quarter of a turn, and then retighten to the specified setting. However, this should not be attempted where angular tightening has been used.

For some screw fastenings, notably cylinder head bolts or nuts, torque wrench settings are no longer specified for the latter stages of tightening, "angle-tightening" being called up instead. Typically, a fairly low torque wrench setting will be applied to the bolts/nuts in the correct sequence, followed by one or more stages of tightening through specified angles.

Locknuts, locktabs and washers

Any fastening which will rotate against a component or housing during tightening should always have a washer between it and the relevant component or housing.

Spring or split washers should always be renewed when they are used to lock a critical component such as a big-end bearing retaining bolt or nut. Locktabs which are folded over to retain a nut or bolt should always be renewed.

Self-locking nuts can be re-used in non-critical areas, providing resistance can be felt when the locking portion passes over the bolt or stud thread. However, it should be noted that self-locking stiffnuts tend to lose their effectiveness after long periods of use, and should be renewed as a matter of course.

Split pins must always be replaced with new ones of the correct size for the hole.

When thread-locking compound is found on the threads of a fastener which is to be re-used, it should be cleaned off with a wire brush and solvent, and fresh compound applied on reassembly.

Special tools

Some repair procedures in this manual entail the use of special tools such as a press, two or three-legged pullers, spring compressors, etc. Wherever possible, suitable readily-available alternatives to the manufacturer's special tools are described, and are shown in use. In some instances, where no alternative is possible, it has been necessary to resort to the use of a manufacturer's tool, and this has been done for reasons of safety as well as the efficient completion of the repair operation. Unless you are highly-skilled and have a thorough understanding of the procedures described, never attempt to bypass the use of any special tool when the procedure described specifies its use. Not only is there a very great risk of personal injury, but expensive damage could be caused to the components involved.

Environmental considerations

When disposing of used engine oil, brake fluid, antifreeze, etc, give due consideration to any detrimental environmental effects. Do not, for instance, pour any of the above liquids down drains into the general sewage system, or onto the ground to soak away. Many local council refuse tips provide a facility for waste oil disposal, as do some garages. If none of these facilities are available, consult your local Environmental Health Department, or the National Rivers Authority, for further advice.

With the universal tightening-up of legislation regarding the emission of environmentally-harmful substances from motor vehicles, most current vehicles have tamperproof devices fitted to the main adjustment points of the fuel system. These devices are primarily designed to prevent unqualified persons from adjusting the fuel/air mixture, with the chance of a consequent increase in toxic emissions. If such devices are encountered during servicing or overhaul, they should, wherever possible, be renewed or refitted in accordance with the vehicle manufacturer's requirements or current legislation.

Note: It is antisocial and illegal to dump oil down the drain. To find the location of your local oil recycling bank, call this number free.

This is a guide to getting your vehicle through the MOT test. Obviously it will not be possible to examine the vehicle to the same standard as the professional MOT tester. However, working through the following checks will enable you to identify any problem areas before submitting the vehicle for the test.

Where a testable component is in borderline condition, the tester has discretion in deciding whether to pass or fail it. The basis of such discretion is whether the tester would be happy for a close relative or friend to use the vehicle with the component in that condition. If the vehicle presented is clean and evidently well cared for, the tester may be more inclined to pass a borderline component than if the vehicle is scruffy and apparently neglected.

It has only been possible to summarise the test requirements here, based on the regulations in force at the time of printing. Test standards are becoming increasingly stringent, although there are some exemptions for older vehicles. For full details obtain a copy of the Haynes publication Pass the MOT! (available from stockists of Haynes manuals).

An assistant will be needed to help carry out some of these checks.

The checks have been sub-divided into four categories, as follows:

1 Checks carried out **FROM THE DRIVER'S SEAT**

2 Checks carried out **WITH THE VEHICLE ON THE GROUND**

3 Checks carried out **WITH THE VEHICLE RAISED AND THE WHEELS FREE TO TURN**

4 Checks carried out on **YOUR VEHICLE'S EXHAUST EMISSION SYSTEM**

1 Checks carried out **FROM THE DRIVER'S SEAT**

Handbrake

☐ Test the operation of the handbrake. Excessive travel (too many clicks) indicates incorrect brake or cable adjustment.

☐ Check that the handbrake cannot be released by tapping the lever sideways. Check the security of the lever mountings.

Footbrake

☐ Depress the brake pedal and check that it does not creep down to the floor, indicating a master cylinder fault. Release the pedal, wait a few seconds, then depress it again. If the pedal travels nearly to the floor before firm resistance is felt, brake adjustment or repair is necessary. If the pedal feels spongy, there is air in the hydraulic system which must be removed by bleeding.

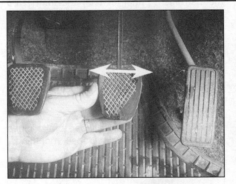

☐ Check that the brake pedal is secure and in good condition. Check also for signs of fluid leaks on the pedal, floor or carpets, which would indicate failed seals in the brake master cylinder.

☐ Check the servo unit (when applicable) by operating the brake pedal several times, then keeping the pedal depressed and starting the engine. As the engine starts, the pedal will move down slightly. If not, the vacuum hose or the servo itself may be faulty.

Steering wheel and column

☐ Examine the steering wheel for fractures or looseness of the hub, spokes or rim.

☐ Move the steering wheel from side to side and then up and down. Check that the steering wheel is not loose on the column, indicating wear or a loose retaining nut. Continue moving the steering wheel as before, but also turn it slightly from left to right.

☐ Check that the steering wheel is not loose on the column, and that there is no abnormal

movement of the steering wheel, indicating wear in the column support bearings or couplings.

Windscreen and mirrors

☐ The windscreen must be free of cracks or other significant damage within the driver's field of view. (Small stone chips are acceptable.) Rear view mirrors must be secure, intact, and capable of being adjusted.

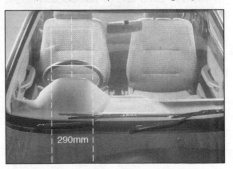

290mm

Seat belts and seats

Note: *The following checks are applicable to all seat belts, front and rear.*

☐ Examine the webbing of all the belts (including rear belts if fitted) for cuts, serious fraying or deterioration. Fasten and unfasten each belt to check the buckles. If applicable, check the retracting mechanism. Check the security of all seat belt mountings accessible from inside the vehicle.

☐ The front seats themselves must be securely attached and the backrests must lock in the upright position.

Doors

☐ Both front doors must be able to be opened and closed from outside and inside, and must latch securely when closed.

2 Checks carried out WITH THE VEHICLE ON THE GROUND

Vehicle identification

☐ Number plates must be in good condition, secure and legible, with letters and numbers correctly spaced – spacing at (A) should be twice that at (B).

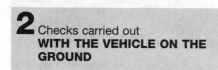

☐ The VIN plate and/or homologation plate must be legible.

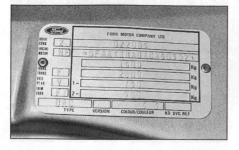

Electrical equipment

☐ Switch on the ignition and check the operation of the horn.

☐ Check the windscreen washers and wipers, examining the wiper blades; renew damaged or perished blades. Also check the operation of the stop-lights.

☐ Check the operation of the sidelights and number plate lights. The lenses and reflectors must be secure, clean and undamaged.

☐ Check the operation and alignment of the headlights. The headlight reflectors must not be tarnished and the lenses must be undamaged.

☐ Switch on the ignition and check the operation of the direction indicators (including the instrument panel tell-tale) and the hazard warning lights. Operation of the sidelights and stop-lights must not affect the indicators - if it does, the cause is usually a bad earth at the rear light cluster.

☐ Check the operation of the rear foglight(s), including the warning light on the instrument panel or in the switch.

Footbrake

☐ Examine the master cylinder, brake pipes and servo unit for leaks, loose mountings, corrosion or other damage.

☐ The fluid reservoir must be secure and the fluid level must be between the upper (**A**) and lower (**B**) markings.

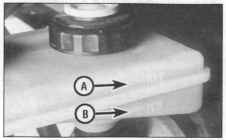

☐ Inspect both front brake flexible hoses for cracks or deterioration of the rubber. Turn the steering from lock to lock, and ensure that the hoses do not contact the wheel, tyre, or any part of the steering or suspension mechanism. With the brake pedal firmly depressed, check the hoses for bulges or leaks under pressure.

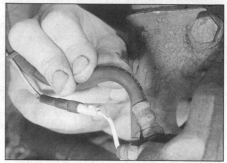

Steering and suspension

☐ Have your assistant turn the steering wheel from side to side slightly, up to the point where the steering gear just begins to transmit this movement to the roadwheels. Check for excessive free play between the steering wheel and the steering gear, indicating wear or insecurity of the steering column joints, the column-to-steering gear coupling, or the steering gear itself.

☐ Have your assistant turn the steering wheel more vigorously in each direction, so that the roadwheels just begin to turn. As this is done, examine all the steering joints, linkages, fittings and attachments. Renew any component that shows signs of wear or damage. On vehicles with power steering, check the security and condition of the steering pump, drivebelt and hoses.

☐ Check that the vehicle is standing level, and at approximately the correct ride height.

Shock absorbers

☐ Depress each corner of the vehicle in turn, then release it. The vehicle should rise and then settle in its normal position. If the vehicle continues to rise and fall, the shock absorber is defective. A shock absorber which has seized will also cause the vehicle to fail.

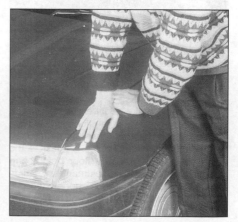

Exhaust system

☐ Start the engine. With your assistant holding a rag over the tailpipe, check the entire system for leaks. Repair or renew leaking sections.

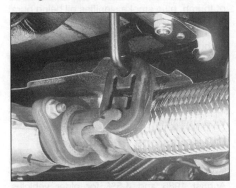

3 Checks carried out **WITH THE VEHICLE RAISED AND THE WHEELS FREE TO TURN**

Jack up the front and rear of the vehicle, and securely support it on axle stands. Position the stands clear of the suspension assemblies. Ensure that the wheels are clear of the ground and that the steering can be turned from lock to lock.

Steering mechanism

☐ Have your assistant turn the steering from lock to lock. Check that the steering turns smoothly, and that no part of the steering mechanism, including a wheel or tyre, fouls any brake hose or pipe or any part of the body structure.

☐ Examine the steering rack rubber gaiters for damage or insecurity of the retaining clips. If power steering is fitted, check for signs of damage or leakage of the fluid hoses, pipes or connections. Also check for excessive stiffness or binding of the steering, a missing split pin or locking device, or severe corrosion of the body structure within 30 cm of any steering component attachment point.

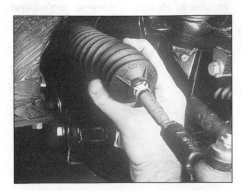

Front and rear suspension and wheel bearings

☐ Starting at the front right-hand side, grasp the roadwheel at the 3 o'clock and 9 o'clock positions and shake it vigorously. Check for free play or insecurity at the wheel bearings, suspension balljoints, or suspension mountings, pivots and attachments.

☐ Now grasp the wheel at the 12 o'clock and 6 o'clock positions and repeat the previous inspection. Spin the wheel, and check for roughness or tightness of the front wheel bearing.

☐ If excess free play is suspected at a component pivot point, this can be confirmed by using a large screwdriver or similar tool and levering between the mounting and the component attachment. This will confirm whether the wear is in the pivot bush, its retaining bolt, or in the mounting itself (the bolt holes can often become elongated).

☐ Carry out all the above checks at the other front wheel, and then at both rear wheels.

Springs and shock absorbers

☐ Examine the suspension struts (when applicable) for serious fluid leakage, corrosion, or damage to the casing. Also check the security of the mounting points.

☐ If coil springs are fitted, check that the spring ends locate in their seats, and that the spring is not corroded, cracked or broken.

☐ If leaf springs are fitted, check that all leaves are intact, that the axle is securely attached to each spring, and that there is no deterioration of the spring eye mountings, bushes, and shackles.

☐ The same general checks apply to vehicles fitted with other suspension types, such as torsion bars, hydraulic displacer units, etc. Ensure that all mountings and attachments are secure, that there are no signs of excessive wear, corrosion or damage, and (on hydraulic types) that there are no fluid leaks or damaged pipes.

☐ Inspect the shock absorbers for signs of serious fluid leakage. Check for wear of the mounting bushes or attachments, or damage to the body of the unit.

Driveshafts (fwd vehicles only)

☐ Rotate each front wheel in turn and inspect the constant velocity joint gaiters for splits or damage. Also check that each driveshaft is straight and undamaged.

Braking system

☐ If possible without dismantling, check brake pad wear and disc condition. Ensure that the friction lining material has not worn excessively, (A) and that the discs are not fractured, pitted, scored or badly worn (B).

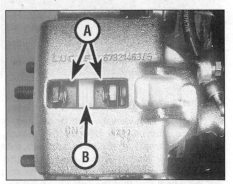

☐ Examine all the rigid brake pipes underneath the vehicle, and the flexible hose(s) at the rear. Look for corrosion, chafing or insecurity of the pipes, and for signs of bulging under pressure, chafing, splits or deterioration of the flexible hoses.

☐ Look for signs of fluid leaks at the brake calipers or on the brake backplates. Repair or renew leaking components.

☐ Slowly spin each wheel, while your assistant depresses and releases the footbrake. Ensure that each brake is operating and does not bind when the pedal is released.

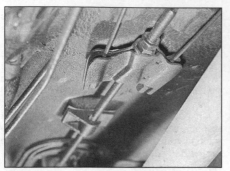

☐ Examine the handbrake mechanism, checking for frayed or broken cables, excessive corrosion, or wear or insecurity of the linkage. Check that the mechanism works on each relevant wheel, and releases fully, without binding.

☐ It is not possible to test brake efficiency without special equipment, but a road test can be carried out later to check that the vehicle pulls up in a straight line.

Fuel and exhaust systems

☐ Inspect the fuel tank (including the filler cap), fuel pipes, hoses and unions. All components must be secure and free from leaks.

☐ Examine the exhaust system over its entire length, checking for any damaged, broken or missing mountings, security of the retaining clamps and rust or corrosion.

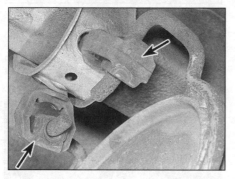

Wheels and tyres

☐ Examine the sidewalls and tread area of each tyre in turn. Check for cuts, tears, lumps, bulges, separation of the tread, and exposure of the ply or cord due to wear or damage. Check that the tyre bead is correctly seated on the wheel rim, that the valve is sound and

properly seated, and that the wheel is not distorted or damaged.

☐ Check that the tyres are of the correct size for the vehicle, that they are of the same size and type on each axle, and that the pressures are correct.

☐ Check the tyre tread depth. The legal minimum at the time of writing is 1.6 mm over at least three-quarters of the tread width. Abnormal tread wear may indicate incorrect front wheel alignment.

Body corrosion

☐ Check the condition of the entire vehicle structure for signs of corrosion in load-bearing areas. (These include chassis box sections, side sills, cross-members, pillars, and all suspension, steering, braking system and seat belt mountings and anchorages.) Any corrosion which has seriously reduced the thickness of a load-bearing area is likely to cause the vehicle to fail. In this case professional repairs are likely to be needed.

☐ Damage or corrosion which causes sharp or otherwise dangerous edges to be exposed will also cause the vehicle to fail.

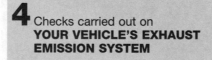

4 Checks carried out on YOUR VEHICLE'S EXHAUST EMISSION SYSTEM

Petrol models

☐ Have the engine at normal operating temperature, and make sure that it is in good tune (ignition system in good order, air filter element clean, etc).

☐ Before any measurements are carried out, raise the engine speed to around 2500 rpm, and hold it at this speed for 20 seconds. Allow

the engine speed to return to idle, and watch for smoke emissions from the exhaust tailpipe. If the idle speed is obviously much too high, or if dense blue or clearly-visible black smoke comes from the tailpipe for more than 5 seconds, the vehicle will fail. As a rule of thumb, blue smoke signifies oil being burnt (engine wear) while black smoke signifies unburnt fuel (dirty air cleaner element, or other carburettor or fuel system fault).

☐ An exhaust gas analyser capable of measuring carbon monoxide (CO) and hydrocarbons (HC) is now needed. If such an instrument cannot be hired or borrowed, a local garage may agree to perform the check for a small fee.

CO emissions (mixture)

☐ At the time of writing, the maximum CO level at idle is 3.5% for vehicles first used after August 1986 and 4.5% for older vehicles. From January 1996 a much tighter limit (around 0.5%) applies to catalyst-equipped vehicles first used from August 1992. If the CO level cannot be reduced far enough to pass the test (and the fuel and ignition systems are otherwise in good condition) then the carburettor is badly worn, or there is some problem in the fuel injection system or catalytic converter (as applicable).

HC emissions

☐ With the CO emissions within limits, HC emissions must be no more than 1200 ppm (parts per million). If the vehicle fails this test at idle, it can be re-tested at around 2000 rpm; if the HC level is then 1200 ppm or less, this counts as a pass.

☐ Excessive HC emissions can be caused by oil being burnt, but they are more likely to be due to unburnt fuel.

Diesel models

☐ The only emission test applicable to Diesel engines is the measuring of exhaust smoke density. The test involves accelerating the engine several times to its maximum unloaded speed.

Note: *It is of the utmost importance that the engine timing belt is in good condition before the test is carried out.*

☐ Excessive smoke can be caused by a dirty air cleaner element. Otherwise, professional advice may be needed to find the cause.

A

ABS (Anti-lock brake system) A system, usually electronically controlled, that senses incipient wheel lockup during braking and relieves hydraulic pressure at wheels that are about to skid.

Air bag An inflatable bag hidden in the steering wheel (driver's side) or the dash or glovebox (passenger side). In a head-on collision, the bags inflate, preventing the driver and front passenger from being thrown forward into the steering wheel or windscreen.

Air cleaner A metal or plastic housing, containing a filter element, which removes dust and dirt from the air being drawn into the engine.

Air filter element The actual filter in an air cleaner system, usually manufactured from pleated paper and requiring renewal at regular intervals.

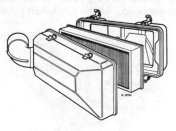

Air filter

Allen key A hexagonal wrench which fits into a recessed hexagonal hole.

Alligator clip A long-nosed spring-loaded metal clip with meshing teeth. Used to make temporary electrical connections.

Alternator A component in the electrical system which converts mechanical energy from a drivebelt into electrical energy to charge the battery and to operate the starting system, ignition system and electrical accessories.

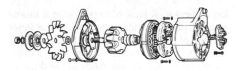

Alternator (exploded view)

Ampere (amp) A unit of measurement for the flow of electric current. One amp is the amount of current produced by one volt acting through a resistance of one ohm.

Anaerobic sealer A substance used to prevent bolts and screws from loosening. Anaerobic means that it does not require oxygen for activation. The Loctite brand is widely used.

Antifreeze A substance (usually ethylene glycol) mixed with water, and added to a vehicle's cooling system, to prevent freezing of the coolant in winter. Antifreeze also contains chemicals to inhibit corrosion and the formation of rust and other deposits that would tend to clog the radiator and coolant passages and reduce cooling efficiency.

Anti-seize compound A coating that reduces the risk of seizing on fasteners that are subjected to high temperatures, such as exhaust manifold bolts and nuts.

Anti-seize compound

Asbestos A natural fibrous mineral with great heat resistance, commonly used in the composition of brake friction materials. Asbestos is a health hazard and the dust created by brake systems should never be inhaled or ingested.

Axle A shaft on which a wheel revolves, or which revolves with a wheel. Also, a solid beam that connects the two wheels at one end of the vehicle. An axle which also transmits power to the wheels is known as a live axle.

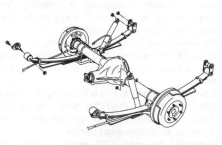

Axle assembly

Axleshaft A single rotating shaft, on either side of the differential, which delivers power from the final drive assembly to the drive wheels. Also called a driveshaft or a halfshaft.

B

Ball bearing An anti-friction bearing consisting of a hardened inner and outer race with hardened steel balls between two races.

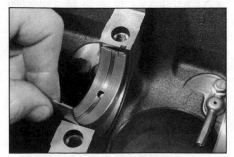

Bearing

Bearing The curved surface on a shaft or in a bore, or the part assembled into either, that permits relative motion between them with minimum wear and friction.

Big-end bearing The bearing in the end of the connecting rod that's attached to the crankshaft.

Bleed nipple A valve on a brake wheel cylinder, caliper or other hydraulic component that is opened to purge the hydraulic system of air. Also called a bleed screw.

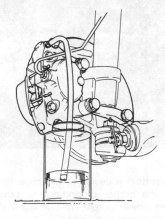

Brake bleeding

Brake bleeding Procedure for removing air from lines of a hydraulic brake system.

Brake disc The component of a disc brake that rotates with the wheels.

Brake drum The component of a drum brake that rotates with the wheels.

Brake linings The friction material which contacts the brake disc or drum to retard the vehicle's speed. The linings are bonded or riveted to the brake pads or shoes.

Brake pads The replaceable friction pads that pinch the brake disc when the brakes are applied. Brake pads consist of a friction material bonded or riveted to a rigid backing plate.

Brake shoe The crescent-shaped carrier to which the brake linings are mounted and which forces the lining against the rotating drum during braking.

Braking systems For more information on braking systems, consult the *Haynes Automotive Brake Manual*.

Breaker bar A long socket wrench handle providing greater leverage.

Bulkhead The insulated partition between the engine and the passenger compartment.

C

Caliper The non-rotating part of a disc-brake assembly that straddles the disc and carries the brake pads. The caliper also contains the hydraulic components that cause the pads to pinch the disc when the brakes are applied. A caliper is also a measuring tool that can be set to measure inside or outside dimensions of an object.

Camshaft A rotating shaft on which a series of cam lobes operate the valve mechanisms. The camshaft may be driven by gears, by sprockets and chain or by sprockets and a belt.

Canister A container in an evaporative emission control system; contains activated charcoal granules to trap vapours from the fuel system.

Canister

Carburettor A device which mixes fuel with air in the proper proportions to provide a desired power output from a spark ignition internal combustion engine.

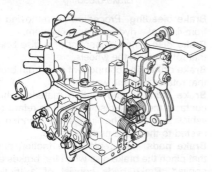

Carburettor

Castellated Resembling the parapets along the top of a castle wall. For example, a castellated balljoint stud nut.

Castellated nut

Castor In wheel alignment, the backward or forward tilt of the steering axis. Castor is positive when the steering axis is inclined rearward at the top.

Catalytic converter A silencer-like device in the exhaust system which converts certain pollutants in the exhaust gases into less harmful substances.

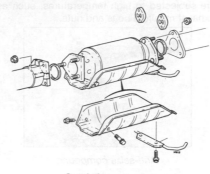

Catalytic converter

Circlip A ring-shaped clip used to prevent endwise movement of cylindrical parts and shafts. An internal circlip is installed in a groove in a housing; an external circlip fits into a groove on the outside of a cylindrical piece such as a shaft.

Clearance The amount of space between two parts. For example, between a piston and a cylinder, between a bearing and a journal, etc.

Coil spring A spiral of elastic steel found in various sizes throughout a vehicle, for example as a springing medium in the suspension and in the valve train.

Compression Reduction in volume, and increase in pressure and temperature, of a gas, caused by squeezing it into a smaller space.

Compression ratio The relationship between cylinder volume when the piston is at top dead centre and cylinder volume when the piston is at bottom dead centre.

Constant velocity (CV) joint A type of universal joint that cancels out vibrations caused by driving power being transmitted through an angle.

Core plug A disc or cup-shaped metal device inserted in a hole in a casting through which core was removed when the casting was formed. Also known as a freeze plug or expansion plug.

Crankcase The lower part of the engine block in which the crankshaft rotates.

Crankshaft The main rotating member, or shaft, running the length of the crankcase, with offset "throws" to which the connecting rods are attached.

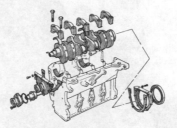

Crankshaft assembly

Crocodile clip See Alligator clip

D

Diagnostic code Code numbers obtained by accessing the diagnostic mode of an engine management computer. This code can be used to determine the area in the system where a malfunction may be located.

Disc brake A brake design incorporating a rotating disc onto which brake pads are squeezed. The resulting friction converts the energy of a moving vehicle into heat.

Double-overhead cam (DOHC) An engine that uses two overhead camshafts, usually one for the intake valves and one for the exhaust valves.

Drivebelt(s) The belt(s) used to drive accessories such as the alternator, water pump, power steering pump, air conditioning compressor, etc. off the crankshaft pulley.

Accessory drivebelts

Driveshaft Any shaft used to transmit motion. Commonly used when referring to the axleshafts on a front wheel drive vehicle.

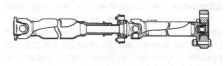

Driveshaft

Drum brake A type of brake using a drum-shaped metal cylinder attached to the inner surface of the wheel. When the brake pedal is pressed, curved brake shoes with friction linings press against the inside of the drum to slow or stop the vehicle.

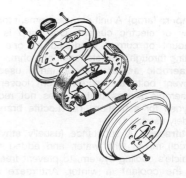

Drum brake assembly

E

EGR valve A valve used to introduce exhaust gases into the intake air stream.

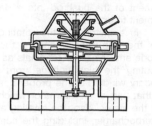

EGR valve

Electronic control unit (ECU) A computer which controls (for instance) ignition and fuel injection systems, or an anti-lock braking system. For more information refer to the *Haynes Automotive Electrical and Electronic Systems Manual.*

Electronic Fuel Injection (EFI) A computer controlled fuel system that distributes fuel through an injector located in each intake port of the engine.

Emergency brake A braking system, independent of the main hydraulic system, that can be used to slow or stop the vehicle if the primary brakes fail, or to hold the vehicle stationary even though the brake pedal isn't depressed. It usually consists of a hand lever that actuates either front or rear brakes mechanically through a series of cables and linkages. Also known as a handbrake or parking brake.

Endfloat The amount of lengthwise movement between two parts. As applied to a crankshaft, the distance that the crankshaft can move forward and back in the cylinder block.

Engine management system (EMS) A computer controlled system which manages the fuel injection and the ignition systems in an integrated fashion.

Exhaust manifold A part with several passages through which exhaust gases leave the engine combustion chambers and enter the exhaust pipe.

Exhaust manifold

F

Fan clutch A viscous (fluid) drive coupling device which permits variable engine fan speeds in relation to engine speeds.

Feeler blade A thin strip or blade of hardened steel, ground to an exact thickness, used to check or measure clearances between parts.

Feeler blade

Firing order The order in which the engine cylinders fire, or deliver their power strokes, beginning with the number one cylinder.

Flywheel A heavy spinning wheel in which energy is absorbed and stored by means of momentum. On cars, the flywheel is attached to the crankshaft to smooth out firing impulses.

Free play The amount of travel before any action takes place. The "looseness" in a linkage, or an assembly of parts, between the initial application of force and actual movement. For example, the distance the brake pedal moves before the pistons in the master cylinder are actuated.

Fuse An electrical device which protects a circuit against accidental overload. The typical fuse contains a soft piece of metal which is calibrated to melt at a predetermined current flow (expressed as amps) and break the circuit.

Fusible link A circuit protection device consisting of a conductor surrounded by heat-resistant insulation. The conductor is smaller than the wire it protects, so it acts as the weakest link in the circuit. Unlike a blown fuse, a failed fusible link must frequently be cut from the wire for replacement.

G

Gap The distance the spark must travel in jumping from the centre electrode to the side

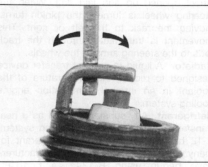

Adjusting spark plug gap

electrode in a spark plug. Also refers to the spacing between the points in a contact breaker assembly in a conventional points-type ignition, or to the distance between the reluctor or rotor and the pickup coil in an electronic ignition.

Gasket Any thin, soft material - usually cork, cardboard, asbestos or soft metal - installed between two metal surfaces to ensure a good seal. For instance, the cylinder head gasket seals the joint between the block and the cylinder head.

Gasket

Gauge An instrument panel display used to monitor engine conditions. A gauge with a movable pointer on a dial or a fixed scale is an analogue gauge. A gauge with a numerical readout is called a digital gauge.

H

Halfshaft A rotating shaft that transmits power from the final drive unit to a drive wheel, usually when referring to a live rear axle.

Harmonic balancer A device designed to reduce torsion or twisting vibration in the crankshaft. May be incorporated in the crankshaft pulley. Also known as a vibration damper.

Hone An abrasive tool for correcting small irregularities or differences in diameter in an engine cylinder, brake cylinder, etc.

Hydraulic tappet A tappet that utilises hydraulic pressure from the engine's lubrication system to maintain zero clearance (constant contact with both camshaft and valve stem). Automatically adjusts to variation in valve stem length. Hydraulic tappets also reduce valve noise.

I

Ignition timing The moment at which the spark plug fires, usually expressed in the number of crankshaft degrees before the piston reaches the top of its stroke.

Inlet manifold A tube or housing with passages through which flows the air-fuel mixture (carburettor vehicles and vehicles with throttle body injection) or air only (port fuel-injected vehicles) to the port openings in the cylinder head.

J

Jump start Starting the engine of a vehicle with a discharged or weak battery by attaching jump leads from the weak battery to a charged or helper battery.

L

Load Sensing Proportioning Valve (LSPV) A brake hydraulic system control valve that works like a proportioning valve, but also takes into consideration the amount of weight carried by the rear axle.

Locknut A nut used to lock an adjustment nut, or other threaded component, in place. For example, a locknut is employed to keep the adjusting nut on the rocker arm in position.

Lockwasher A form of washer designed to prevent an attaching nut from working loose.

M

MacPherson strut A type of front suspension system devised by Earle MacPherson at Ford of England. In its original form, a simple lateral link with the anti-roll bar creates the lower control arm. A long strut - an integral coil spring and shock absorber - is mounted between the body and the steering knuckle. Many modern so-called MacPherson strut systems use a conventional lower A-arm and don't rely on the anti-roll bar for location.

Multimeter An electrical test instrument with the capability to measure voltage, current and resistance.

N

NOx Oxides of Nitrogen. A common toxic pollutant emitted by petrol and diesel engines at higher temperatures.

O

Ohm The unit of electrical resistance. One volt applied to a resistance of one ohm will produce a current of one amp.

Ohmmeter An instrument for measuring electrical resistance.

O-ring A type of sealing ring made of a special rubber-like material; in use, the O-ring is compressed into a groove to provide the sealing action.

O-ring

Overhead cam (ohc) engine An engine with the camshaft(s) located on top of the cylinder head(s).

Overhead valve (ohv) engine An engine with the valves located in the cylinder head, but with the camshaft located in the engine block.

Oxygen sensor A device installed in the engine exhaust manifold, which senses the oxygen content in the exhaust and converts this information into an electric current. Also called a Lambda sensor.

P

Phillips screw A type of screw head having a cross instead of a slot for a corresponding type of screwdriver.

Plastigage A thin strip of plastic thread, available in different sizes, used for measuring clearances. For example, a strip of Plastigage is laid across a bearing journal. The parts are assembled and dismantled; the width of the crushed strip indicates the clearance between journal and bearing.

Plastigage

Propeller shaft The long hollow tube with universal joints at both ends that carries power from the transmission to the differential on front-engined rear wheel drive vehicles.

Proportioning valve A hydraulic control valve which limits the amount of pressure to the rear brakes during panic stops to prevent wheel lock-up.

R

Rack-and-pinion steering A steering system with a pinion gear on the end of the steering shaft that mates with a rack (think of a geared wheel opened up and laid flat). When the steering wheel is turned, the pinion turns, moving the rack to the left or right. This movement is transmitted through the track rods to the steering arms at the wheels.

Radiator A liquid-to-air heat transfer device designed to reduce the temperature of the coolant in an internal combustion engine cooling system.

Refrigerant Any substance used as a heat transfer agent in an air-conditioning system. R-12 has been the principle refrigerant for many years; recently, however, manufacturers have begun using R-134a, a non-CFC substance that is considered less harmful to the ozone in the upper atmosphere.

Rocker arm A lever arm that rocks on a shaft or pivots on a stud. In an overhead valve engine, the rocker arm converts the upward movement of the pushrod into a downward movement to open a valve.

Rotor In a distributor, the rotating device inside the cap that connects the centre electrode and the outer terminals as it turns, distributing the high voltage from the coil secondary winding to the proper spark plug. Also, that part of an alternator which rotates inside the stator. Also, the rotating assembly of a turbocharger, including the compressor wheel, shaft and turbine wheel.

Runout The amount of wobble (in-and-out movement) of a gear or wheel as it's rotated. The amount a shaft rotates "out-of-true." The out-of-round condition of a rotating part.

S

Sealant A liquid or paste used to prevent leakage at a joint. Sometimes used in conjunction with a gasket.

Sealed beam lamp An older headlight design which integrates the reflector, lens and filaments into a hermetically-sealed one-piece unit. When a filament burns out or the lens cracks, the entire unit is simply replaced.

Serpentine drivebelt A single, long, wide accessory drivebelt that's used on some newer vehicles to drive all the accessories, instead of a series of smaller, shorter belts. Serpentine drivebelts are usually tensioned by an automatic tensioner.

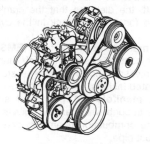

Serpentine drivebelt

Shim Thin spacer, commonly used to adjust the clearance or relative positions between two parts. For example, shims inserted into or under bucket tappets control valve clearances. Clearance is adjusted by changing the thickness of the shim.

Slide hammer A special puller that screws into or hooks onto a component such as a shaft or bearing; a heavy sliding handle on the shaft bottoms against the end of the shaft to knock the component free.

Sprocket A tooth or projection on the periphery of a wheel, shaped to engage with a chain or drivebelt. Commonly used to refer to the sprocket wheel itself.

Starter inhibitor switch On vehicles with an

automatic transmission, a switch that prevents starting if the vehicle is not in Neutral or Park.

Strut See MacPherson strut.

T

Tappet A cylindrical component which transmits motion from the cam to the valve stem, either directly or via a pushrod and rocker arm. Also called a cam follower.

Thermostat A heat-controlled valve that regulates the flow of coolant between the cylinder block and the radiator, so maintaining optimum engine operating temperature. A thermostat is also used in some air cleaners in which the temperature is regulated.

Thrust bearing The bearing in the clutch assembly that is moved in to the release levers by clutch pedal action to disengage the clutch. Also referred to as a release bearing.

Timing belt A toothed belt which drives the camshaft. Serious engine damage may result if it breaks in service.

Timing chain A chain which drives the camshaft.

Toe-in The amount the front wheels are closer together at the front than at the rear. On rear wheel drive vehicles, a slight amount of toe-in is usually specified to keep the front wheels running parallel on the road by offsetting other forces that tend to spread the wheels apart.

Toe-out The amount the front wheels are closer together at the rear than at the front. On front wheel drive vehicles, a slight amount of toe-out is usually specified.

Tools For full information on choosing and using tools, refer to the *Haynes Automotive Tools Manual.*

Tracer A stripe of a second colour applied to a wire insulator to distinguish that wire from another one with the same colour insulator.

Tune-up A process of accurate and careful adjustments and parts replacement to obtain the best possible engine performance.

Turbocharger A centrifugal device, driven by exhaust gases, that pressurises the intake air. Normally used to increase the power output from a given engine displacement, but can also be used primarily to reduce exhaust emissions (as on VW's "Umwelt" Diesel engine).

U

Universal joint or U-joint A double-pivoted connection for transmitting power from a driving to a driven shaft through an angle. A U-joint consists of two Y-shaped yokes and a cross-shaped member called the spider.

V

Valve A device through which the flow of liquid, gas, vacuum, or loose material in bulk may be started, stopped, or regulated by a movable part that opens, shuts, or partially obstructs one or more ports or passageways. A valve is also the movable part of such a device.

Valve clearance The clearance between the valve tip (the end of the valve stem) and the rocker arm or tappet. The valve clearance is measured when the valve is closed.

Vernier caliper A precision measuring instrument that measures inside and outside dimensions. Not quite as accurate as a micrometer, but more convenient.

Viscosity The thickness of a liquid or its resistance to flow.

Volt A unit for expressing electrical "pressure" in a circuit. One volt that will produce a current of one ampere through a resistance of one ohm.

W

Welding Various processes used to join metal items by heating the areas to be joined to a molten state and fusing them together. For more information refer to the *Haynes Automotive Welding Manual.*

Wiring diagram A drawing portraying the components and wires in a vehicle's electrical system, using standardised symbols. For more information refer to the *Haynes Automotive Electrical and Electronic Systems Manual.*

Note: *References throughout this index are in the form - "Chapter number" • "page number"*

Haynes Manuals – The Complete List

Title	Book No.
ALFA ROMEO	
Alfa Romeo Alfasud/Sprint (74 - 88)	0292
Alfa Romeo Alfetta (73 - 87)	0531
AUDI	
Audi 80 (72 - Feb 79)	0207
Audi 80, 90 (79 - Oct 86) & Coupe (81 - Nov 88)	0605
Audi 80, 90 (Oct 86 - 90) & Coupe (Nov 88 - 90)	1491
Audi 100 (Oct 76 - Oct 82)	0428
Audi 100 (Oct 82 - 90) & 200 (Feb 84 - Oct 89)	0907
AUSTIN	
Austin Ambassador (82 - 84)	0871
Austin/MG Maestro 1.3 & 1.6 (83 - 95)	0922
Austin Maxi (69 - 81)	0052
Austin/MG Metro (80 - May 90)	0718
Austin Montego 1.3 & 1.6 (84 - 94)	1066
Austin/MG Montego 2.0 (84 - 95)	1067
Mini (59 - 69)	0527
Mini (69 - Oct 96)	0646
Austin/Rover 2.0 litre Diesel Engine (86 - 93)	1857
BEDFORD	
Bedford CF (69 - 87)	0163
Bedford Rascal (86 - 93)	3015
BL	
BL Princess & BLMC 18-22 (75 - 82)	0286
BMW	
BMW 316, 320 & 320i (4-cyl) (75 - Feb 83)	0276
BMW 320, 320i, 323i & 325i (6-cyl) (Oct 77 - Sept 87)	0815
BMW 3-Series (Apr 91 - 96)	3210
BMW 3-Series (sohc) (83 - 91)	1948
BMW 520i & 525e (Oct 81 - June 88)	1560
BMW 525, 528 & 528i (73 - Sept 81)	0632
BMW 5-Series (sohc) (81 - 91)	1948
BMW 1500, 1502, 1600, 1602, 2000 & 2002 (59 - 77)	0240
CITROEN	
Citroen 2CV, Ami & Dyane (67 - 90)	0196
Citroen AX Petrol & Diesel (87 - 94)	3014
Citroen BX (83 - 94)	0908
Citroen CX (75 - 88)	0528
Citroen Visa (79 - 88)	0620
Citroen Xantia Petrol & Diesel (93 - Oct 95)	3082
Citroen XM Petrol & Diesel (89 - 97)	3451
Citroen ZX Diesel (91 - 93)	1922
Citroen ZX Petrol (91 - 94)	1881
Citroen 1.7 & 1.9 litre Diesel Engine (84 - 96)	1379
COLT	
Colt 1200, 1250 & 1400 (79 - May 84)	0600
DAIMLER	
Daimler Sovereign (68 - Oct 86)	0242
Daimler Double Six (72 - 88)	0478
DATSUN (see also *Nissan*)	
Datsun 120Y (73 - Aug 78)	0228
Datsun 1300, 1400 & 1600 (69 - Aug 72)	0123
Datsun Cherry (71 - 76)	0195
Datsun Pick-up (75 - 78)	0277
Datsun Sunny (Aug 78 - May 82)	0525
Datsun Violet (78 - 82)	0430

Title	Book No.
FIAT	
Fiat 126 (73 - 87)	0305
Fiat 127 (71 - 83)	0193
Fiat 500 (57 - 73)	0090
Fiat 850 (64 - 81)	0038
Fiat Panda (81 - 95)	0793
Fiat Punto (94 - 96)	3251
Fiat Regata (84 - 88)	1167
Fiat Strada (79 - 88)	0479
Fiat Tipo (88 - 91)	1625
Fiat Uno (83 - 95)	0923
Fiat X1/9 (74 - 89)	0273
FORD	
Ford Capri II (& III) 1.6 & 2.0 (74 - 87)	0283
Ford Capri II (& III) 2.8 & 3.0 (74 - 87)	1309
Ford Cortina Mk IV (& V) 1.6 & 2.0 (76 - 83)	0343
Ford Cortina Mk IV (& V) 2.3 V6 (77 - 83)	0426
Ford Escort (75 - Aug 80)	0280
Ford Escort (Sept 80 - Sept 90)	0686
Ford Escort (Sept 90 - 97)	1737
Ford Escort Mk II Mexico, RS 1600 & RS 2000 (75 - 80)	0735
Ford Fiesta (inc. XR2) (76 - Aug 83)	0334
Ford Fiesta (inc. XR2) (Aug 83 - Feb 89)	1030
Ford Fiesta (Feb 89 - Oct 95)	1595
Ford Fiesta Petrol & Diesel (Oct 95 - 97)	3397
Ford Granada (Sept 77 - Feb 85)	0481
Ford Granada (Mar 85 - 94)	1245
Ford Mondeo 4-cyl (93 - 96)	1923
Ford Orion (83 - Sept 90)	1009
Ford Orion (Sept 90 - 93)	1737
Ford Sierra 1.3, 1.6, 1.8 & 2.0 (82 - 93)	0903
Ford Sierra 2.3, 2.8 & 2.9 (82 - 91)	0904
Ford Scorpio (Mar 85 - 94)	1245
Ford Transit Petrol (Mk 1) (65 - Feb 78)	0377
Ford Transit Petrol (Mk 2) (78 - Jan 86)	0719
Ford Transit Petrol (Mk 3) (Feb 86 - 89)	1468
Ford Transit Diesel (Feb 86 - 95)	3019
Ford 1.6 & 1.8 litre Diesel Engine (84 - 96)	1172
Ford 2.1, 2.3 & 2.5 litre Diesel Engine (77 - 90)	1606
FREIGHT ROVER	
Freight Rover Sherpa (74 - 87)	0463
HILLMAN	
Hillman Avenger (70 - 82)	0037
HONDA	
Honda Accord (76 - Feb 84)	0351
Honda Accord (Feb 84 - Oct 85)	1177
Honda Civic (Feb 84 - Oct 87)	1226
Honda Civic (Nov 91 - 96)	3199
HYUNDAI	
Hyundai Pony (85 - 94)	3398
JAGUAR	
Jaguar E Type (61 - 72)	0140
Jaguar MkI & II, 240 & 340 (55 - 69)	0098
Jaguar XJ6, XJ & Sovereign (68 - Oct 86)	0242
Jaguar XJ6 & Sovereign (Oct 86 - Sept 94)	3261
Jaguar XJ12, XJS & Sovereign (72 - 88)	0478

Title	Book No.
JEEP	
Jeep Cherokee Petrol (93 - 96)	1943
LADA	
Lada 1200, 1300, 1500 & 1600 (74 - 91)	0413
Lada Samara (87 - 91)	1610
LAND ROVER	
Land Rover 90, 110 & Defender Diesel (83 - 95)	3017
Land Rover Discovery Diesel (89 - 95)	3016
Land Rover Series IIA & III Diesel (58 - 85)	0529
Land Rover Series II, IIA & III Petrol (58 - 85)	0314
MAZDA	
Mazda 323 fwd (Mar 81 - Oct 89)	1608
Mazda 626 fwd (May 83 - Sept 87)	0929
Mazda B-1600, B-1800 & B-2000 Pick-up (72 - 88)	0267
MERCEDES-BENZ	
Mercedes-Benz 190, 190E & 190D Petrol & Diesel (83 - 93)	3450
Mercedes-Benz 200, 240, 300 Diesel (Oct 76 - 85)	1114
Mercedes-Benz 250 & 280 (68 - 72)	0346
Mercedes-Benz 250 & 280 (123 Series) (Oct 76 - 84)	0677
Mercedes-Benz 124 Series (85 - Aug 93)	3253
MG	
MGB (62 - 80)	0111
MG Maestro 1.3 & 1.6 (83 - 95)	0922
MG Metro (80 - May 90)	0718
MG Midget & AH Sprite (58 - 80)	0265
MG Montego 2.0 (84 - 95)	1067
MITSUBISHI	
Mitsubishi 1200, 1250 & 1400 (79 - May 84)	0600
Mitsubishi Shogun & L200 Pick-Ups (83 - 94)	1944
MORRIS	
Morris Ital 1.3 (80 - 84)	0705
Morris Marina 1700 (78 - 80)	0526
Morris Marina 1.8 (71 - 78)	0074
Morris Minor 1000 (56 - 71)	0024
NISSAN (See also Datsun)	
Nissan Bluebird 160B & 180B rwd (May 80 - May 84)	0957
Nissan Bluebird fwd (May 84 - Mar 86)	1223
Nissan Bluebird (T12 & T72) (Mar 86 - 90)	1473
Nissan Cherry (N12) (Sept 82 - 86)	1031
Nissan Micra (K10) (83 - Jan 93)	0931
Nissan Micra (93 - 96)	3254
Nissan Primera (90 - Oct 96)	1851
Nissan Stanza (82 - 86)	0824
Nissan Sunny (B11) (May 82 - Oct 86)	0895
Nissan Sunny (Oct 86 - Mar 91)	1378
Nissan Sunny (Apr 91 - 95)	3219
OPEL	
Opel Ascona & Manta (B Series) (Sept 75 - 88)	0316
Opel Ascona (81 - 88)	3215
Opel Astra (Oct 91 - 96)	3156
Opel Corsa (83 - Mar 93)	3160
Opel Corsa (Mar 93 - 94)	3159
Opel Kadett (Nov 79 - Oct 84)	0634

Title	Book No.
Opel Kadett (Oct 84 - Oct 91)	3196
Opel Omega & Senator (86 - 94)	3157
Opel Rekord (Feb 78 - Oct 86)	0543
Opel Vectra (88 - Oct 95)	3158
PEUGEOT	
Peugeot 106 Petrol & Diesel (91 - June 96)	1882
Peugeot 205 (83 - 95)	0932
Peugeot 305 (78 - 89)	0538
Peugeot 306 Petrol & Diesel (93 - 95)	3073
Peugeot 309 (86 - 93)	1266
Peugeot 405 Petrol (88 - 96)	1559
Peugeot 405 Diesel (88 - 96)	3198
Peugeot 406 Petrol & Diesel (96 - 97)	3394
Peugeot 505 (79 - 89)	0762
Peugeot 1.7 & 1.9 litre Diesel Engines (82 - 96)	0950
Peugeot 2.0, 2.1, 2.3 & 2.5 litre Diesel Engines (74 - 90)	1607
PORSCHE	
Porsche 911 (65 - 85)	0264
Porsche 924 & 924 Turbo (76 - 85)	0397
PROTON	
Proton (89 - 97)	3255
RANGE ROVER	
Range Rover V8 (70 - Oct 92)	0606
RELIANT	
Reliant Robin & Kitten (73 - 83)	0436
RENAULT	
Renault 5 (72 - Feb 85)	0141
Renault 5 (Feb 85 - 96)	1219
Renault 9 & 11 (82 - 89)	0822
Renault 12 (70 - 80)	0097
Renault 15 & 17 (72 - 79)	0763
Renault 18 (79 - 86)	0598
Renault 19 Petrol (89 - 94)	1646
Renault 19 Diesel (89 - 95)	1946
Renault 21 (86 - 94)	1397
Renault 25 (84 - 92)	1228
Renault Clio Petrol (91 - 93)	1853
Renault Clio Diesel (91 - June 96)	3031
Renault Espace (85 - 96)	3197
Renault Fuego (80 - 86)	0764
Renault Laguna (94 - 96)	3252
Renault Mégane Petrol & Diesel (96 - 97)	3395
ROVER	
Rover 111 & 114 (95 - 96)	1711
Rover 213 & 216 (84 - 89)	1116
Rover 214 & 414 (89 - 96)	1689
Rover 216 & 416 (89 - 96)	1830
Rover 618, 620 & 623 (93 - 97)	3257
Rover 820, 825 & 827 (86 - 95)	1380
Rover 2000, 2300 & 2600 (77 - 87)	0468
Rover 3500 (76 - 87)	0365
Rover Metro (May 90 - 94)	1711
SAAB	
Saab 90, 99 & 900 (79 - Oct 93)	0765
Saab 9000 (4-cyl) (85 - 95)	1686

Title	Book No.
SEAT	
Seat Ibiza & Malaga (85 - 92)	1609
SIMCA	
Simca 1100 & 1204 (67 - 79)	0088
Simca 1301 & 1501 (63 - 76)	0199
SKODA	
Skoda Estelle 105, 120, 130 & 136 (77 - 89)	0604
Skoda Favorit (89 - 92)	1801
SUBARU	
Subaru 1600 & 1800 (Nov 79 - 90)	0995
SUZUKI	
Suzuki SJ Series, Samurai & Vitara (82 - 97)	1942
Suzuki Supercarry (86 - Oct 94)	3015
TALBOT	
Talbot Alpine, Solara, Minx & Rapier (75 - 86)	0337
Talbot Horizon (78 - 86)	0473
Talbot Samba (82 - 86)	0823
TOYOTA	
Toyota Carina E (May 92 - 97)	3256
Toyota Celica (Feb 82 - Sept 85)	1135
Toyota Corolla (fwd) (Sept 83 - Sept 87)	1024
Toyota Corolla (rwd) (80 - 85)	0683
Toyota Corolla (Sept 87 - 92)	1683
Toyota Corolla (Aug 92 - 97)	3259
Toyota Hi-Ace & Hi-Lux (69 - Oct 83)	0304
Toyota Starlet (78 - Jan 85)	0462
TRIUMPH	
Triumph Acclaim (81 - 84)	0792
Triumph Herald (59 - 71)	0010
Triumph Spitfire (62 - 81)	0113
Triumph Stag (70 - 78)	0441
Triumph TR7 (75 - 82)	0322
VAUXHALL	
Vauxhall Astra (80 - Oct 84)	0635
Vauxhall Astra & Belmont (Oct 84 - Oct 91)	1136
Vauxhall Astra (Oct 91 - 96)	1832
Vauxhall Carlton (Oct 78 - Oct 86)	0480
Vauxhall Carlton (Nov 86 - 94)	1469
Vauxhall Cavalier 1300 (77 - July 81)	0461
Vauxhall Cavalier 1600, 1900 & 2000 (75 - July 81)	0315
Vauxhall Cavalier (81 - Oct 88)	0812
Vauxhall Cavalier (Oct 88 - Oct 95)	1570
Vauxhall Chevette (75 - 84)	0285
Vauxhall Corsa (93 - 97)	1985
Vauxhall Nova (83 - 93)	0909
Vauxhall Rascal (86 - 93)	3015
Vauxhall Senator (Sept 87 - 94)	1469
Vauxhall Vectra Petrol & Diesel (95 - 98)	3396
Vauxhall Viva HB Series (ohv) (66 - 70)	0026
Vauxhall Viva & Firenza (ohc) (68 - 73)	0093
Vauxhall/Opel 1.5, 1.6 & 1.7 litre Diesel Engines (82 - 96)	1222
VOLKSWAGEN	
VW Beetle 1200 (54 - 77)	0036
VW Beetle 1300 & 1500 (65 - 75)	0039
VW Beetle 1302 & 1302S (70 - 72)	0110

Title	Book No.
VW Beetle 1303, 1303S & GT (72 - 75)	0159
VW Golf Mk 1 1.1 & 1.3 (74 - Feb 84)	0716
VW Golf Mk 1 1.5, 1.6 & 1.8 (74 - 85)	0726
VW Golf Mk 1 Diesel (78 - Feb 84)	0451
VW Golf Mk 2 (Mar 84 - Feb 92)	1081
VW Golf Mk 3 Petrol & Diesel (Feb 92 - 96)	3097
VW Jetta Mk 1 1.1 & 1.3 (80 - June 84)	0716
VW Jetta Mk 1 1.5, 1.6 & 1.8 (80 - June 84)	0726
VW Jetta Mk 1 Diesel (81 - June 84)	0451
VW Jetta Mk 2 (July 84 - 92)	1081
VW LT vans & light trucks (76 - 87)	0637
VW Passat (Sept 81 - May 88)	0814
VW Passat (May 88 - 91)	1647
VW Polo & Derby (76 - Jan 82)	0335
VW Polo (82 - Oct 90)	0813
VW Polo (Nov 90 - Aug 94)	3245
VW Santana (Sept 82 - 85)	0814
VW Scirocco Mk 1 1.5, 1.6 & 1.8 (74 - 82)	0726
VW Scirocco (82 - 90)	1224
VW Transporter 1600 (68 - 79)	0082
VW Transporter 1700, 1800 & 2000 (72 - 79)	0226
VW Transporter with air-cooled engine (79 - 82)	0638
VW Transporter (82 - 90)	3452
VW Vento Petrol & Diesel (Feb 92 - 96)	3097
VOLVO	
Volvo 66 & 343, Daf 55 & 66 (68 - 79)	0293
Volvo 142, 144 & 145 (66 - 74)	0129
Volvo 240 Series (74 - 93)	0270
Volvo 262, 264 & 260/265 (75 - 85)	0400
Volvo 340, 343, 345 & 360 (76 - 91)	0715
Volvo 440, 460 & 480 (87 - 92)	1691
Volvo 740 & 760 (82 - 91)	1258
Volvo 850 (92 - 96)	3260
Volvo 940 (90 - 96)	3249
YUGO/ZASTAVA	
Yugo/Zastava (81 - 90)	1453

Title	Book No.
TECH BOOKS	
Automotive Brake Manual	3050
Automotive Carburettor Manual	3288
Automotive Diesel Engine Service Guide	3286
Automotive Electrical & Electronic Systems	3049
Automotive Engine Management and Fuel Injection Systems Manual	3344
Automotive Tools Manual	3052
Automotive Welding Manual	3053
In-Car Entertainment Manual (3rd Edition)	3363
CAR BOOKS	
Automotive Fuel Injection Systems	9755
Car Bodywork Repair Manual	9864
Caravan Manual (2nd Edition)	9894
Haynes Technical Data Book (89 - 98)	1998
How to Keep Your Car Alive	9868
Japanese Vehicle Carburettors	1786
Small Engine Repair Manual	1755
SU Carburettors	0299
Weber Carburettors (to 79)	0393

CL05.01/98

All the products featured on this page are available through most motor accessory shops, cycle shops and book stores. Our policy of continuous updating and development means that titles are being constantly added to the range. For up-to-date information on our complete list of titles, please telephone: (UK) +44 1963 440635 • (USA) +1 805 498 6703 • (France) +33 1 47 03 61 80 • (Sweden) +46 18 124016 • (Australia) +61 3 9763 8100

Preserving Our Motoring Heritage

< *The Model J Duesenberg Derham Tourster. Only eight of these magnificent cars were ever built – this is the only example to be found outside the United States of America*

Almost every car you've ever loved, loathed or desired is gathered under one roof at the Haynes Motor Museum. Over 300 immaculately presented cars and motorbikes represent every aspect of our motoring heritage, from elegant reminders of bygone days, such as the superb Model J Duesenberg to curiosities like the bug-eyed BMW Isetta. There are also many old friends and flames. Perhaps you remember the 1959 Ford Popular that you did your courting in? The magnificent 'Red Collection' is a spectacle of classic sports cars including AC, Alfa Romeo, Austin Healey, Ferrari, Lamborghini, Maserati, MG, Riley, Porsche and Triumph.

A Perfect Day Out

Each and every vehicle at the Haynes Motor Museum has played its part in the history and culture of Motoring. Today, they make a wonderful spectacle and a great day out for all the family. Bring the kids, bring Mum and Dad, but above all bring your camera to capture those golden memories for ever. You will also find an impressive array of motoring memorabilia, a comfortable 70 seat video cinema and one of the most extensive transport book shops in Britain. The Pit Stop Cafe serves everything from a cup of tea to wholesome, home-made meals or, if you prefer, you can enjoy the large picnic area nestled in the beautiful rural surroundings of Somerset.

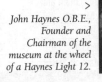

> *John Haynes O.B.E., Founder and Chairman of the museum at the wheel of a Haynes Light 12.*

< *Graham Hill's Lola Cosworth Formula 1 car next to a 1934 Riley Sports.*

The Museum is situated on the A359 Yeovil to Frome road at Sparkford, just off the A303 in Somerset. It is about 40 miles south of Bristol, and 25 minutes drive from the M5 intersection at Taunton.
Open 9.30am - 5.30pm (10.00am - 4.00pm Winter) 7 days a week, *except Christmas Day, Boxing Day and New Years Day*
Special rates available for schools, coach parties and outings Charitable Trust No. 292048